UNDERSTANDING SPORT PSYCHOLOGY and HUMAN BEHAVIOR

Incentives For Better Health & Wellness Through Exercise

AN INDIVIDUAL GUIDE FOR ACHIEVING YOUR GOALS

August John Hoffman, Ph.D.
California State University Northridge and Compton Community College

Contributing Authors:
Julie Wallach • Bruce Gaims

PEARSON

Custom
Publishing

Printed in the United States of America

10 9 8 7 6 5

ISBN 0-536-97606-6

2005500018

MR

Please visit our web site at *www.pearsoncustom.com*

PEARSON CUSTOM PUBLISHING
75 Arlington Street, Suite 300, Boston, MA 02116
A Pearson Education Company

Acknowledgments

Writing a textbook or an article addressing such exciting topics as health and sport psychology has been personally rewarding and very inspirational for me, however, this task requires tremendous effort, patience, and insight from several people, not just the primary author. As such, writing this book would have been virtually impossible were it not for the kind support and encouragement that I received from several individuals whom I would like to now recognize. First, my family for their patience and support during those long evenings when I promised to be finished "in an hour" that turned out to be several hours while working on this manuscript. I first would like to thank my lovely wife Nancy and our beautiful children Sara and A.J. I wish to offer my thanks in your love and support to help me through this project. My teaching assistant in psychology 321 (research methodology) at California State University Northridge Ms. Julie Nichole Wallach offered inspiration and new ideas when I thought the topic was complete or when I suffered from "writer's block." She has completed her own chapter in the text and I am confident that she will someday soon be completing her own book. Ms. Wallach's editing skills in the completion of this manuscript was very helpful and her ideas were always fresh, new and dynamic. I would also like to thank Mr. Bruce Gaims of Gaims Fitness who offered tremendous support and encouragement while writing this text. Bruce has been a wonderful training partner of mine for many years who always seems to be several feet ahead of me when we run or exercise together. Mr. Gaims also has contributed to this text by writing a chapter that looks at the psychological experiences of sport activity and exercise. Bruce is in my opinion the ideal model of health and fitness who balances the physical with the psychological demands of life—these things I shall always try to incorporate into my own life. I would also like to thank Coach Greg Goosen, former football coach of Notre Dame High School (1975–1977) who offered his views in coaching skills describing the necessary characteristics in the successful relationship between the athlete and coach.

Additionally, I would like to thank personal friend Ms. Lynne Cox, world record holder in numerous long distance swimming records. Ms. Cox has an incredible passion for the water and swimming where we both met at U.C. Santa Barbara in 1979. Her comments and friendly advice in chapter 9 (*The Female Athlete*) also served as motivating factors in the completion of this text. Finally, I would also like to thank my former doctoral committee members at UCLA who provided me with what I feel was the "hardware" in polishing and developing basic writing skills, Dr. James Bruno, Dr. Rodney Skager and Dr. Noreen Webb in the Graduate School of Education. Dr. Bruno's insight and truly genuine ideas regarding culture, time and our interrelationships with one another provided much information for me to discuss in this text regarding collectivism and individualistic culture in modern society. Dr. Bruno and Dr. Rodney Skager served as mentors for me during my tenure at UCLA and both helped me develop the skills that I now recognize as critical in writing and discussing empirical research in the social sciences. It was here at UCLA where I feel that I made the transition from a conventional thinker to a critical and innovative thinker. Finally, my love and thanks go forward to my parents and family who provided me with the psychological strength, aptitude and love to complete this project.

Table of Contents

Contents

Contents

Foreword

*"Our Destiny May Be Predetermined—But We Choose
The Path That Takes Us There"*

■ PSYCHOLOGICAL MOMENTUM DISCOVERED

As a child I was raised with expectations to try my best at whatever goals I had set out to achieve—no matter what they were or how simple or complex the task. My Father, Augie Lincoln Hoffman, is a very strong and competitive individual where I am sure I have either inherited or learned these skills necessary in maintaining determination to achieve my goals. Conversely, my mother, Lillian Hoffman is a very artistic and passionate individual who is also very determined and positivistic in achieving goals. Parents are the single most important influence in shaping the mentality and personality that equips the child with the necessary psychological skills in achieving their goals and maintaining wellness and balance in their life. The combination of these two philosophies from my parents was (and continues to be) an important element in my understanding how goals are achieved despite the challenging nature to many tasks we may set out to accomplish. My two older sisters and I were taught by our parents that winning or losing came second to effort—effort meant everything to our parents. When someone puts forth their effort to achieve something very important in their life it usually reflects what kind of a person they are and the values they have. Furthermore, as children we were taught that we were in control of and responsible for achieving our goals, whether that meant learning fractions in grade school, learning how to swim, or getting into college. It is here, I think, early in childhood during the critical and formative years, when we learn whether we are in control of the events in our lives (intrinsic control) or whether events control our lives (extrinsic control). Children need us to teach them to look critically at what is deep inside them—what they are capable of achieving only through mental focusing on their positive skills and understanding how it relates to their physical development. Only through understanding this dynamic relationship between physical development and psychological principles can we achieve our challenging goals throughout our lives that provide a unique identity for each of us.

Many years ago a memorable event occurred that helped me realize my inner strength as a person, as a student, and as an athlete. At a family party my cousin and I had begun a friendly contest to see who could complete the most consecutive sit-ups. I was 10 and my cousin was 13 and he had already completed 1000. Not to be outdone, I had set out to complete 1050, and then he completed 1100, and this went on most of the evening and early morning. We were both exhausted at the end of the evening, but I had learned that if we set our goals and proceed at a relatively relaxed pace, our bodies can progress for remarkable periods. It was also at this point where I first came up with the idea to try to break the Guinness Book of World Records number of consecutive sit-ups, which was 21, 000 in 1980. Something about that evening many years ago helped me to realize something very important to human success and endeavor. Our behavior is not necessarily controlled by what our body does physically, *but by what our minds and psyche (i.e., levels of self-efficacy and self-esteem) convinces the body of what it has the potential to do.* I also discovered an important concept relative to marathon training: When you focus on doing too much too soon, the body physically shuts itself off and a means of self-protection. The body begins to cramp, develops pain more quickly, and in general, our tolerance to pain drops significantly. Regardless of the goal, whether an 8 year old is trying to learn to ride a bicycle or a NCAA track and field athlete is trying to break a national record, the process of and methodology in achieving goals is the same: If the belief system and psychological momentum does not exist, then the goal will not be realized. In the Spring of 1981 I graduated from the University of California Santa Barbara and was accepted to the graduate program (Masters of Arts) in clinical psychology at Radford University. It was here where I began my formal training and studies in psychology and how they relate to psychological momentum, athletic competition and psychological preparation and improving physical stamina and tolerance to pain. After one year of intense stamina training and preparing for my record attempt, I was able to finish my Masters Thesis: "Effects of Psychological Momentum on the Performance Among American Athletes" (1982) and combined my personal experiences in exercise and physical training and incorporated these experiences in my empirical research involving athletes and improving athletic performance. I later broke the Guinness Book of World Records in consecutive sit-ups (29, 051 in just over 10 hours) in 1982 and one year later broke the world record in consecutive jumping jacks (40, 014). My experiences, philosophy and views regarding training, self-esteem and achieving goals despite numerous obstacles are described and elaborated in detail in this book as we review current theory in psychology. My goal is to help the reader understand how psychological theory may be applied to their personal goals and help them be successful in their lives, regardless what their goals are. Finally, this book is about you achieving your personal and professional goals and to help you realize your full potential. It doesn't matter what the goals are, if you wish to lost 10, 20, 30 lbs. or more, or if you wish to complete a marathon for the first time (26.2 miles), or complete a degree program that you may have procrastinated for years—the concepts discussed in this book are meant for you. No fancy concepts, no expensive things to buy, simply a philosophy and mental focusing technique that will allow you to better understand how the mind and body work together and achieve your personal goals.

■ How Do I Begin To Believe In Myself?

In my opinion, most people are capable of achieving much, much more in their lives but are limited by negative belief systems or unhealthy cognitive schemas that they learned early in childhood. As B. F. Skinner noted, many common problems that people experience in their lives (i.e., depression, substance abuse) are caused simply by poor choices that we make and the reinforcing consequences that are associated with those choices. These poor choices are further exacerbated by the unhealthy and erroneous cognitive belief systems that are associated with unhealthy behaviors (i.e., "I can never lose the weight that I have been trying to lose for years . . . It's my destiny to remain this way my whole life."). Furthermore, if we remain in a state of depression long enough we begin to believe that we are helpless to make any positive changes in our life. This is what Martin Seligman (1975) refers to as *learned helplessness*. If we wish to change our behavior, then change the environment that contributes to the unhealthy choices and begin thinking about positive choices that we are all capable of making in our lives. Believe that it is your destiny to live a healthier and happier life, and it will become just that! Many people feel that they know the answers and the steps to improving their lives, but are simply unprepared to execute the healthy choices and decisions that will improve the quality of their life. In this book we help provide you with the tools to make the positive choices that ultimately will lead to a happier and more productive lifestyle. This book, based on my own personal experiences and theories by leading sport psychologists, will help you realize your true potential and will help you get "into the zone" in your life.

August John Hoffman, Ph.D.
Spring 2005

Introduction to Sport Psychology: Why This Text Is Necessary

This text was written with one goal in mind: To help individuals achieve wellness and physical health by understanding how psychology influences sport and exercise activity. As a sport psychology and research psychology instructor for several years, I came to realize that there are many individuals who have the capacity to train and exercise and improve their health, but simply lack the specific knowledge in motivating themselves to achieve their physical training and exercise goals. The purpose of this book is very simple: To help people achieve their goals by better understanding psychological principles and applying these principles in exercise and sport for better health. Increasingly more individuals are becoming aware of the importance of health, wellness and increased activity and exercise. As this book was being written, Hardee's® restaurant introduced their new "Monsterburger©" a double-burger of almost *two-thirds* of a pound of beef, four bacon strips, cheese and mayonnaise all combined to total almost 1500 calories (calories that total *more* than two of McDonald's® Big Mac's sandwiches)! To put this into perspective, an individual would need to run almost 2 miles to burn off the calories from these highly caloric foods. Is it any wonder that we are truly in the midst of an obesity epidemic? Despite the numerous warnings from medical and health specialists, the trend of increasing portion sizes together with high caloric foods is becoming increasingly evident in our society. The need to identify healthy foods, exercise programs that reach the needs of all individuals, and educating ourselves for improved diets has never been more important. The goals of teaching sport psychology are unique in the sense that we wish to incorporate theory into practice—how can we best teach students the principles of motivation, visualization, and increased stamina and strength from the "textbook" approach that also may be incorporated into practice and training on the field or on the court? When we first teach students who are interested in sport psychology how to think independently and incorporate theory into their own training skills, we as instructors are teaching not only academic theory but also practice as a way of life that improves wellness and the overall quality of living.

Imagine you have been golfing for several years, and your favorite putt is within two to three feet from the cup. You've made this type of putt hundreds (if not thousands) of times before. However, now many people are watching you as you approach the green. Furthermore, you are playing with friends and the golf match depends on you making this putt. You line up the putt, concentrate, but something somehow just doesn't feel right. You miss the putt—what happened? Many times in athletic and sport competition athletes can focus too much and actually become distracted in what otherwise is a normal or routine behavior. Sport psychology is a vital component of psychology today because sports have become proliferated and assimilated into our society—when we win at something—anything, we feel better about ourselves and those who contributed to the win. Sport psychology refers to the application of psychological principles to sport and athletic activity. A sport psychologist is an individual who is trained to understand sport activity and human behavior and delineate those factors that improve performance. However, sport psychologists wear several hats on and off the court—a sport psychologist may help encourage an athlete who is feeling down after a disappointing play, or a sport psychologist may occasionally serve as a trainer, a counselor, and motivator. This book will explore the several factors that are associated with successful athletic performance—the personality characteristics of the athlete, the environment that triggers successful (and unsuccessful) performance, and the relationship between coaching and individual performance. There are many agencies that recognize, formalize and monitor the development and structure of issues in sport psychology: The American Association of Aerobics and Fitness Association (AAAFA), American College of Sports Medicine (ACSM), The Association of for the Advancement of Applied Sport Psychology (AAASP) and the Amateur Athletic Union (AAU). There are many similarities among general psychologists and sport psychologists. For example, both psychologists and sport psychologists are concerned with observing and understanding human behavior and both areas engage in empirical research to improve functioning and performance in society, and teachers of psychology try to find ways to stimulate and motivate learning among students very similar to the coach who tries to motivate and stimulate his or her athletes during competition.

While this text may be helpful for anyone who is interested in improving their performance relative to sport and exercise, it really was written for several groups who are concerned with better understanding human functioning. The first group would include undergraduate students who may be interested in studying various courses within the discipline of psychology. Sport psychology will focus on concentration factors as they relate to athletic performance, guided imagery and visualization skills, controlling temper and emotions in key situations, reducing aggression in competitive sports, and the psychosocial issues that are relative to competitive environments. Thus, many of the same topics that we discuss in traditional psychology courses will also be addressed in this text, but most importantly how the psychological variables influence athletic performance and sport performance. A second group of individuals that may be interested in this text include individuals interested in motivation and exercise. *The key to successful training and exercise is in identifying and achieving your goals and feeling good in the process.* Thus, this text is also devoted to the individual who wishes to train for optimal physical health (i.e., keeping your weight at ideal levels, blood pressure, etc.) and psychological benefits (i.e., relieving stress from the job). In a word, this text is designed to help people who train and exercise for health, fun and to feel better. We should pause for a moment here and consider the importance of this concept—imagine participating in an exercise routine that is healthy, fun and challenging all at the same time! Exercise does not have to be (nor should it ever be) dull and mundane. We know as psychologists that people tend to repeat those behaviors that are most enjoyable and rewarding, so the key to maintaining a healthy exercise routine is to enjoy what you do and feel passion in your training. We can apply the concepts of operant conditioning in psychology to your exercise routine, because behaviors that are rewarding (which we tend to repeat) and other behaviors that are painful and difficult tend to be extinguished. Thus, we gravitate to engage in those behaviors that make us happy and discontinue activities that we do not enjoy. This basic law in psychology has its roots in operant conditioning and is also known as the "Law of Effect": People repeat those behaviors that promote positive reinforcement (i.e., "You look great!! What have you been doing?") and we avoid those behaviors that are not rewarding in some way (i.e., pain, sore muscles, etc.).

Perhaps a final group of individuals that may benefit from this text are coaches, fitness instructors and health trainers. We have devoted several chapters that focus on motivating specific populations of individuals, such as children (making exercise a fun activity in schools and how to combat childhood obesity), the changing world of the female athlete competitive athlete in sports, and health and fitness with the physically challenged.

As a health and fitness instructor and psychology professor for several years, I had (and still continue to have) the unique and fortunate opportunity to train individuals who are interested in improving their physical health and to use my psychological training to help motivate them in achieving their personal goals. Within the last fifteen years I have seen one characteristic continually surface time and again when training and working with individuals in health and fitness: *Only those people who actually think they can achieve their goals eventually do achieve their goals.* Conversely, those people who experience difficulty in achieving their goals or become frustrated usually also have one thing in common: *They do not think they are capable of achieving their personal health-related goals.* They may not outright admit it, but after talking to them and gaining their trust over time, several clients confide that they have "always had a weight problem . . . and I just accepted that I would always be this way" or "I never was able to complete and finish a program to achieve my fitness goals . . . something always came up or I just lost interest." These comments and the tremendously important issue of helping people achieve and maintain healthy lifestyles provided the motivation and impetus in writing this book because I personally firmly believe this: Anyone is capable of achieving their goals if they have two key points in mind: a) The belief in their own ability to achieve their goals (i.e., a positive belief system where you feel in control of your own behavior); and b) Developing realistic standards and expectations in the process of attaining these goals.

Chapter 1:
Where Did Sport Psychology Come From?

Sport psychology has not always existed within the discipline of psychology. Sport psychology is a relatively new area in psychology that explores the relationship between psychological principles, sport activity, competition and athletic experiences. While athletes have known for many years (centuries, in fact) that understanding psychological principles improves sport performances, only within the last 100 years have we been able to shape sport psychology into a true science that utilizes the empirical data and the scientific method. Most researchers and sport psychologists agree that the first empirical research addressing psychological phenomena and sport activity was conducted by Norman Triplett (1897). Here Triplett analyzed the impact of other competitors (cyclists) on an individual athlete. His research findings demonstrated the fact that when athletes compete with other athletes, in most cases performance increases. This study was further supported in much later research by Richard Zajonc (1965) who demonstrated the "social facilitation effect." The social facilitation effect states that the impact of audience or an observer can have either a positive or negative influence on athletic performance, depending on how comfortable the athlete is in performing the task. In other words, both Triplett (1897) and Zajonc (1965) had similar findings, even though their research was conducted almost 70 years apart. Zajonc determined that depending on the degree of difficulty of the task (what he called either "dominant" or "non-dominant" tasks), an audience can either facilitate performance or inhibit performance. With dominant (easy) tasks, large groups tend to facilitate performance, whereas large groups tend to inhibit performance with non-dominant (complex) tasks. Triplett found that individual athletes involved with specific synchronized performance are facilitated when other groups of athletes perform with them. Sports that require synchronized performance, such as rowing, bicycling and swimming seem to excel when performed in concert with other athletes. Even running seems to be facilitated (in terms of running faster times) when runners can "pace" themselves with other athletes. There have been many reasons for the long overdue scientific study and analysis of sport and athletic behaviors. For several decades (even in some cases today) a bias against athletes and sports existed in academia. Traditional academics and scholars had felt that sports and athletic competition were not valid topics of research, and even complained of athletes not being devoted enough to scholarly work. Today we are happy to recognize that the majority of NCAA athletes are indeed scholars and successful students who combine the rigors of undergraduate academic work with the physical demands of sport. In fact, the majority of NCAA athletes have grade point averages that exceed 3.0 who go on to successful professional careers.

The history of sport psychology has seen tremendous variation from the time of the early Greeks. Most people are aware that ancient Greeks first introduced the Olympics centuries ago, but the actual development of sport psychology didn't evolve until the late 18th Century in the Soviet Union shortly after the Bolshevik Revolution in 1917. As the government of the Soviet Union controlled various components of public and private lifestyles, a growing movement towards dominating sports existed to express nationalistic pride. The government recognized the importance of physical activity and encouraged all citizens to participate in daily exercise. The government also expressed strong interest in creating the image of military and economic superiority to the world, and began to illustrate the strength of the country by dominating sports and international competition. Several famous (and infamous) leaders throughout the world have tried to correlate military and economic superiority through superior athletic performance (i.e., Hitler, Mao Tse Tung) which resulted in more attention to exploring psychological influence in sport performance. Soon the "Socialist Approach" dominated the world of sport (1960–1980), where the government invested tremendous resources to identify and recruit very young athletes (age 3) to begin training at remote and highly concentrated camps. Children were separated from their families for years, exposed to highly rigorous and intense training programs over twelve hours daily. Clearly, the Western philosophical ideology of "playing for fun" did not apply to the Soviet Socialist Approach to athletic training.

Different forms and methods of motivation, such as intrinsic and extrinsic motivation were developed in the Soviet Union to enhance performance. Intrinsically motivated athletes included those athletes who participated in the sport activity for the sheer enjoyment of the sport—extrinsic motivation refers to a form of athletic performance that is entirely motivated for external (extrinsic) factors, such as money, attention and tangible rewards. Most commonly athletes have a combination of both intrinsic and extrinsic forms of motivation to excel in sports. More recently, athletes from underdeveloped or economically deprived countries are participating in sports as a means of economic support. For example, several athletes from the Soviet Union (and now Russia) participate in sports as a career, and approach their competition as a job. For many of these athletes, their only means of support is through winning and achieving success through their sport. Thus, tremendous pressure exists among athletes from underdeveloped countries solely as a means to exist and survive in an economy that is struggling to survive.

The link between psychological preparation and superior athletic performance did not become apparent in the United States until the late 18th century with the work by Coleman Roberts Griffith who was a professor at the University of Illinois. Griffith created an institution called the Athletic Research Laboratory (1925) at the University of Illinois that many agree was a trigger for the development of sport psychology in the United States. The Athletic Research Laboratory helped shatter the myth and bias held against athletes and the use of scientific procedures in understanding sport psychology. Griffith is considered to be the founder of sport psychology in North America and was a pioneer in engaging in research that was addressed motor skills and personality characteristics. The concept of sport psychology in general was slow to develop throughout North America due to perhaps the erroneous assumption that sports and academics were separate entities, as well as the bias that athletic endeavors did not involve (or deserve) scientific analysis or the components of the scientific method. These unfortunate sport stereotypes persisted in American universities through the 1960's era, and it wasn't until academicians such as Franklin Henry and John Lawther began to incorporate these courses in traditional educational environments. These biases, however blatantly incorrect, persisted until the late 1960–1970 era, where we begin to see more research being published regarding the links between psychological momentum, visualization and rehearsal skills and athletic performance. New training centers were being created, and the International Society for Sport Psychology (ISSP) was created in 1968. Empirical research and tremendous success was being achieved by researchers, coaches and athletes who began to recognize the importance of emotional and psychological control in the world of the elite athlete, and by 1980 the United States Olympic Committee (USOC) instituted a sport psychology advisory board to be implemented by the highly successful 1984 Olympics held in Los Angeles, California.

■ STYLES OF CULTURE INFLUENCING TEAM & INDIVIDUAL SPORTS

The collectivistic culture and the individualistic culture are important characteristics that influence how people communicate, relate and interact with one another. Culture itself is defined as a collection of beliefs and values shared by a group of individuals. Culture defines who we are in terms of our own identity as well as the norms that shape the behaviors of others who comprise the group. When cultural values are violated, sanctions usually result. We teach cultural values through our religion, our social and professional activities, and our recreational activities including sport and athletic behavior. The values that are taught to children and people within society are also reflected through sports and competitive activities. How are the concepts of collectivistic and individualistic cultures relative to sport psychology? Actually, both of these concepts are very important to sport psychology because they influence how we relate to other people (i.e., such as an individual relates to his or her teammates in group sports) and how we make decisions during competitive environments that often determine the outcome of winning versus losing. Perhaps no other topic addressing sport psychology today is more important than understanding the effective components of team work, communication and trust—the dynamics of group functioning and effective performance. The contrast between a highly effective, dynamic and collaborative team as compared to a loosely organized ball club that lacks trust among team mates is profound. Today in modern sports, coaches, owners and players are beginning to discover that becoming a team means more than just having the best players—good team work makes good players. This chapter will explore a seldom discussed topic when addressing sport psychology and the dynamics of winning: How the team culture can influence players to become more responsible to each other and create a sense of "positive interdependency" while playing with each other.

The differences between "positive" and "negative" interdependency are that *positive* interdependency refers to a healthy and productive form of dependency seen in all successful teams. Positive interdependency means relying on your team mates to be responsible among each other and to organize the style of play that is best for the team. Positive interdependency means the ability to make personal sacrifices for others than enhances team performance and winning; it is the realization that the team exists for a group of individuals playing together for a common goal. Conversely, negative interdependency means playing for one's self, for money, for attention, and primarily for extrinsic values. The form of negative interdependency can destroy team morale by a sense of egoism that permeates the entire team. When players play for themselves individually and do not focus on the other players on the team, individuals do not play cohesively. The team has created a set of individual identities rather that a single set of a collective identity. We will discuss further how the concepts of interdependency, collective identity and values can dramatically influence the style of play among athletes in chapter 6 (Collective versus Individualistic Cultures and Sport).

Perhaps a better understanding of the differences in individual and team sports may be assisted by a review of the differences between the concepts of collectivistic and individualistic cultures. Kitayama (1997) has explored these cultural differences to some extent and has described the Western culture as being predominantly self-oriented where individuals view daily activities as opportunities for self-improvement and individual gain. Conversely, the Eastern cultures view day to day interaction and activities with others as a means of self-analysis and opportunities to improve our relations with others. In a word, then, collectivistic cultures emphasize the importance of the group and how individuals should work for the overall benefit of the group or society itself. Individualistic cultures are very different, where emphasis is placed on individual success and gain, even at the expense of the group. I think it is very clear to see the negative impact of a highly individualistic culture on team sports. During the 2004 NBA playoff series, the Los Angeles Lakers were expected to win the championship because they had the best players the NBA had to offer: Shaquille O'Neil, Kobe Bryant, Rick Fox, and others. However, one important ingredient was missing in this recipe—the players were experiencing difficulty in communicating with each, there was rivalry among the players, and the consensus was that no one on the team wanted to play as a team. The result was a very disappointing loss and Shaquille O'Neil was traded and Rick Fox later retired from basketball.

Conversely, let's review the 2004 Olympic Games in Greece. Many new teams in basketball were challenging the United States—remember, prior to these games, the United States had lost only twice in the history of the modern games. However, again due to the problems of poor communication enhanced by the individualistic culture and the emphasis of "Me First" or self-centered mentality, the United States lost *twice*. Spain (a relative newcomer to the game) played exceedingly well and their style of play was characterized by communication, drive, self-criticism (instead of criticizing others) which is basically the essence of the collectivistic culture. Thus, teaching communication skills and to value the importance of others as a vital link of the team are critical components of collectivism. The motivating factor in the individualistic culture is the need to improve the self at the cost of the group and to identify your own needs regardless of the needs of the group, whereas the motivating factor of behavior in the collectivistic culture is self-analysis, sacrificial behavior and critical review of the self to enhance the group. Individuals who have been exposed to the collectivistic philosophy make personal sacrifices to enhance the welfare of the group and are considered to be part of a collective identity with their team.

▄▄ THE DEVELOPMENT OF THE SPORTS SOCIAL IDENTITY

The sports social identity is important to understand when exploring how individualistic and collectivistic cultures have influenced the style of play among athletes. What actually defines the athletic personality in addition to the culture where one lives is the sports social identity: An athlete's definition of who he or she is, including personal attributes such as education, gender, ethnicity and age. Components of the sports social identity may include:

Training and Practice History   **Personality Characteristics**

Components of the Sports Social Identity

Interests and Activities   **Locus of Control (Internal Versus External)**

Figure 1a   Components of the Sports Social Identity

▄▄ CHAPTER 1 QUESTIONS & REVIEW

1. Define the term "sport psychology" and describe how sport psychology has evolved as a discipline in science today;

2. Describe the contributions of Coleman Roberts Griffith—how did his work gradually lead to the development of sport psychology in the United States?

3. Why did bias exist in the field of sport psychology, especially in the area of academics? In your opinion, is this bias justified? Identify three ways that coaches, athletes and educators may help address this bias;

4. Explain how the culture of the athlete may impact his or her style of play; Describe the relationship between individualistic and collectivistic cultures with team and individual sport competition;

5. Describe the Sports Social Identity—What are the four components of the Sports Social Identity and explain how they combine to influence athletic performance.

Chapter 2:
Personality Characteristics and Modern Sport: From Freud to Bandura

When we discuss the variables that make successful athletes superior athletes, the term "personality" comes to mind. The elite or successful athlete is an individual with such positive personality characteristics that include responsibility, persistence and determination, resilience and a positive frame of mind. However, before we talk about the ideal personality of the successful athlete, we need to accurately identify and describe what the term means. What exactly do we mean when we talk about a personality? Can we actually see a personality? Of course not—but we will soon discover that in the field of psychology and sport psychology we will be discussing and addressing many concepts and topics that are based not on direct, observable facts but rather constructs. Constructs in psychology refer to psychological phenomenon that we agree exist but are not capable of being directly measured. Examples of psychological constructs that impact sports include aggression, anxiety, happiness and jealousy. A personality is also based on a construct—things that we all agree exist but defy empirical and quantitative analysis. For our purposes in sport psychology we will define the term personality as a combination of skills, aptitudes, attitudes and traits that consistently emerge and characterize an individual's behavior within a wide range of environments. The term "personality" is extremely powerful—it basically describes how we generally feel about someone most of the time, in either a positive or negative perspective. But in order to determine specifically what types of personality components make athletes successful, we must first explore the history of the development of the term personality and understand how personality characteristics actually influence behavior. As with many topics in psychology, we shall first begin our review of the personality with name of Sigmund Freud.

Freud's theory of psychoanalysis has represented a milestone of accomplishments in research addressing personality theory. Perhaps Freud's greatest contributions to the field of psychology addresses the role of the unconscious mind and behavior itself, where Freud argued that our most significant decisions and choices are influenced not by conscious decisions but rather unconscious mechanisms. Freud has made a tremendous contribution to the field of psychology, and is considered by many to be the founder of modern psychology. Some of the significant contributions that Freud has made include the defense mechanisms (unconscious efforts to protect the ego when overwhelmed with anxiety), the psychosexual stages of development (oral, anal, phallic, latent and genital), the psychodynamic theory of the personality (id, ego and superego), and perhaps his magnum opus, the Oedipal Complex. These important contributions will be discussed at some length and we will also view the traditional Freudian psychoanalytic theory with a particular emphasis on athletic and sport competition. For example, Freud argued that the motivating forces among all groups of people are the unconscious drives or urges that contribute to aggression and sexuality. Freud further argued that these unconscious drives or urges are addressed in a variety of activities that we engage in with other people. The cultures and norms within society may also influence how these instincts are addressed, and during the Victorian era many thoughts and impulses were repressed due to the social and moral constraints that were common during this period of time. For example, if an athlete who participated in a particularly aggressive sport makes a very aggressive hit or tackle, he is congratulated for his aggression by his coaches, but criticized among other members in society. From the psychodynamic perspective, the athlete is "working through" his aggressive impulse via catharsis. This is the goal for all people, according to Freud, the capacity to address or "work through" our aggressive instincts in a socially acceptable manner that would not conflict with the moral restraints of society.

In some of his earlier research, Freud noted that several of his patients (the most famous being "Anna O") complained of physical problems such as paralysis, blindness, and numbness and tingling in the hands. Early on in his career, Freud worked essentially as a medical doctor (a neurologist) where he began to see an increasing number of clinical cases where patients experienced serious medical problems but lacked any organic cause—in other words, the paralyzed patients did not encounter any trauma to the central nervous system, the blind patients did not have any physical impairment with the optic nerve, etc. This peculiar psycho-physiological phenomenon led to Freud's greatest discovery, a discovery that ultimately changed his focus from physical ailments and conditions to psychological conditions causing physical disorders—a term Freud called "conversion disorders." Put in simple terms, Freud hypothesized that the tremendous social pressure and repression from the Victorian era influenced his clients to suppress their true biological urges—both aggressive and sexual. This form of repressed energy needed to be released in some way, and the physiological problems were actually a result of the stored or pent up energy and anxiety that could not consciously be released during the Victorian era. Thus, according to Freud, a young woman who suppressed her sexual urges with her hands resulted in numbness and tingling in the hand; a woman who wanted to see something that was socially taboo or inappropriate during the Victorian era became blind; and a woman who wanted to engage in extramarital affairs with her lover became paralyzed (literally unable to move or ambulate to her socially taboo lover). Incidentally, all of Freud's patients during this time period were women.

■■■ CONSCIOUSNESS, PRECONSCIOUS & THE UNCONSCIOUS

If you were to ask an athlete why he or she has selected a particular sport that they prefer to play, you might hear any type of responses, such as: "I like it" or "Because I am good at it." Thus, the athlete is consciously aware of activities and sports that they excel in. Consciousness refers to a form of awareness, and that this awareness fluctuates and changes throughout the day. Remember also that the choices that these athletes make are conscious choices, meaning we feel that we are aware of the decisions that we make and act on them. However, as we mentioned earlier, many important decisions are made not on the conscious level, but rather on the unconscious level. We will now discuss the three forms of consciousness (conscious, preconscious and unconscious) and identify the characteristics that influence the choices athletes make when selecting sports and competitive environments. As you may recall, Freud argued that our conscious decisions that we make are strongly influenced by the unconscious mechanisms that we are not aware of. The unconscious is thus described as the part of the mental activity and processing that we are unaware of and the conscious mind is described as simply awareness. Finally, the preconscious is described as an "in between link" between conscious activity and the unconscious mind. The preconscious serves as a bridge between conscious behaviors and activities and the unconscious mind. Additionally, the preconscious mind refers to the level of the mind that is not actually conscious, but if we try hard enough and focus on an activity we may be able to recall distant memories or activities. For example, if I ask you to describe an event on a specific holiday or vacation several years ago (i.e., a trip to Catalina) with some concentration and effort we may be able to recall specific events that did occur. Thus, the events were not existent on a conscious level, but with some effort we were able to recall specific details of the event back to consciousness.

■■■ THE PERSONALITY ACCORDING TO FREUD

When we typically describe someone's personality, what kinds of things are we really referring to? When we say that someone has a "really great personality" what do we mean? The term personality is a very complicated topic, and in order to understand how athletic behavior operates under a variety of competitive environments we must first define the term itself. The term personality is described as a collection of stable traits, dispositions, demeanor and attitudes that typically characterize how one behaves under a variety of situations. In other words, the term personality is used to describe how someone usually responds and typically behaves under various circumstances. Stop and think for a moment—are there certain types of personality characteristics that are ideal and optimal for successful athletes? Think about two or three very successful athletes in different sports—are there similarities regarding the personalities of these athletes? Are they regarded by people as hard workers, reliable, trustworthy, determined, and do they stay focused despite distractions? Probably most successful athletes do fit these characteristics and we may generalize that their personality does make a profound difference in the performance of the specific sport.

■■■ THE TOPOGRAPHIC THEORY: ID, EGO & SUPEREGO

Freud described the personality as consisting of three variables: The ego, id and superego. The ego is best described as the part of the personality that is the "executive" of the personality that balances the needs of the id and superego. The ego must somehow satisfy the instinctual needs of the id and superego and thus conform to the demands of society. Because of the need to meet the demands of society, Freud argued that the ego operates or functions on what is regarded as the "reality principle" which means operating and functioning within the parameters of the rules of society. For example, if you as a student are sitting in a classroom trying to pay attention to a lecture but find yourself becoming hungry, you may be tempted to leave early—however, the ego portion of the personality may encourage you to wait for the next break before leaving class. Thus, the ego keeps the powers of the id and superego in check and helps to balance and control behaviors that conform to social norms and protocol. The id is very different from the ego, and is described as the raw and animalistic portion of the personality—it is described as doing what you want, when you want and how you want it. The id often is characterized and described as the child of the personality. The id refers to the instinctual energy that we all have and must be resolved in some way. For example, the id works through a concept Freud referred to as the "pleasure principle"—maximizing gratification and pleasure while minimizing cost and effort. Think of the pleasure principle as similar to the principles of Hedonism—whatever feels good must be good for you and anything that requires cost and effort is not good. The id is the source of all instinctual energy and operates without regard to social norms or laws. Thus, Freud argued that individuals who live their lives without regard to the laws of society and live according to their own pleasure principles really are being controlled by instinctual urges and impulses that we call the id. The final component of the personality according to Freudian psychoanalysis is the superego. In many ways, the superego is the antithesis of the id. The superego is often compared to the moral conscious of the personality, as the superego directs our behavior in terms of what we should or ought to be doing. Perhaps most importantly regarding the superego is the influence of the ego ideal, where the superego prevents us from engaging in morally reprehensible or illegal behaviors. The superego does not develop until sometime later in childhood, and helps balance the opposite needs of the id. For example, imagine you have been trying to improve your physical health and have been eating only healthy and organic foods. As you walk to class, you see a vending machine with your favorite candy—the id of course is telling you that purchasing this candy from the vending machine "just this one time" can't hurt. However, the superego keeps you in check, and prevents you from buying the candy. The ego plays into this interchange by balancing the needs and serves as a compromise by suggesting to you: "why not eat some fruit instead?"

■ CAN PERSONALITIES CHANGE?

Freud was really the first theorist to discuss how the personality develops from infancy through adulthood, and how our relationships with our parents and significant persons in our family may have had profound influences on how we make important choices in our lives. For example, Freud argued that our relationships with our parents may influence our choices in professional careers, our relationships with others, even the type of spouse that we may consider for marriage. Many individuals ask the question: "Can an individual's personality change or be modified?" Perhaps the best response to this question is that *behaviors* can change, but traits, dispositions and characteristics that comprise the personality tend to remain static. Freud would certainly agree with this statement, as he maintained that the human personality is fixed and based on inherent instincts that involve aggression and sexuality. When discussing the different types of personalities and the influence of athletic performance, Freud would argue that particularly aggressive individuals actually seek out those activities such as contact sports to "work through" their aggression while playing active sports. This would allow the person to literally hit and tackle others and reduce their aggressive impulses in a socially accepted manner, such as football activities or boxing matches. While Freud was not known for his particularly optimistic views regarding the human condition, he did feel that people are capable of making contributions to society. However, Freud's views regarding the personality are predominantly fixed and deterministic; in other words, Freud argued that human behavior and personality are controlled by biological urges and destructive instincts that manifest themselves in a variety of ways. Freud further described human behavior and motivation as occurring through two primary forces: sexual drives (a term he referred to as *libidos*) and later in his life he focused more on a counterbalancing force, *thanatos,* or the destructive death force. These two diametrically opposed forces have profound influences on how people interact with others. For example, a person may argue in a very hostile manner or drive his or her car in a very aggressive style, or an athlete may select to play in very physical and aggressive sports, such as rugby or football. These examples illustrate how the aggressive instinct may influence not only what we do in terms of behaviors, but also our relationships with people and our choices and decisions in life. Additionally, Freud would probably comment that while people are capable of occasionally making positive and healthy choices in their lives, the biological tendency to engage in destructive behaviors due to the presence of aggressive instincts will always be present in our behavior and manifest itself either directly or indirectly.

■ THE PSYCHOSEXUAL STAGES OF DEVELOPMENT

Now that we have briefly discussed the personality according to Freud, how does the personality progress and develop from childhood to adulthood? What exactly are the circumstances that influence our personality development and how can we modify the personality to make us happy in our lives? Many individuals have commented on how the personality may develop, but Freud was the first theorist to offer a comprehensive theory describing how the personality develops and is influenced through five stages of growth: the oral stage (from birth to about one year of age); the anal stage (from one year to about three years of age); the phallic stage (from three years to about five years); the latent stage (from six years to about eleven years of age); and finally the genital stage (from adulthood on through late adulthood).

■ ORAL STAGE OF DEVELOPMENT

The oral stage represents a period of time where the infant develops a relationship with his or her mother by gratifying their needs by stimulating the mouth, tongue and oral area in general. The mouth and oral area are the primary areas where the infant receives pleasure and gratification by sucking and nursing. According to Freud, infants derive a very primitive form of pleasure by attending to their needs orally, and too much or too little attention to this area may lead to personality problems later in adult life. For example, too much pleasure at the oral stage according to Freud may lead to a "fixation" where as adults we unconsciously strive to achieve gratification from anxiety by excessive drinking (i.e., alcoholism), overeating, chewing nails, and other forms of oral activity. Freud argued that these oral activities are an unconscious attempt to relieve anxiety and psychologically "go back" (regress) to a period of time marked by calmness and security.

■ ANAL STAGE

In Freud's second stage of psychosexual development, the child develops the ability to control bowel movements and bladder control. Children at this stage are learning to conform to the regulations and rules of society and learn to become responsive to their physiological signals that indicate the need to use the bathroom. Freud argued that between the ages of one to three years, children are beginning to learn and be responsive to rules and regulations in their relationship with parents and peers. Bowel control, or what is commonly referred to as "potty training" is very important to children as they perceive this responsibility as the first task that they can successfully achieve and have autonomy and control over. Children respond to parents' reaction to their child's ability to control their bladder and bowel, such as their ability to sleep at night without wetting the bed. At this point in time, children are responding to their ability to identify tasks and successfully accomplish them. Children also begin to learn to share activities with other children and are beginning to learn to interact with others at this period of time. From the sport psychology perspective, this is an especially important period of time as children learn communication skills and compatibility that are essential characteristics in team sports. During the anal stage, children learn to coordinate activities and are becoming skilled in motor activities that may be important in sports later in development. In terms of personality characteristics, children develop specific behaviors relative to control and responsibility and order during the anal stage. For example, successful athletes must adhere to rigorous training schedules, show up to practice on time, and develop organizational skills that influence individual performance. These skills are critical for ideal and exceptional performance among athletes, and must be learned during the anal stage. Athletes that historically have had problems in conforming to team training standards and practice schedules may have rebelled against parental training techniques during this period of time. Finally, how children learn and respond to guidance, supervision and training by parents during the anal stage often determine how they respond to direction and supervision as adults.

■ PHALLIC STAGE & IDENTIFICATION: TEACHING CHILDREN EXERCISE AS A WAY OF LIFE

In the phallic stage (ages three to five), the child discovers the source of pleasure is through stimulation of the genitalia, and that the Oedipal Complex must be resolved. According to Freud, the classic interpretation of the Oedipal Complex is that all children have an unconscious drive to possess or have intercourse with the opposite sex parent and terminate the existence or murder the same sex parent. The rivalry that the young boy feels toward his father is labeled as *castration anxiety,* where the young boy unconsciously fears that his father will remove his penis and testicles. Freud based this interpretation from the classic Greek tragedy by Sophocles as a universal experience and necessary for healthy sexual maturity. When the child realizes that they cannot destroy their same-sex parent, they learn to identify with them and imitate their behaviors. Now, the young boy wants to do things with his father and play with him during daily activities. The key term to focus on here is *identification* of the same sex parent during the phallic stage—the child realizes that it is unrealistic to try to remove his father, thus he becomes his best friend and develops an alliance with him. This concept of identification is critical in terms of sports and athletic behaviors among children, because many children imitate and adapt to the behaviors and activities that their parents are participating in. For example, if a young boy or girl between the ages of three, four or five years sees his or her parent stretching and exercising as part of their daily routine, most children will imitate these behaviors into their own routine when they become adults themselves. This imitative form of behavior is no different from young people adopting behaviors relative to eating habits and obesity, or watching media programs and becoming influenced by the content that they are exposed to. The key point to emphasize here is that if you wish to teach and train children to have healthy and active lifestyles when they are older, you need to serve as a model for them during the stage of identification as Freud suggests. Consider this period of time to be the most sensitive when children begin to incorporate healthy activities into their own lifestyle that will hopefully stay with them as they mature. Many young athletes begin their athletic careers by interacting in sports and learning sports during these critical ages—3, 4, 5 and 6 years are vital years in learning some sports. Perhaps more importantly, the child is learning to form relationships with significant persons in his life, and developing a bond of trust that is vital in any relationship with family members or team members in a team sport.

▬▬ LATENCY STAGE & GENITAL STAGE

The psychosexual stage of latency is described as a period of dormancy involving sexual attention, and is experienced between the ages of 5 or 6 through puberty. During this period of time, Freud described all sexual energy and attention as basically being inactive, where the young child now focuses his attention towards his same-sex playmates and is unconscious of sexual drives. Finally, during the genital stage of psychosexual development (puberty through adulthood), the young adult faces the challenge of engaging in a healthy sexual relationship with another person, and is capable of communicating and expressing their needs to maintain a loving and happy relationship with another person.

▬▬ EMPIRICAL DATA AND FREUDIAN THEORY: WAS FREUD RIGHT?

When Freud originally presented this information to the public, he was criticized and derided as being eccentric and even perverted in describing his views of children and their relationships with their parents. Remember, Freudian theory was introduced during the peak of moral restraint and repression during the Victorian era, and even to suggest a sexual link or connection between child and parent was widely condemned. However, people gradually began to accept some of Freud's views, and even anecdotally if we see how children respond to opposite-sex parents, we see that young girls do tend to cherish their fathers and young boys also have very close emotional bonds with their mothers. However, empirical evidence is not conclusive in many of Freud's theories and is still under speculation among many scholars. Indeed, many researchers view his therapeutic exchanges involving latent sexual drives with his patients (such as the previously mentioned Anna O.) were actually projections of his own repressed views of sexuality commonly known as "counter-transference" in the psychoanalytic field (Webster, 1995). In sum, perhaps a final reason why Freud continues to be a topic of discussion in psychology and his views remain pervasive is because these theories were highly theoretical—where they could not be proven *not* to exist (i.e., how can one "prove" that a psychological construct such as an ego actually exist?).

■ ALFRED ADLER AND INDIVIDUAL PSYCHOLOGY: THE ATHLETE BECOMING STRONGER THROUGH CONTRIBUTIONS TO SOCIETY

Alfred Adler was at one time a close and trusted friend of Freud. However, the two gradually experienced disagreements in theory that ultimately led to their estrangement as colleagues and friends. The two theorists differed sharply; Adler argued that people and their personality are not separated into parts, whereas Freud argued that the id, ego and superego comprise the personality. Additionally, Adler argued that the personality is indivisible, and the motivating component of behavior is a sense of inferiority that provides the impetus for us to excel and strive to achieve our goals. For example, a young boy may have been teased by his peers as being "slow" and unable to compete with others. This initial criticism of physical skills and prowess usually provides the impetus in developing (compensating) for excellence in physical skills, such as playing basketball. Adler would then argue that these conscious feelings of inferiority caused by the derision and ridicule of the peers will motivate the young boy to improve his basketball skills, where he practices until late in the evening and is very motivated to excel. If we discuss the basketball skills of now retired basketball star Larry Byrd, Byrd argued that only through determination and long hours of practice was he able to improve to the levels of being an NBA star. Byrd commented during a post-game interview that he often would report to the basketball court two to three hours early just to practice and warm-up by shooting free throws. One may consider this very positive work ethic by Larry Byrd an important part of the culture that children need to learn when playing in any group activity, such as sports.

■ STYLES OF LIFE & THE COLLECTIVE IDENTITY

Individual performance that focuses on team work and group performance will create a form of collective identity—where the team has merged into one force, as opposed to simply groups of individuals. Adler referred to this style of learning that children adapt to as a "style of life." The style of life that Adler refers to is learned typically by children between the ages of three or four years, and the style of life includes important values that can lead the child to either healthy development or unhealthy development. An example would be children learning to continue to work toward their goals in spite of initial difficulty, as opposed to simply giving up or relying on others. Another example would include teaching children to share and play in groups—to rely on group members to achieve a common goal. The essential point is that children need to be taught positive examples of how to interact and work with others to accomplish goals. More importantly, children need to be taught how to utilize the potential strength of the group (or team) and that group performance is always stronger than individual performance. These values are typically taught to children in either a collective society (emphasis on the group's success through individual sacrifices) or an individualistic society (emphasis on individual success at the cost of the group), and that these styles of life may be translated into styles of team work, where positive styles of life taught to a child become manifested into positive styles of sport performance and team work.

> Social Interest: "It is the individual who is not interested in the welfare of others who has the greatest difficulty in life . . . and provides the greatest injuries to others . . . it is from this where all failures develop (Alfred Adler, 1870–1937).

Perhaps one of Adler's greatest areas of contributions to psychology is the notion of social interest and contributing to society. Adler argued that all persons have an innate drive to contribute to society that serves as a form of individual identity and helps to create and identify a sense of purpose regarding our own life. Parents need to teach children the value of assisting others and making sacrifices that contribute to the human condition. Adler further notes that all infants have in some way benefited from the sacrifices of others, and people are inherently and automatically motivated to help others because of our own initial dependency on others as infants. However, Adler comments that children who have been provided with too much attention or material wealth may not be able to develop social interest, as they focus on their own needs at the expense of society. Regrettably, we are beginning to see more of these types of behaviors in our society that are exhibited through a sense of entitlement at the cost of other people. This sense of expectation and entitlement may be a result of the individualistic culture that is becoming more evident and pronounced in our society (see collectivistic and individualistic cultures—page 8). When we teach children that their own needs are more important than the needs of others, behaviors of the child then become egoistic and self-serving.

■■■ TEACHING CHILDREN SPORTS AS A FORM OF CREATIVE POWER

As coaches and parents of young children, Adler encouraged us to help teach children the importance of relying on the cooperation of others in creating something of value. This is manifested not only in classrooms when teaching children to share and interact with others, but also in sports and recreation. Teaching children to participate and cooperate in a variety of team sports and activities helps them to value the input and creativity of others. It also teaches them the important ability in relying on others and valuing diverse contributions from others. Additionally, Adler notes that our primary method of achieving individual value, a sense of personal worth and identity only is capable by making sacrifices for the benefit of others—this is the essence of the collectivistic culture which also may be demonstrated through the concept of team sports. We receive more satisfaction internally when we give more to society and make sacrifices for the improvement of society. Adler further noted that those persons who have high levels of social interest have a beginning sense of "incompleteness" as a child, and this sense of incompleteness is addressed and mollified by participating in a variety of group activities and individual sacrifices. When the group or team advances in competition, our sense of incompleteness is reduced as we have contributed to achieving something that is only accomplished through the combined efforts of a team.

This important component and philosophy is relevant not only to social interaction with children, but may be observed with adult team sports and how members interact with another. When professional athletes feel that they are interacting and contributing with one another and playing truly as a team and one unit, their efforts are coordinated and become significantly more powerful. However, when the social interest declines and the focus is on individual performance, the strength and power of the team becomes significantly damaged and compromised. We have seen this phenomenon in many professional teams, where intrinsic values (shared cooperation and responsibility) are compensated for extrinsic values (money, salaries, attention, and media exposure). Engaging in a competitive sport as a team member and contributing to the team itself, representing a country, or a particular group or culture may be powerful motivating forces in athletic competition. Athletes who have had exposure to the individualistic culture and the sense of entitlement may not recognize the need to make sacrifices for the team itself. They are incapable of utilizing the "creative power" that Adler cites in his research because they are unaware of the very things that motivate them. Individual athletes can only play as a team if they recognize that their individual value as a team member is enhanced with the combined efforts of other team members. Further, Adler argues that individuals must identify and use their own "creative power" that can be used as a vital and successful ingredient in team sports. The creative power that each of us has is essential in identifying a goal and working towards it with others. This was another significant difference between Freud and Adler, where Adler recognized that the creative power in all of us exists and allows us the freedom to make positive choices in our lives. Freud, however, argued that the destructive and dark forces of the unconscious mind limit our ability to make socially cooperative and creative choices that would enhance society. Indeed, Freud commented that the individual is more focused in extrinsic factors and egoistic advantages at the cost of society and others.

Which theorist most accurately describes behavior as it relates to society? Was Adler correct regarding his views of the socially cooperative and motivated person in achieving their goals through the use of their creative power? Or was Freud correct, maintaining that each person has destructive and egoistic motives that are immune to recognizing and understanding social and cooperative strategies in society? Perhaps the answer to this question lies more in understanding how we relate to others and our overall capacity to change based on our environmental exchanges with one another. Clearly, if we teach individuals to value and contribute to society and recognize that participating in team activities is one way to appreciate the value and worth of others, then people are capable of working together for a common goal. The important concept that we need to remember as coaches, parents and educators is that children's behavior is a reflection of the values that they have been exposed to. Sport provides an opportunity to exhibit and demonstrate the values that we teach our children. Thus, we need to teach children and people in general to share, to contribute and to cooperate in activities that benefit society as a whole, not just an individual.

■ CARL GUSTAV JUNG AND THE COLLECTIVE UNCONSCIOUS: SPORT AND THE COLLECTIVE UNCONSCIOUS

Both Sigmund Freud and Alfred Adler described human behavior and the personality as components operating from the unconscious mind. Carl Gustav Jung (1875–1961) was a very gifted and intelligent thinker who also was part of the original "Freudian Circle" with Alfred Adler. However, similar to Adler, Jung and Freud began experiencing theoretical disagreements over psychoanalytic theory, and ultimately in 1913 the two had reached an impasse and remained *incommunicado* for the duration of their professional careers. The original and primary source of agreement among each of these three talented psychoanalytic theorists was the role that the unconscious mind played in behavior, and that the only true way in understanding the mechanisms of the unconscious was through dream analysis. Each of the three theorists also agreed that the unconscious mind contained the true and deep-seated drives and wishes regarding our relationships with people. However, Carl Jung's departure from traditional psychoanalytic theory stems from his description of spiritual matters (mysticism), the collective unconscious, and the archetypes in describing human behavior. Additionally, Carl Jung characterized human behavior as more motivated in the drive to achieve self-realization and insight; thus, Jung argues that individuals are more rational in their thought processes and more importantly capable of making rational and free decisions in their lives. This was a dramatic change from classical Freudian psychoanalytic theory. We shall begin our first description of Jungian psychoanalytic theory with the collective unconscious.

■ THE COLLECTIVE UNCONSCIOUS AND THE ATHLETIC ARCHETYPE

The collective unconscious was a new concept in psychoanalytic theory introduced by Jung. The collective unconscious was a revolutionary concept that described the contents of the unconscious as a collection of primitive and ancient concepts and images that we have inherited from our ancestors. Stored within the collective unconscious is another original feature described by Jung as the "archetype." The archetype is a symbolic image that is stored within the collective unconscious mind that has deep meaning and interpretation relative to our history and culture. For example, archetypes may include topics depicting religion, art, history and what I regard as the competitive nature of humans. If we investigate and explore how specific archetypes relate to human competition and sports, we may better understand and improve athletic behavior and ethics. One universal and dominant type of archetype is the "shadow" or the dark archetype. The dark archetype refers to the antagonist that resides deeply within each of us; the shadow archetype represents the capacity to engage in negative and destructive behaviors as a means of advancing our own lives. A primary motivating factor of human behavior according to Jungian psychoanalytic theory is the universal drive to first realize that we each share a highly destructive "dark shadow" and then to develop individual and unique processes to counteract the destructive force of the shadow. According to Jung, the only way we can overcome our shadow is through insight and recognition of the negative forces that we all share and to realize the positive forces that we also share that may overpower the negative forces. While Jung actually did not comment as sports and athletic activity as a viable mechanism in counteracting the dark forces, we may speculate that the negative force mentioned in the collective unconscious may be addressed through cooperative team work and excelling in physical achievement through sports. By selecting physical goals (i.e., exercise and weight management) and achieving them through cooperative activities with others we may counteract the negative archetype of the dark shadow and create positive and healthy forces that are contained in the collective unconscious.

According to Jung, we can only achieve the good in our lives by first recognizing the capacity that we all have in engaging in destructive and unethical behaviors. This duality of the personality is commonly referred to the "anima" and the "animus" or the male/female component of our being. Jung theorized that all males have the feminine side (anima) as all females have the masculine (animus) side that contributes to balance. The collective unconscious and archetypes may also be interpreted in sports activities and how athletes relate to one another. Athletes who are known for their particularly ethical style of interaction with other athletes are also aware of the dark side or the shadow. In sports and athletic behaviors, I contend that athletes also have the dark side or the shadow in how they display their skills and the style of their interaction with others. For example, the athlete may display negative and unethical qualities in the style of play that is contained in their collective unconscious or they may choose to counter the dark side of their collective unconscious by engaging in ethical conduct.

Finally, Jung argued that the most important archetype is the *self*—the self archetype refers to the complete and whole individual. The self archetype represents our identity and how we represent ourselves to the world. Many individuals feel unbalanced in their lives because they tend to devote too much attention in one aspect of their life (i.e., work, leisure, etc.) and tend to ignore other critical areas, such as their physical health. Jung's *mandala* archetype represents unity and balance in our lifestyle, and this can only be achieved through a combined and balanced interaction of physical activity (such as through sports and athletic participation) and intellectual or professional challenges. Too much of either activity yields an imbalance in one's life which may result in stress and depression. According to Jung, the primary motivating unconscious drive that we all share is to reach a balance among all of the archetypes: Anima and animus, the shadow or the antagonist and the protagonist; extraversion and introversion, somatic (athletic skills) and psychological development and so on. When this balance is achieved, we then develop the final archetype of *mandala*.

■■■ THE BEHAVIORAL APPROACH AND EXERCISE: WE REPEAT THOSE ACTIVITIES THAT PRODUCE POSITIVE CONSEQUENCES

The behavioral approach historically has been viewed very differently from all other disciplines of psychology, and for good reason. The behavioral approach argues that many of the basic concepts and ideas that have traditionally viewed as fundamental in psychology, such as the personality, emotions, attitudes and traits, are simply psychological constructs that defy scientific explanation and analysis. The last three dominant theorists that we have described in psychoanalysis (Freud, Adler and Jung) argued behavior from a very theoretical perspective; many of these concepts are simply impossible to verify and quantify under the scientific method. The behaviorists, as a result, argued that any topic discussed in the discipline of psychology should be viewed as a "true science" and thus, arbitrary terms such as moods, feelings and personality were simply rejected due to the lack of a scientific consensus on exactly what these terms actually mean. Some of the more famous names in the specific discipline of behaviorism in psychology include E. L. Thorndike, John Watson, Pavlov and Skinner. What each of these important theorists had in common was that they were all studying under the discipline of behaviorism and they felt that the key component to understanding human behavior was in first understanding the complex process of *learning. The basic and fundamental rule in behaviorism is that behavior tends to be repeated when it produces positive consequences, and that behavior is reduced or terminated when it produces negative consequences.* In health and sport psychology, this simple but yet very important and fundamental law is vital when attempting to help athletes reach their goals through training and physical exercise. Additionally, this rule is important for individuals of all ages or level of ability and physical health. The most frequently cited factor why athletes and individuals who are concerned with improving their health stop exercising is because: "It didn't feel good to me" or "I didn't like what I was doing . . . It was hard to get up in the morning, going day after day and not see any changes."

◼◼◼ USING BEHAVIORISM AS A MEANS OF IMPROVED PERFORMANCE: DOING WHAT FEELS GOOD

Because the behaviorists argued that it was virtually impossible to understand the arbitrary characteristics of the personality (i.e., how can we look in the "black box" to view the personality?), they argued the only way to understand behavior and the personality was by better understanding the environment and those variables that triggered (elicited or emitted) the behavior in the first place. Thus, the key factor in understanding behavior comes not from the person or the athlete, but rather the specific environment that influences behavior: People may learn behavior from a series of rewards of punishments and can also unlearn behavior from their environment. According to the behaviorists, if you want to better understand an individual and their behavior, then first begin by exploring the environment that they are exposed to.

A common question that many people ask regarding health and exercise is how to develop the motivation, consistency and determination that is necessary to achieve one's own health goals. Regardless whether or not someone wishes to lose weight, achieve personal goals (i.e., running a marathon under four hours), or simply just exercise to feel better, the key point to this chapter (and this text) is that all persons are capable of achieving their individual goals. The behaviorists would argue, however, that the best way to achieve your personal goal is not through more "focused thinking" or through the development of determination. Remember, the behaviorists argued that these psychological constructs were impossible to verify and measure overtly, so they disregarded them. However, the behaviorists would agree that if we can change or somehow manipulate our environment, we can influence people to continue their attendance and participation to health and fitness thereby allowing them to achieve their own personal goals.

The behaviorists would also claim that the individual is changing his or her behavior through changes in one's environment. If we allow individuals to experience a realistic system of rewards, where they are rewarded for consistent participation in an exercise program, they will be significantly more likely to complete the program. For example, let's say you have a friend (we'll call him 'Ted') who has been trying to lose about 15 pounds for over one year. It's not that he finds it impossible to lose weight, but he finds himself continuously going up and down and putting the weight back on after a few weeks of losing it. How can we keep Ted on a consistent and healthy weight management program where he will be happy, focused and stay at his desirable weight? According to the behaviorists, the first thing we have to do is to identify those types of environments that trigger the unhealthy eating behaviors in the first place. Remember, the behaviorists argued that the situation and the environment are the key factors that trigger our behaviors—thus, change the environment and the behavior will change. For example, as his friend, perhaps you have noticed that Ted tends to eat unhealthy foods only when he goes to particular restaurants or when he is depressed. Additionally, you have observed that he eats unhealthy foods when he is with a certain group of people from work. You have also noticed that if Ted is unhappy he usually calls you to talk, and usually you go for a short walk to discuss Ted's problems. Thus, if Ted is rewarded for contacting you to discuss his problems rather than engage in unhealthy eating habits, he will significantly be more likely to repeat these behaviors in the future.

According to the behaviorists, the logical explanation is to change the variables in the environment that seem to trigger the unhealthy eating habits in the first place. As Ted's friend, you encourage him to communicate his source of frustration and to avoid those environments that produce the unhealthy eating habits. You have also noticed that he feels better while walking and communicating his source of frustration to you. Thus, rewarding Ted by listening to him and providing support is the key to engage in healthy behaviors that will not contribute to his weight problem. Furthermore, you have created a system pattern that reinforces and rewards the healthy behaviors (talking about sources of frustration rather than engaging in poor eating habits)—and you make it a point to bring it to Ted's attention. Things that seem simple and so easy to do—such as a comment: "You really look great today . . . have you been exercising?" or "I've noticed that you look trimmer . . . keep working and exercising . . . you look great!" When perceived by the recipient (Ted) as being true and authentic, these comments are tremendously helpful in the individual in maintaining a particularly difficult training regimen or diet. Remember—once Ted himself realizes that he can achieve his goals by the reward system that you have provided, he will be able to maintain his own program. *The key is in helping individuals first realize that they have the capacity to achieve their own goals.* This is most commonly achieved by developing the "token economy system" that creates a unique environment of rewards for individuals maintaining their program. These programs have been most effective in substance abuse programs, health and exercise programs, and weight management programs. We will now describe in some detail an example of a successive approximation (shaping) program for a health management program for Ted.

■ ACHIEVING YOUR HEALTH GOALS THROUGH SHAPING: ONE STEP AT A TIME

We began this section of the chapter addressing behaviorism and how environmental cues may trigger either healthy styles of behavior or unhealthy and maladaptive styles of behavior. What prompted Skinner to publish much of his research addressing the fundamental principles of learning and the technology of change in human behaviors was the dramatic numbers of unhealthy behaviors people engage in. Furthermore, Skinner was troubled by how many people were actually responsible in maintaining their unhealthy physical and psychological states by their false belief systems. In his widely acclaimed text: *Beyond Freedom and Dignity,* Skinner argues that people always have the capacity to change any type of behavior they wish, but they typically lack the information about the environment that elicits the behavior they wish to change. Furthermore, Skinner comments that individuals who wish to change some form of behavior usually engage in unhealthy mental frameworks or thoughts where they convince themselves that they have no control over what happens to them or that they have no control over their environment. Nothing could be further from the truth—while we cannot change specific environments that trigger a variety of unhealthy behaviors, we certainly can decide where we work, where we live, and where we spend our free time. The reality of the situation is actually quite simple—we are responsible for the choices we make and how we spend our time with others. If we are unhappy with work, change the work environment; if we are unhappy in a personal relationship, seek counseling or a new spouse; if we are unhappy in school, change your major. Admittedly, this approach is very pragmatic, and Skinner was criticized as being insensitive to these factors. However, much of what Skinner argues in hid operant conditioning principles is quite accurate. We make conscious choices in the environments where we live and socialize—for example, someone who has a problem gambling should avoid the supermarket that is selling lottery tickets, and should not take a vacation anywhere near Las Vegas. Additionally, someone who is trying to lose weight should avoid the bakery or avoid supermarkets when they are feeling hungry. These things, of course, we have control over. Skinner argues that our poor choices or irrational decisions that we make are the causal factors that lead to our problems. What Skinner proposes to reduce aggression, over-population, substance abuse, crime and so on is really a technology of change in behavior. This technology of behavior means having a scientific understanding of the antecedent conditions that influence our choices and decision-making processes. Skinner further believed that the fantasies of our ability to make entirely free choices in our environment are responsible for many of the problems that we see today in society. Similar to Huxley's Brave New World, Skinner argues that we can condition people to change their unhealthy behaviors that include over-population, crime, war, and substance abuse.

What we actually do is usually a result of what we've been taught through a system of rewards and punishments: If we wish to change our behavior, then we should change the reward system (and environment) that occurs when we engage in the unhealthy or maladaptive behavior. If we revisit our example of Ted, and Ted complains to you that he is unhappy about his work, his weight problem and his relationship with his girlfriend, we should examine exactly what is happening in his relationship with his friends. When people stop and listen to the maladaptive behaviors and the behaviors keep continuing, we (as listeners) are actually contributing to the problem. Thus, Skinner argues that often people who reward the maladaptive behaviors (i.e., the "enablers") are unaware that they are *de facto* are contributing to its reoccurrence! How then, do we stop maladaptive behaviors through the principles of behaviorism? The process of shaping is very popular and most effective, as individuals are provided with the tools to change their behaviors slowly, and are progressively rewarded with each successful step.

■ SHAPING: CHANGING UNHEALTHY BEHAVIORS GRADUALLY IN BABY STEPS

Propose program for overweight clients

What exactly is shaping? Shaping is a principle of learning described by the behaviorists that involves learning in small ("baby") steps where each successfully mastered step is rewarded. The key factor to note here is that most problems in learning are due to complex and multifaceted theoretical constructs that are often confusing to both child and adult. If people tend to repeat those behaviors in smaller steps that produce favorable or positive consequences, then an effective shaping program offers clear and structured goals in progressive and predictable steps. After each step is mastered, a small reward is given. The problem in learning and educational technology is that we often push too much and expect too much from children and adults to process information in a short period of time. In the shaping program, we individually tailor a specific program based on the individual's capacity to learn. This is precisely the problem with many individuals who wish to lose weight or who wish to dramatically alter or change their physical appearance. Let us return to the example of Ted, where Ted has been fluctuating from his ideal weight of 180 lbs. to 220 lbs. As we mentioned earlier, Ted does manage to lose his weight, but his real problem is in maintaining a healthy lifestyle where he can keep the weight off and not "fixate" or experience obsessive thoughts over food. Perhaps you know someone similar to Ted who is experiencing similar problems in weight management. Now, consider the following shaping program for Ted in weight management:

The Problem: To help Ted maintain a healthy diet and activity level without weight constantly fluctuating.

Ted's Health Program: Sensible Fitness Through Shaping

Startup: Ted weighs in at the gym and is provided with a tour of the facility. He is introduced to other gym members and health trainers, and is familiarized with the facility. He meets with his trainer (Mary) who will be working with Ted. Ted has been provided with a thorough physical examination by his doctor and has been cleared for physical health training. His cholesterol is somewhat high, and the nutritionist has provided him with a diet. Ted is very serious and confident in his program, and he is encouraged and rewarded for his commitment to this program. Ted orients himself with his gym and begins to understand how to use the equipment. He meets again with Mary at the end of the tour and discusses his goals, his concerns and his anxiety of "starting something all over again . . . only to be disappointed again." Mary encourages Ted to remain positive, to work with her and most importantly to enjoy his program of fitness at the gym. Ted feels very positive about his relationship with his trainer, because she appears to believe in his abilities to achieve his goals and seems invested in his welfare and success in the program—Mary appears very enthusiastic and does not have the appearance of doing this just because it is her job. Finally, at the end of the orientation process, Mary sits down with Ted and completes a "Fitness Contract." The contract is not "legally binding" of course, but rather "psychologically binding." In other words, Ted is making a personal and formal commitment to himself and to Mary to participate fully in the weight management program and to give it his best effort. This means adhering to his diet in a realistic manner, coming to the gym promptly at 7:00 am for one hour (at least) three times during the week. He signs the contract and for some reason he feels very excited—as if this time, perhaps, his commitment will be fully realized so that he may achieve his realistic goals in a very realistic period of time.

His contract may look something like this: (figure 2a)

I, Ted Johnson, will make a commitment to report to the gym and work under the supervision of trainer Mary Smith for a period of time of one year. I will come to the gym at 7:00 am for a minimum of three times a week (Monday, Wednesday, and Friday) and will participate in an aerobic or cardiovascular exercise program for at least 30 minutes, followed by a weight circuit of 20 minutes. Finally, I will complete my exercise program with at least 15 minutes of stretching and "warm down" exercises. Additionally, while participating in this exercise program, I have made a commitment to monitor my caloric intake and have been advised to use a low-carbohydrate diet recommended by my nutritionist. I promise to faithfully adhere to these regulations, and if I violate any one of them (i.e., if I decide to "sleep in" one morning, I have promised my health trainer Mary promise to myself, my family and friends to let them know about my decisions to improve my health so they may also offer support to me. Most importantly, I will make it a point each time I come to the gym to train to have fun and use my time wisely.

Signed: <u>*Ted Johnson*</u>
Witnessed: <u>*Mary Smith*</u>
Date: <u>*October 2004*</u>

Figure 2a   Hoffman Health Triangle

Week 1: Ted does not weigh in—his trainer (Mary) recommends that too frequent checking of the scale regarding weight loss (or gain) can actually be counterproductive. When Ted first walks on to the gym stretching mat, he feels somewhat intimidated by the new environment and the new people there—he thinks that he will be the only person there that has a weight problem, and that everyone will look like models and bodybuilders. He is pleasantly surprised—the people who are there working out with him are just "normal people" like him—exercising, training, and they seem to be enjoying themselves. Furthermore, they say "hello" to Ted and welcome him to the gym—he already feels better and knows that this decision was right for him! Ted begins his routine of stretching and works with Mary. Mary provides direct and hands-on skills for Ted helping him to realize the healthy and productive stretching routines, and also helps him become aware of what his body responds positively to. During this time, Mary is frequently providing positive and encouraging comments to Ted, such as: "Good work Ted . . . that's it, try to stretch slowly and feel how your leg muscles respond."

Week 2: Ted is adapting to the program well and is very excited that this time things really seem to be changing. Somehow (perhaps because of the "contract" he has signed) things seem more serious, legitimate and sincere. He has told several of his friends and family members about the program and he can already feel some of the positive changes that are occurring in his body. His muscles are "a little sore" but it is a "good type of soreness . . . the type that let's you know that you are doing something good for your body." His legs and hamstring muscles are responding to the demands made on them by the increased walking and treadmill activity he has started. Ted now looks forward to exercising with his trainer but also feels capable to be exercising autonomously. Mary has Ted stretch his hamstrings, quadriceps and lower body, followed by abdominal exercises. After 15 minutes of stretching and stomach work, Mary again tells Ted that he is doing well, While participating in the stretching program, several other gym members walk by and say hello to Ted. Ted is now receiving various forms of positive attention from other members and is gaining control over events that determine his weight and weight management. Most importantly, Ted is enjoying his time spent with Mary and the other members in the gym and is gaining confidence in his ability to train independently. During the second week of training and health management, Ted has learned what flexibility means and also what types of foods to eat that are most healthy. Ted now brings carrot and celery snacks with him as he drives to work and makes a conscious effort to drink more water. He already feels better—ironically, more energy and stamina has helped him stay focused throughout the day.

Reward: His reward for successfully completing the second week: Mary has provided Ted with two tickets to a movie of his choice.

Week 3: Week three and things are really taking place—Ted is adapting to his program and now looks forward to his training and exercise program. The exercise that he once dreaded and avoided he now embraces—he finds himself talking more and more to people about health and fitness, and he finds that he is now more secure when around food. Other things in his life now appear to be under control—now he finds himself more prompt when reporting to work, assignments are in early, and he finds that he has more patience in driving and his temperament seems somehow more relaxed—stated very simply, he appears more relaxed and balanced. Ted now feels more confident when exercising and he knows how his body should respond while completing his exercise program. Ted is also more realistic regarding his diet and exercise and allows more time to complete his training programs. Most importantly, Ted now trains for himself and feels good in the process of doing so—if he feels a little tired one day, he spends more time stretching and lets his body adjust to the physical demands of his program. Ted now really looks forward to going to the gym and saying hello to everyone that is exercising. He is also finding that his fears of everyone being perfectly fit and exemplifying the "glamour model" image at the gym was really a myth, as many of the people in the gym appear to be just like himself! He has created a new social base while at the gym, and more importantly he feels more confident in every other aspect of his professional and personal life. Work is more successful for him and he appears to have more energy as he is working late in the evening. It is the end of week three, and things are progressing very well for Ted.

Reward: As his reward for successful completion of week three: Taking his friend to a movie and going for a walk at the beach.

Week 4: As expected things were going too well without some form of a relapse. Shortly into the fourth week of Ted's training program, he started experiencing some frustration in his work—it seems that his employer rejected a report that he had submitted earlier that day and was greeted with some criticism from the employer as well. As if that were not enough, his car broke down and that was an additional financial expense. Later that evening he was feeling very frustrated, and retreated to the bakery near his home and bought several brownies and cookies. He knew that this was a violation of his contract, but he felt he "owed himself" a treat. Later the next day after feeling very guilty, he discussed the issue with Mary his trainer. Mary informed Ted that we need to anticipate times and various experiences where we will have relapses and fall into the old unhealthy behavioral patterns. She further encouraged him to maintain his exercise schedule but also told him of the violation of the contract—a fifty dollar ($50.00) donation to a charity of his choice. This experience actually turned out to be a very positive learning experience for Ted, as he now has more realistic standards and expectations for himself. He resumes his program with a more realistic approach and once again is excited about his training and how it feels to be a part of a successful experience.

Week 5: Over a month has now gone by since Ted's exercise program has started—now he is allowed by his trainer to weigh himself on the scale (remember, after Ted began the program over a month he was not allowed to weigh himself—the logic being if we weigh ourselves too much, we do not allow enough time to pass to actually lose the weight and may actually become frustrated). Ted is nervous—but confident as he steps on the scale with his trainer next to him. He is very pleased to discover that he has in fact lost two (2) pounds in about one month—this is very good, despite the relapse he experienced last week. Mary congratulates him and encourages him to continue his program—now he knows that he can change his weight, his life and his destiny by making very positive and small changes in a very consistent manner. This again is the essence and the crux of the shaping program—small steps of improvements that are consistently and gradually rewarded.

Two points of interest here are important to note from a psychological perspective: a) Perhaps the most important point that must be addressed is the fact that Ted has dispelled his personal belief that he was destined to be overweight throughout his life—Clearly, Ted is not alone in this faulty and inaccurate belief system. Many individuals who wish to stop smoking, lose weight, improve their exercise program, or simply stop any compulsive and unhealthy behavior often convince themselves that they have no control over their behavior and ultimately their destiny. *This simply is not true!!* The first time Ted got on the scale during week 5 of his training program, he realized that he was capable of achieving his goals. Many people prevent themselves from achieving their goals by these faulty belief systems and "negative self-talk" dialogues—this is what Skinner was referring to by the processes of behavior modification and the token economy systems, as well as the current shaping program we are discussing now with Ted- by changing the environmental factors that elicit the unhealthy behaviors, we gradually change the behavior itself so the individual now believes that he or she may achieve their goal. This is precisely why Skinner argued that many unhappy and depressed people are actually victims by their own unhealthy choices—the sooner the individual changes their environment that brings out the unhealthy behavior, the sooner their belief system becomes more adaptive and positive.

In the example with Ted, he basically had two choices in his life: a) He could have continued his unhealthy lifestyle and blamed others for his misery and unhappiness that was associated with his weight problem. He also could have joined various weight support groups that actually justify obesity but unfortunately provide little incentives to lose the weight and thus achieve a healthier balance in living; or b) Ted could have made a rational decision to change his life and realize that he had the power and the ability to make positive and healthy changes for himself. Thankfully, this is what Ted actually did. No one (including myself) who is familiar with health and training claim that these changes are easy. However, with support, realistic goals and a positive belief system, I believe anything is possible.

■ THE TRAP OF OBESITY: COGNITIVE DISTORTIONS & LEARNED HELPLESSNESS

Aaron Beck (1967) explained how people like Ted can develop negative viewpoints of themselves and the world around them. Beck noted that sometimes people who suffer from depression and obesity tend to have highly unrealistic and pessimistic views of the world around them. Furthermore, many individuals who suffer from depression and obesity have inaccurate opinions of the world in general and view themselves as being helpless with no control over the events that affect their lives. In Ted's example, he took responsibility for his relapse due to the events taking place at his work, but he was also able to resume his diet and exercise program. Ted was fortunate in the sense that even though he broke one of the rules of his contract by eating the wrong types of food, he accepted responsibility for this behavior and was able to correct it in the future. Furthermore, he was able to identify the causes and environmental antecedent conditions that triggered or elicited the counterproductive behavior of binge-eating cookies. According to Beck, individuals who suffer from depression often portray themselves as being much worse off than they actually are, and view their professional situation (such as at work) or their personal relationships typically suffer as a result of these distorted perceptions. Beck referred to these negative viewpoints as "cognitive distortions" and regarded cognitive distortions as the single most important factor that contributes to depression and counterproductive behavior. The combination of cognitive distortions, low self-esteem and negative experiences may form clinical depression.

Often related to the cognitive distortions that Beck describes is the concept of "learned helplessness" (Seligman, 1976). Learned helplessness refers to a lack of effort in trying to improve one's circumstances or situations due to repeated past failures. What makes learned helplessness particularly frustrating for therapists, family and friends is that often the "answer" or the solution to the problem is very obvious, but for a variety of reasons, the individual fails to act on the solution. For example, in the case of overeating, Ted may know that he tends to overeat with a particular group of friends, but he goes out with them anyway and binges on unhealthy food. A second example would be the battered housewife who is continuously stalked by her jealous husband or boyfriend. Every time she tries to escape his control, he tracks her down and physically assaults her and verbally abuses her—he may even threaten her family and friends if she tries to escape in the future. Imagine every time you try to run away from someone and they find you and physically assault you—eventually you are going to "give up" especially if the legal system fails to intervene and protect you. Eventually, the young woman simply gives up and stops trying to escape her jealous boyfriend—this is the classic example of learned helplessness: Failure to escape an unhealthy or dangerous situation due to repeated past failures. How is Seligman's (1976) learned helplessness relative to Ted and the problem of obesity? If we have repeatedly tried to diet and lose weight, only to regain the weight and even add more of the weight in the future, many people eventually tend to give up entirely because of the frequent negative experiences of failure. Many of the overweight people simply feel that they are "destined to remain overweight forever . . . or God wanted my body to be this way." Thus, overweight individuals eventually stop trying because they feel that no matter what they try to do, it ultimately will end up as a failure. This is the crux of the epidemic of obesity that currently plagues our society—individuals who feel helpless and out of control in their eating habits and lifestyle. We need to restructure our environments that will help trigger healthier, active lifestyles that will not promote obesity. Examples may include more frequent walks to the supermarket, turning the television off and going for a walk or bicycle ride, teaching children healthier eating habits (fruit snacks instead of cookies), placing limits on watching television programs or using the computer (especially for video games). These examples are clear examples of how environmental factors may trigger either healthy or unhealthy activities that directly impact our health. Remember what Skinner describes as a key component in understanding behavior—in order to better change the behavior, change the environment. It is of little use to encourage the overweight person to "try harder" or to "use more willpower" when faced with difficult daily choices ("Do I order the salad with skim milk or the fried chicken with gravy?"). *The key in changing behavior is in changing those environmental situations that elicit the positive and healthy behavior and simultaneously discourage the negative or counterproductive behaviors.*

Negative Schemas Leading to Counter-Productive Choices and Behaviors:

Environmental Factors   **»**   **Eating Unhealthy Foods (Bakery) / Sedentary Activities Television & Video Games; Fear of Change & Failure; Developing Unrealistic Goals**

Individual Belief Systems   **»**   **I Have No Choice in Being Overweight—My Destiny is in Remaining Inactive & Obese / I Have No Control in My Decisions and Behaviors That Impact My Life**

Personal Support Systems   **»**   **No Support / Family or Friends Are Critical of Change & Skeptical of Your Ability in Making Positive Changes. Your Friends Say "We Like You As You Are—Why Change?"**

Positive Schemas Leading to Healthy Choices and Behaviors:

Environmental Factors   **»**   **Eating Healthy Foods (Keeping Healthy Snacks Handy)**
Engaging in Aerobic Activities & Regular Exercise Daily Structured Activities (Work & Exercise) To Stay Focused

Individual Belief Systems   **»**   **Internal Attributions: I Am in Control of My Choices and My Destiny—I Can Make Healthy and Positive Changes in My Life; I Am a Valuable, Dynamic, Creative and Unique Individual Who is Capable of Making Positive Changes**

Personal Support Systems   **»**   **Positive Familial Support; Realistic Goals Set; Friends are Supportive and Positive Role Models; Employment and Work-related Friends Also Are Supportive and Encouraging You; Your Family and Friends Are Proud of You!**

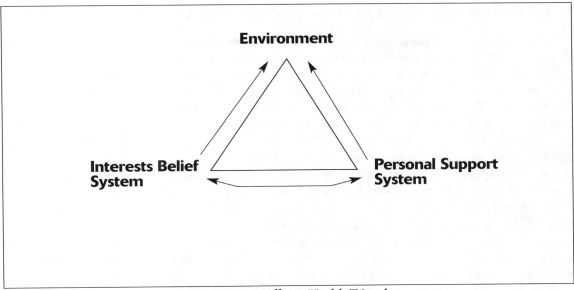

Figure 2a   Hoffman Health Triangle

Week 6: Ted has now recovered from his recent relapse from week 5—he is further encouraged that despite his setback, he has still lost 2 lbs. and remains very optimistic about his program. His health trainer Mary consistently is encouraging him to continue his training and reminds him that all programs periodically have periods of stagnancy. Ted has now been participating in his program about six weeks and can really feel positive changes in his body—he feels lighter, more energetic and happier. Ted's ability to focus and concentrate is now extended beyond his ability before his dieting and exercise program, and all areas of his life have become positively impacted. His friends and family members (the personal support system) are providing him with encouragement and helping him to maintain realistic goals. He is now attending the gym on average about five days a week, but he does not criticize himself if he occasionally misses a day. He is training for fun and health and has created a program of training that is healthy and realistic that he can complete. Ted's relationships with people have also noticeably changed for the better— he appears more patient in his exchanges and interactions with co-workers and friends, and seems more relaxed in his professional relationships. He feels that finally he is achieving the "balance" in his life that he always knew that he was capable of achieving.

Week 7: During the beginning of week seven, Ted has made several positive changes in his physical health and has noticed improvements in related areas, such as his professional relationships with co-workers and his personal relationships with his friends. He feels more "balanced" but wants to incorporate more psychologically motivating skills into his program. He contacts Mary and she makes several interesting suggestions. The first suggestion that Mary makes addresses a more skilled program in helping Ted to stretch and relax his muscles prior to his training. Although Ted's strength has been improving consistently over the last several weeks, he has noticed that he has been cramping (especially in the hamstring area) and would like to find out the reasons. Mary suggests spending more time doing flexibility and stretching and preparing his body physically prior to the exercise program. Mary specifically makes the recommendation of the Self Induced Relaxation Procedure (SIRP), which is a term that describes a particular sequence of psychological and stretching exercises that focuses on all of the major muscle groups.

■■■ SELF-INDUCED RELAXATION PROCEDURE (SIRP)

Before Ted actually began his training and exercise program several weeks ago, he was so inundated with work and frequently stressed-out, he had completely forgotten the sensation of feeling and being totally relaxed. It was almost like the moment he jumped out of bed at 6:00 am his life was on the go, eating whatever and wherever he could—he was experiencing a series of headaches, upset stomach and even ulcers. The stress and anxiety was really beginning to take its toll on Ted—he felt as though he could never really relax. Ted also noticed that his stress and frustration that was associated with work was also gradually influencing how his body responded physically—he was experiencing somatic complaints, such as difficulty in sleeping, migraine headaches, upset stomach and even ulcers. Mary explained to Ted that since the stress factors at work were psychological factors influencing his physical health, he must combine a psychological and physical approach to his exercise program. She further explained to Ted that the mind / body duality work together as one, and when we train in the gym we should also focus on psychological factors that influence physical performance. In the SIRP program, we combine mental visualization and guided imagery techniques with a systematic muscle relaxation procedure to improve physical performance, flexibility, mental focus and concentration. Ted was very enthusiastic to Mary's suggestion to learn more about the SIRP procedure.

The SIRP is a systematic and controlled psychological and physical process that helps people clarify and understand the distinctions between physical discomfort (muscle cramping) and psychological balance and comfort (true relaxation). The idea is actually quite simple—as with Ted, many of us are so constantly bombarded with stress that we tend to forget what our muscles should feel like in terms of relaxation. Quite literally, we are walking in a constant state of tension and discomfort. The idea and the logic behind the SIRP is actually quite simple—teach individuals to "relearn" the distinction between stress and muscle contractions and relaxation. This is done by a series of clenching and contracting muscles, feeling the tension and intentional discomfort, and then relaxation. The key to this exercise is to focus on the differences in physical sensation between physical discomfort and relaxation. Additionally, when we are aware of the signals that contribute to stress and tension, we can address them and make changes so that the stress does not contribute to more serious stress-related disorders (i.e., ulcers, migraine headaches, and even possible heart attacks). In the first step of SIRP, subjects are encouraged to lie down in a comfortable position on their backs. If possible, dim any bright lights and keep outside or extraneous noises to a minimum. Additionally, loosen any tight or constrictive clothing now lying on your back, take several deep breaths—holding your breath for a few seconds, then releasing. Notice the sensation between inhaling and exhaling.

The SIRP is a technique used to assist athletes such as Ted to develop a balance between psychological relaxation and balance (a term referred to in psychology as "psychological momentum." Psychological momentum is a term used in sport psychology that refers to an added or gained psychological power which influences an individual's mental attitude and increases significantly his or her physical strength, stamina and power. While the outcome of the SIRP is very similar for many athletes in terms of successful results and outcomes in competition, the individual process in achieving and maintaining psychological momentum varied from athlete to athlete and from sport to sport. Ted began using the SIRP to help control anxiety and stress at work and also to help improve his exercise program at the gym:

> "Prior to beginning your exercise, find a quiet, comfortable place where you will not be disturbed and where you can sit down or lie down. If you were glasses or contact lens . . . remove them. If you are wearing restrictive clothing, loosen it . . . make yourself as comfortable as possible, with your hands at your sides, and you are ready to begin. Close your eyes, and take three deep breaths, inhaling and exhaling slowly . . . Feel your body beginning to relax. Continue to notice yourself breathing and inhale and exhale methodically and slowly. As the breathing exercises continue, now begin focusing on intentionally contracting each of the major muscle groups for three seconds,

then release. The idea of this program is that you are literally relearning how to notice the distinction between true relaxation (comfort) and a contracted (discomfort) state. Most of us (either in sports or other employment occupations) are in such stressful environments for prolonged periods of time that we forget the true distinction between relaxation and contraction." Subjects are given specific instructions, such as: "Now clench both of your fists . . . close them and squeeze tighter and tighter . . . as you squeeze them, notice the pleasant and relaxed feeling in your body as you slowly release the contraction. Now continue this process with the muscle groups in your forearms, your leg muscles, calves, and so on."

The development of the imagery techniques is a key component of the SIRP. Through the development of imagery techniques, most elite athletes can begin to train themselves to recognize what key physical characteristics and cues are beneficial to performance, and what characteristics are negative in performance. For example, in many cases, breathing is a vital component to successful performance. When the athlete can control and monitor his or her breathing, the body physically performs in more desirable ways and we improve our stamina. Through controlled and deep breathing, we supply our body with more oxygen, thereby allowing the muscles more energy to respond to the demands being made. The imagery techniques allow the athlete to control his or her breathing. In the SIRP program, athletes are instructed to focus on the process of the maneuver or physical task at hand, not necessarily how many to complete or even to focus on winning or losing. In other words, athletes are encouraged to mentally rehearse the guided exercises of breathing and to visualize a calming or relaxing environment, such as an isolated beach or lake. The visualization allows the body to mentally picture a calming environment that in turn will make the body physically respond in a most efficient manner.

After incorporating the SIRP in as little as three weeks, Ted began noticing several improvements in his demeanor and psychological outlook at work and his exercise program at the gym. He was able to stay more mentally focused and was concentrating more while completing a variety of projects at work. Ted also commented that he seemed more confident in achieving his goals—and when he felt more confident about his ability to achieve goals, his overall self-esteem and self-efficacy also improved. Even co-workers and friends at the gym noticed the differences in his appearance since he began incorporating the SIRP. Some of the other advantages that Ted noticed since he started using the SIRP included:

a. Raised or lowered tension level (after his second physical at his doctor's office, Ted's blood pressure actually dropped);
b. Passive or active concentration skills;
c. Physical and mental relaxation skills;
d. Increased focus and self-confidence;
e. Increased endurance and tolerance to pain;
f. Improved consistency in athletic performance and reduced variability of performance;
g. The ability to systematically analyze your own behavior.

The Purpose of the SIRP

Through the development of the mental rehearsal processes (SIRP), Ted was able to train and to recognize the important cues are in competitive situations. Through practice and mental rehearsal of what he should be attending to, Ted was able to focus more on relevant issues that facilitated his physical performance and isolated his negative performance. Once the SIRP has become successfully mastered by other athletes, they will be able to focus on relevant factors that facilitate optimum performance, and delete negative factors that result in poor performance.

Execution Phase

These procedures should be rehearsed daily for 30 to 40 minutes in private. The order of the steps are very important and must be followed in respective order: Prior to beginning your exercise, find a quiet, comfortable place where you will not be disturbed and where you can sit down or lie down. If you were glasses or contact lens . . . remove them. If you are wearing restrictive clothing, loosen it . . . make yourself as comfortable as possible, with your hands at your sides, and you are ready to begin. Close your eyes, and take three deep breaths, inhaling and exhaling slowly . . . Feel your body beginning to relax. Continue to notice yourself breathing and inhale and exhale methodically and slowly. As the breathing exercises continue, now begin focusing on intentionally contracting each of the major muscle groups for three seconds, then release.

a. Close your eyes, and take three deep breaths—as you exhale, relax your body as much as possible;

b. Now clench both fists. Close them tightly, and feel the discomfort or tension as you squeeze them tightly—Let your fingers become loose, and notice the pleasant sensation, in particular noticing how your body responds to discomfort (clenching) to comfort (relaxation). Quite literally you are re-teaching yourself to distinguish the cues from discomfort (negative) to comfort (positive);

c. Continue this procedure with the next muscle group—the elbows, then the shoulders, abdomen, quadriceps, calves and feet/toes—all following the same procedure of clenching and relaxation.

Now that you are completely relaxed and calm, you are ready for the mental imagery technique. In this phase, imagine the specific routine or exercise you are about to execute—if you are trying to lose weight and eat different foods that are healthy, imagine how your body appears and feels once you achieve the desired weight. As the successful athlete performing the routine of exercises—you are going to focus on the process in a series of flowing, continuous movements that are de facto effortless, fluid, and flawless. Feel your body responding to the manner in which you need it to respond . . . If you are stretching, reaching further and further, feeling the muscles respond with flexibility . . . if you are playing basketball and shooting a three point shot, visualize the ball going through the hoop . . . if you are a golfer, visualize the golf ball entering the cup after you have read the break correctly . . . If you are doing sit-ups, bar-dips or pull-ups or any aerobic routine, visualize your body responding smoothly and with effortless motion, and you are ahead of the other competitors. Finally, always remember that your body physically only responds to what you mentally have programmed it to do . . . if you think you are winning and have the psychological advantage—then you do have the advantage. To be "in the zone" physically you must first be "in the zone" mentally.

Week 8: In just eight weeks Ted has completely refurbished and overhauled the content his mind and body. Whereas in the beginning of his program he simply indicated that he "just wanted to drop a few pounds," now Ted is a very good example of how the "average person" can make dramatically positive changes in the physical and psychological health with the aid and assistance of a truly motivated trainer. Ted now gets on the scale after completing the eighth week and is proud to say that he has dropped five (5) lbs. *Most importantly, the weight is being kept off by Ted because he has discovered a balance and a routine that his body has adapted to and something he enjoys.* He eats healthy foods and his life is not controlled by thoughts of food or eating. His weight is kept off and he feels confident that he will keep it off because he has very realistic goals regarding food—most importantly, his diet is reasonable and balanced. He also is very happy to incorporate the SIRP into his program—it provides for him what he calls the "psychological edge." Ted now realizes that the physical health of an athlete is only part of the goal—the other part of the goal is in achieving mental and psychological balance. Ted further realizes that his body only accomplishes and achieves what his mind and psyche tell it to do—when we think of positive and realistic goals, only then can we achieve these goals.

Week 9: Ted feels more confident than ever about maintaining his program. His trainer Mary now spends less time with him because he is exercising more and more autonomously—however, Ted still prefers feedback and information regarding his progress. Ted is also experimenting with new exercise routines in the gym and this helps him to remain motivated and committed to his program. Ted has been able to set realistic goals about his weight and actual participation in the program, and he verbalizes these goals to his family and friends. He varies his program frequently so he does not "burn out" and frequently finds different partners to train with (commonly called "work out buddies"). Ted now feels confident that he will be able to continue his training program autonomously because he feels motivated when he exercises and looks forward to going to the gym. He periodically "touches base" with his trainer Mary for support and feedback, but finds now that his is training with increasing independence. Ted compares his valuable experiences with Mary as someone who initially gave him the psychological "push" that he needed to get started. Ted is very thankful of his relationship with Mary because she helped him realize that he does have the capacity to be successful and now he is capable of exercise training under his own supervision;

Week 10: Mission Accomplished! Ted has done it!—he has achieved his goals of dropping between five to ten pounds and has successfully incorporated a new style of living into his life that is balanced. Furthermore, he is motivated to continue training and exercising most of all because he enjoys what he is doing and he likes the effect on both his mind and body. Ted feels that this training program is different because he has made the successful changes in his routine himself and his program is more realistic. The important factor in keeping Ted an active member in exercise and training is the enjoyable factor that he associates with his program. The key to staying motivated for Ted is summarized into five basic concepts:

■ KEY COMPONENTS TO HEALTH & FITNESS

a. **Identifying the Goal.** If you remember earlier in this section we discussed the psychological principle that people cannot achieve what they do not first know what they are striving for. For Ted, the initial goal was just to drop a few pounds. However, after discussing his plan with Mary, Ted realized that there is much more to health and training than losing weight. His initial goal was to lose (and keep off) five to ten lbs. As Ted continued working in his exercise program, his goals became less extrinsic (physical appearance-oriented) and more internal-oriented. In other words, Ted started focusing more on how the exercise made him *feel* rather than how the exercise made him *look*. Additionally, Ted was able to find activities that he found most enjoyable and had fun while performing the exercises. This enabled him to regularly engage in the exercise program so that he will be more likely to keep off the weight;

b. **Maintaining a Positive Support System.** Ted realized that the more his trainer (Mary), his family and friends were supporting him and encouraging him to continue, the better his chances were at succeeding in his goals. If you will recall in the previous section addressing operant conditioning and learning principles, people tend to repeat those behaviors that produce positive or favorable consequences and avoid those behaviors that produce negative consequences. As Ted progressed towards his goals of fitness, his trainer, family and friends provided him with feedback and positive reinforcement ("you're doing great Ted! You look fantastic . . . keep up the good work") that gradually pulled him toward his goal of health and fitness. Thus, a reciprocal relationship developed where his family and friends provided positive encouragement and support, and this support in turn motivated him to work harder to achieve his goals—he further believed as time progressed that he was capable of achieving these goals; One other important point that Ted discovered was that when he told his friends and family about his program, they were more likely to ask him how his progress was coming along. These frequent reminders were actually very helpful in motivating him to stay focused in his training program;

c. **Self-Efficacy.** The term self-efficacy refers to an internal belief system that you can achieve your goals. Self-efficacy comes from gradual and persistent efforts in achieving your goals; Remember what Adler said about our initial feelings of inferiority: All people begin their lives feeling relatively inferior, and this psychological sense of inferiority provided the impetus and motivation to develop and master our skills in an activity that we excel in. Believe in your ability to achieve your goals gradually. If you find that you are becoming frustrated—slow down and re-evaluate the program. Fitness and health may be achieved in a variety of ways—your responsibility is to find which method suits you best; In Ted's example, Ted soon discovered that the more he participated in his training program the better capable and competent he felt about accomplishing his goals—the relationship between successful goal attainment and self-efficacy is a highly reciprocal one, where the more often we are successful in actually achieving our goals, the greater our perception (self-efficacy) and personal belief system is in achieving future goals;

d. **Stay the Course:** Be aware that no matter how exciting and dynamic the exercise routine happens to be—change is inevitable and ultimately a good thing. Be consistent in training by experimenting with different procedures, working different muscle groups, and "shock" or surprise the muscle groups. Frequently change your routine and work different muscles. Be flexible—both psychologically and physiologically. This procedure will prevent you from falling into "mental or psychological slumps" and help you to maintain an active and dynamic exercise program; Ted discovered that when he occasionally experienced his slumps in training, the more he changed his routine and did some exercises differently (i.e., even changing the order in performing the exercises) this alleviated some of the mundane experiences he felt;

e. **Enjoy the Process.** Perhaps the single most important axiom in all of health training is in learning what activities you enjoy most. This is essential because we tend to repeat those activities that provide the most physical and psychological benefit to us. Enjoy your exercise program and remain open to learning new methods that may benefit your training program. Ted found that when he completed each and every exercise program on each day, at the end of his training he actually felt more energized and positive. The program was very successful for Ted because he had discovered an exercise routine that his body had physically adapted to, and with the help of Mary he was able to incorporate information about nutrition that provided the health changes that he was looking for. We are pleased to say that Ted is still training and exercising and is living a well balanced and healthy lifestyle.

Key Components to Health and Fitness

a. <u>Identifying the Goal.</u> **What are your goals in training? What do you wish to accomplish? Are your goals extrinsically oriented (physical appearance) or are your goals also intrinsically oriented (training and exercising for the experience and enjoyment of the activity)?**

b. <u>Maintaining a Positive Support System.</u> **Who else knows about your new training goals? Who (besides yourself) believes in your ability to achieve your goals? Who offers support and constructive and helpful suggestions? Who cares about you and your program so you may achieve your goals? Who is willing to listen to your concerns about training and exercising and offer feedback to your ideas? Most importantly, when you have your "down" days or slumps—do you have a support group that will push you forward? Identify your support groups and let them know what you are doing!**

c. <u>Self-Efficacy.</u> **Do you believe enough in yourself to begin this program? How much do you believe in yourself that you can achieve your goals? Remember, self-efficacy and successful completion of the program are reciprocal—the more often you complete your goals, the more competent you will view yourself for future tasks and projects. Furthermore, success in health and fitness generalizes to all other important areas in our lives: Work, personal relationships, and so on. Nothing breeds success like success!**

d. <u>Stay the Course.</u> **Everyone at some point becomes tired or burned out. Be persistent, drive toward your goals. Change routines, programs and work-out partners to avoid burn-out. Be flexible, both psychologically and physiologically; Do not be afraid to try new activities in your program—keep growing and learning!**

e. <u>Enjoy the Process.</u> **The most important characteristic to training is to enjoy the process and experience the physical and psychological benefits that are associated with training. Operant Conditioning theory tells us that we repeat behaviors that are intrinsically rewarding— Allow yourself to enjoy something good for the body!**

Figure 2b

■■ CHAPTER 2 QUESTION & REVIEW

1. Briefly describe Freud's theory of psychoanalysis, including the topographic theory, the five stages of psychosexual development, and the aggressive instinct as a predominant motivator of behavior. Explain how the phallic stage (ages 3–5) in the psychosexual stages of development may serve to influence the role of sports and identification among parents and children;

2. Briefly describe Jung's view of the collective unconscious and the term "archetypes." Explain how Jung differed from Freud in theory, and comment on the possibility of the existence of the "athletic archetype" in comparison with the "anima" (female) and "animus" (male) archetypes of the collective unconscious;

3. Describe how shaping may be used to develop an exercise program for a resistant child or teenager who is not familiar with any type of exercise program;

4. Explain how Adler's theory of psychoanalysis compares to theories in sport psychology—how does the theory of "feelings of inferiority" influence athletic development among children and adults? Elaborate on Adler's concept of the "creative power" and how this may utilized in a constructive manner to enhance health and exercise;

5. Create your own personal contract of health and training (use Ted's example).

Chapter 3:
Observational Learning and Teaching Children Skills as a Means of Enjoying Sport Activity:
A Critical Period for Learning

The previous discussion regarding the personality characteristics of the athlete described learning and behavior as relative to one another—in Freudian theory, the personality is influenced by the inherent biological and conflicting drives that influenced our behavior in society. Freud argued that the Human Condition is characterized by sexual and aggressive instincts. Further, these instincts are often manifested through a variety of contact sports, such as football or rugby. In Adler's case, the personality is influenced by unconscious feelings of inferiority. Thus, if we are born with difficulty in running or walking, we have subconscious drives that may push us towards sports that involve these activities, such as track and field or jogging. Jung argued that the archetypes contained in the collective unconscious also influence our behaviors in an attempt to find some form of balance. The anima and the animus will merge by combining typically aggressive activities (such as playing football) with other more artistic talents, such as artwork or ballet. Interestingly, many National League Football players weighing over 300 lbs. study and participate in activities such as ballet to combine both diametrically opposed archetypes for complete balance (*mandala archetype*). Even the now former great lineman for the Los Angeles Rams Rosie Grier engages in crochet and knitting activities. A new and very dynamic form of learning that addresses sport activity is observational learning. Observational learning involves usually a model (such as a parent or older sibling) where younger children watch their activity and try to imitate it.

Observational learning is an important topic in psychology and understanding human behavior. There are important characteristics regarding observational learning that are necessary to understand in order for learning to occur. For example, we need to understand the relationship between the observer and the model that the observer happens to be watching. If the model is a positive one (such as a parent) and the observer is a young child, their relationship is dynamic and therefore highly likely to lead to learning and therefore imitated by the child. Observational learning is generally credited with the work by Albert Bandura (Bandura, 1969; 1977b) and his classic research at Stanford University with the "Bobo doll (an inflated doll)" study. In this study, Bandura and colleagues showed young children two sets of videos, one depicting adults playing aggressively with toys (hence the name "Bobo" doll study) where dolls were punched repeatedly by the adult models and the other group of children playing cooperatively and non-aggressively. The children who were exposed to the experimental videos (aggressive adults playing with the Bobo doll) were shown to play more aggressively in post-treatment phase of the study than children who were not exposed to the aggressive adult style of play in the video. The data in several studies suggests that children (and adults) tend to repeat behaviors that they see, especially if the models are portrayed in a positive manner.

▄▄ TECHNIQUES OF OBSERVATIONAL LEARNING: POSITIVE AND NEGATIVE ROLE MODELS

Children who watch a variety of behaviors do not have to be rewarded in order to imitate the behavior. Additionally, even if children watch a model being rewarded via video tape or being punished for a particular behavior, the result is long lasting. For example, children who watch other children being rewarded for a particular behavior (i.e., sharing toys) will be significantly more likely to share their toys with other children. Similarly, if children watch other children being punished for some undesirable behavior, they are significantly less likely to imitate the behavior that they see being punished. Additionally, who the model is typically has a profound impact whether or not the behavior is emulated. For example, if children perceive the model as being very similar to themselves, they significantly more likely to imitate the behavior. Furthermore, if the child has a positive relationship with the model (i.e., if the model is a friend of the observer), the behavior more than likely is imitated.

Children will also imitate a variety of different types of models. For example, Charles Barkley (retired center for the Phoenix Suns) had a reputation for playing very aggressively and physically with other players in the National Basketball Association. During an interview after one particularly physical game, Barkley admitted to the interviewer that he would continue playing his style of basketball and that parents needed to supervise their children in terms of appropriate and ethical styles of play: "Professional athletes should not be role models . . . Hell, I know drug dealers who can dunk . . . can drug dealers be role models too?" Additionally, in a later interview Barkley was quoted: "Just because I can dunk a basketball doesn't mean I should raise your kids" (Barkley on Parenthood). Finally, in another quote regarding Barkley's views on his role as a basketball player and his audience: "*I am not a role model* . . . I am paid to wreak havoc on the basketball court . . . parents should be [the child's] role model" (emphasis mine). In other words: "Do as I say and not as I do." While this cavalier and non-conformist statement might sound appealing to adolescents, it only exacerbates the problem of potential aggression. Barkley is wrong and the research strongly supports the idea that young children aspire to be like and emulate those figures that are positively portrayed in the media. Whether he likes it or not, when the media portrays you as a sports star, you automatically become *ipso facto* the role model for the public—this responsibility comes with the job and the salary that he is earning. High profile movie stars or athletes that do not want this responsibility should reconsider their careers as the media will change their lives significantly. Furthermore, (quite ironically) Barkley became an even more popular and sought after athlete after making these comments. Unfortunately, there are numerous other athletes that maintain display less than desirable forms of athletic behavior that are being adapted by young athletes today (i.e., During the 2004 national league baseball championship series Dodger baseball player Milton Bradley takes off his baseball jersey in right field after one fan throws a bottle onto the field, seemingly to challenge the unruly fan).

More recent research addressing media and violence continues to support the hypothesis that exposure to violence has a profound influence on children in engaging in more aggressive styles of play. Villain (2001) and Johnson and colleagues (2002) argue that when children are exposed to gratuitous violence and aggressive forms of behavior via the media, they are significantly more likely to engage in similar forms of behavior. The media and entertainment industry have taken issue with these results and claim that they are only providing the types of entertainment that the public wants to see. The issue is still highly contentious and revolves around the "chicken and the egg" argument. One point is still very clear, and that is when we portray individuals as being positive role models, regardless of the behaviors they engage in, children are significantly more likely to imitate it. According to recent estimates, children are inundated with exposure to gratuitous violence. One recent study (Villani, 2001) estimated that children see (on average) approximately 10,000 acts of violence annually, and perhaps more importantly, over 40% of these violent acts were committed by what was perceived to be the positive role model or a physically attractive individual.

An additional area of concern is the link not only between exposure to graphic visual violence, but also how music portrays violence towards underrepresented minority groups (gay and lesbian individuals, persons of color, etc.) typically seen in music videos. Violence towards women is a relatively common theme in some rap videos and rap music, and the recent statistics suggest that over 20% of college-age women have been exposed to some form of sexual trauma typically experienced in "date rape" (Silverman and colleagues, 2001). How then, do we combat these highly negative and disturbing results? First, we need to change who our "role models" are—role models need to be just that, positive individuals who display exemplary behaviors. Additionally, closer supervision to children and adolescents who are exposed to the music videos and television programs. Finally, and perhaps most importantly, perhaps the best idea is simply to (God forbid!) turn off the video game, the MTV music video or the television program and engage in healthy and physically active behaviors that bring people together in a positive environment. Research consistently shows that when children reduce the numbers of hours watching television and music videos and engage in other active programs, violence significantly is reduced (Silverman and colleagues, 2001).

We may better understand the components of observational learning by reviewing three critical elements that must exist if behavioral change is going to occur: a) *Characteristics that are associated with the model* (i.e., is the model physically attractive? Is the model perceived to be warm, nurturing, and desirable?); b) *Characteristics that are associated with the observer.* Research indicates that the personality type of the observer is important in determining whether or not the observer imitates the model's behavior. For example, more autonomous and independent children are less likely to imitate the model that dependent children. Additionally, children are significantly more likely to imi-

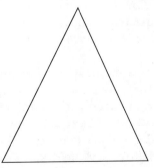

Figure 3a

tate and conform to a variety of behaviors when they have relatively low levels of self-esteem; and *c) Environmental factors.* Research suggests that people are most likely to imitate those behaviors where the appropriate behavioral response is ambiguous and unclear.

▄▄ OBSERVATIONAL LEARNING, EXERCISE & THE CRITICAL PERIOD

An important characteristic to review in developmental psychology is the term "critical period." The term critical period refers to a limited period of time to learn an important cognitive or physical component to behavior. The term critical period is used most often when describing the behaviors of young children who are learning languages, math skills or who are learning some physical function that is adaptive in behavior, such as walking or crawling. The other important characteristic to note with the critical period is that the opportunity to learn the behavior or cognitive information is typically limited to a few months or years. If the child is not exposed to the stimulation of the environment that triggers learning the language or cognitive information, then his or her chances of learning later in life are severely limited. Thus, the critical period is very important in terms of adequate learning and adaptation. Without the appropriate forms of stimulation by parents, the child is clearly at a disadvantage when learning in the environment.

It is well known that children who are most exposed to various forms of intensive cognitive (such as reading) and physical stimulation are offered the highest advantages of learning. Parents are (and should remain) the strongest influence in behavior in the child's life. Children adopt the values, attitudes and styles of behaviors among adults. If we as parents tend to eat unhealthy foods or snack foods too often, children clearly imitate those behaviors and suffer the consequences of obesity. If children see you eat a dessert after a meal all of the time, soon they too will expect cookies and ice-cream after each lunch and dinner. If children see you recline on the couch all day Saturday and Sunday watching game shows or ball games rather than exercising or gardening, they too will spend all of their free time watching television. If your children see you park as close as possible to the supermarket to avoid walking, or use the elevator all of the time and avoid stairs, they too imitate these behaviors. In a word, if our children are lazy and obese, we need to realize that we probably have set poor guidelines and perhaps ourselves have been poor role models for health and fitness. As parents, teachers, educators and family friends we need to take responsibility to change this very dangerous and unhealthy trend that we in fact are setting. It just requires a few minor changes, such as eating healthy snacks (i.e., fruit after dinner instead of cookies), going for a walk after eating a meal instead of watching television, playing active games and sports with your family, and so on. *Remember—the greatest contributor to obesity is lack of activity and sedentary behavior, not necessarily what you eat.*

How does the term "critical period" relate to sports and athletic activities among children? Actually, I would make a strong argument that there is a very strong link between types of parental activities that children are exposed to and involved with and likelihood to engage in similar activities when they are older. Children and adults are clearly becoming a more sedentary and inactive group of individuals. We are relying more and more on video simulation of sports and athletic activities (i.e., why actually play baseball in a hot and dusty park field when you can enjoy the game in your air-conditioned home playing a baseball video game?). Even in terms of recreation, children are using electric or gas-powered scooters and not using their own muscles and physical force to propel themselves when using their wagon or scooter. More and more toys, wagons and scooters have become self-propelled where the child uses virtually no effort of their own in coordinating the activity. More and more primary-grade schools and high schools have dramatically cut-back or eliminated entirely the physical education courses, so students are not offered enough opportunity for exercise and activity. When children are not taught by a role model (such as their parents or older siblings) how to develop a healthy and active lifestyle that incorporates exercise, it is very difficult for them to change as they develop and develop their own routines and daily activities. Research continually suggests that when parents teach children how to engage in healthy exercise that is combined with a healthy diet, they are significantly more likely to maintain these activities throughout their lives. If these children are not taught these activities by age ten or twelve, it is very difficult to change their routines as they become older. Therefore, as parents we need to start early and teach children what is healthy and adaptive so they may lead happier and more adaptive lifestyles. In this sense, then, teaching children exercise programs is very similar to languages, reading or math skills—the sooner they learn them, the more proficient they are in continuing these behaviors.

To illustrate the broad scope of the problem of obesity among children, consider the following: Approximately 9 million American children over the age of 6 are now obese due to inactivity and poor eating habits. The Institute of Medicine recommends less television, more exercise and healthier foods. Furthermore, Dr. Jeffery Koplan, Chairman for the panel's report and former head of the Center for the Disease Control and Prevention states: "No single factor or sector of society bears all of the blame for the current [obesity] problem . . . and no single group or sector can solve it." The panel also recommended that children in school receive at least 30 minutes of daily activity, such as physical education. (*Daily News*, 10/02/04). Additionally, the Los Angeles Times reports: "Over the last 30 years, the rate of childhood obesity has tripled among children from ages 6 to 11, and doubled for those from age 2 to 5 as well as 12 to 19" (*The Los Angeles Times*, October 1, 2004).

■ THE CRITICAL PERIOD FOR EXERCISE & ACTIVITY FOR CHILDREN: BETWEEN THE AGES 5 AND 10 YEARS

Research suggests that children are most likely to be receptive to exercise and health programs if they are incorporated early on in their lives, and the most important ages for these activities appear to be between 5 years and 10 years. The logic is simple and very dynamic: If you want your child to remain healthy and develop the skills to maintain good physical health as they mature into adults, teach them yourself where you are the positive role model. Engage them in an activity that they like that also involves eye-hand coordination, running, jumping, and cardiovascular or aerobic activities. If they see you and your spouse or other family members engaging in these activities, they too will join you so they can have fun. Walking, jogging, stretching, gardening, basketball, baseball, jump-rope, and many other simple activities are the key to motivate your children to get off the couch, shut off the video game and get outside. The table below is a sample model of some of the activities that children should be involved with at specific ages. Remember, some children may advance faster or more slowly than others, so some differences may occur with this chart:

Beginning Exercise Program for the Critical Period (5–10 years)

a. **Age 5:** 15 minutes of *daily* outdoor activity involving gross motor skills (hands and feet movement). Child should be capable of kicking a large ball, coordinate some eye-hand activities (such as throwing a ball and catching a large, soft ball such as a beach ball); Child should be able to jump up in the air with both feet; Walk up and down stairs; consistent walking distances over 10 minutes. Child should also be able to balance on one foot, run short distances without stumbling or falling; Child should also be able to swim short distances ("survival swim") to get to shallow water or to land if falls in water.

b. **Age 6:** 30 minutes of *daily* outdoor activity involving organized sport activity. Children at this age should be throwing with more accuracy, catching balls at distances of approximately 10–15 feet and running with greater speed and coordination. The differences between ages 5 and 6 are significant, as typically most 6 year old children are now increasing their social interaction with friends at school and may be interested in joining organized sport activities at school. Children now play in organized sport programs, such as Little League Baseball or Basketball programs at school. Parental involvement is very important at this point, support, encouragement, direction and supervision are essential components for successful experiences in sports. Parents and caregivers should also frequently offer praise so the child is enjoying the activity. The specific activity or sport may be modified so the child may participate in the sport. For example, some young children (5–6 years) may have difficulty in actually hitting a ball in baseball. In cases such as these, modifications may be necessary such as hitting a ball from a "T" rather than actually pitching a ball to them.

c. **Age 7.** 40 minutes of aerobic activity, such as kicking a ball on a field with other children in a soccer game or walking at a brisk pace. Children are becoming more advanced in physical skills and coordination, and now are throwing and catching with improved eye-hand coordination. Children are becoming more active in team sports and should now have the capacity to understand in sharing responsibilities, positions, and different types of activities in the recreational program they are attending.

d. **Age 8.** 45 minutes of continuous and improved physical exercise. Children at this stage of development should have an appreciation of the different types of sports programs that exist and should have an opportunity to interact and engage in active play in a variety of these sports. Sports that are the healthiest and most popular place a demand on the aerobic capacity of the child and are stimulating to participate in with other children. Examples of popular team sport activities that 8 year olds should have some experience with include: Baseball, soccer, football (non-contact—"flag" football); basketball, and swimming. Children at this age may be deciding what types of sports they prefer to participate in and are developing their own preferences.

e. **Age 9.** 50 minutes of continuous recreational activity. Children are associating more sports activities as a means of identifying with peers and school activities and should have more frequent exposure to a variety of exercise programs. Children should be also developing intrinsic motivation and participating now because it is "fun" and they enjoy the activity.

f. **Age 10.** 60 minutes of continuous recreational activity. Children should be participating in more complex sports and understanding concepts such as play diagrams and strategies. Play and recreational sport are now integrated into the child's routine of daily activities and the child looks forward to playing sports and exercise as a means of social interaction. Child now may be viewing sports and recreational as a form of an identity, such as a factor in selecting a particular high school or college program.

Perhaps the most important component in each of these critical stages of exercise development is the appreciation of sport as a means of enjoyment and recreation. Perhaps the most difficult factor in working with adults in a health and fitness program is in helping them to "relearn" the process of exercise as a fun activity and not something to dread or avoid.

▬ CHAPTER 3 QUESTION & REVIEW

1. Briefly describe the concept of observational learning and how we may use the principle of observational learning to teach children healthy forms of exercise;

2. Identify three components necessary for observational learning to occur and provide examples;

3. Describe the concept of the critical period and observational learning. What are the ages of the critical period of exercise programs for children? In your opinion, why is it important to teach children during the critical period an exercise and sport program? Can you think of other examples that incorporate the concepts of a critical period?

4. Create an exercise program involving different activities for children during the sport critical period (ages 5–10 years).

5. Do you believe professional athletes have an inherent obligation to be positive role models? Justify your reasoning.

Chapter 4:
Understanding Motivational Skills That Enhance Your Training: When You Believe You Can Achieve Something—You Will!

We have been discussing the importance of exercise and activities as key elements to physical health. We've established the fact that inactivity combined with poor diet leads to an increase in obesity. As a society we need to collectively change our patterns and habits of behaviors that lead to poor health. More importantly, however, before behaviors can change we need to first develop and understand the motivational skills that are necessary to activate the change. This chapter will focus on motivational concepts from a historical and current perspective and will also emphasize key theories that will help individuals to remain motivated in their training and exercise program. The first thing that we need to establish is the definition of motivation, and this can be sometimes difficult in psychology. When discussing the term motivation, we most often use it in a relatively positive way. For example, the "motivated athlete" or the "motivated student" usually conveys many positive concepts, such as good worker characteristics, showing up to practice on time, studying and trying hard, and so on. The term motivation does not actually specifically refer to either a positive or a negative component, but rather a description of the intensity and level of the drive of the behavior. Thus the term motivation refers specifically to a form of an incentive or drive intensity that helps us achieve a goal. The motivational direction may be either positive or negative, and the intensity of the motivational drive may vary as well from situation to situation. The key to understanding and improving athletic behavior is first in understanding what are the components that trigger motivation and attitude. The differences between winning and losing, success and failure often depends on the athlete's understanding how to control his or her levels of motivation. The key to good coaching also involves understanding the motivational concepts of the athlete within a variety of different competitive situations. We will now explore some of the specific topics that focus on motivational theory.

■ ATTRIBUTION THEORY: UNDERSTANDING THE REASONS WHY WE ENGAGE IN BEHAVIORS

When individuals wish to understand and improve their behaviors regarding health and fitness, they may explore some factors that are relevant to support systems, their environment, and their relationships with people, such as coaches and health trainers. Perhaps a key element to explore when trying to investigate athletic performance are the reasons or attributions people have regarding events that occur in their lives. When people feel that they are in control of the events of their lives and have some control in the outcome of their events, they have what is called an intrinsic or internal attribution system. Individuals who feel that things happen to them outside of their control and that they have no ability to control or direct events in their lives have an external attribution system. Research clearly supports the hypothesis that when individuals feel that they do not have control in their events (i.e., "we lost because the referee was biased against us!") have more negative experiences in the lives and are more susceptible to depression and failure. Conversely, those individuals who feel that they have the ability to control events in their lives tend to report feeling less depression, more happiness, and in general are more successful experiences in their life.

■■■ TEACHING EXTRINSIC & INTRINSIC ATTRIBUTIONS: KEEP TRYING!

Whether or not an individual has an internal or an external locus of control largely depends on what we teach our children as parents, coaches and teachers and how they respond to failure. For example, if a child who is learning to play catch, throw a ball, or hit a ball with a baseball bat experiences difficulty and simply gives up he is more likely to feel less capable of achieving his goal in the future. Parents need to help teach children who are learning components in sports to keep trying in light of initial failure. When children learn to overcome initial failure with the assistance and guidance of their parents or coach, they begin to develop the foundation of a belief system and incorporate self-esteem. An individual with an intrinsic attribution perceives that they are in control in the events that unfold in their lives, and that they have the ability to monitor and determine their fate. Parents can teach children to have an internal attribution (also referred to as internal locus of control) by developing the persistence and determination in learning the skills to complete tasks after initial failure. Parents should also support children in learning tasks that failure does happen and that we should view failure as an opportunity to learn and improve our behaviors. Through gradual support and supervision, parents should instruct children how to accomplish their goals by providing them with the information to correct their mistakes. This allows children to become convinced that they do have the ability to learn from their mistakes and that they in fact have the capacity to make positive changes in their life—this is the essence of the intrinsic attribution theory: The ability to realize that you control events in your life as they unfold.

Conversely, parents may intervene when a child fails at a particular sports-related task and prevent their child from learning from his or her mistakes. When this happens, the child does not learn how to correct the mistakes that they will make in the future and they will become more dependent on others to help them in learning the sports-related task. Additionally, the child who is not afforded the opportunity to correct his or her mistakes independently when learning how to throw a ball or hit a baseball with a bat may be more apt to develop an extrinsic attribution due to the inaccurate perception that they cannot change their faulty behavior. This misperception is further amplified when the (well-intentioned) parent frequently intervenes and comes to the child's rescue. For example, a parent that blames a coach for not putting in their child or the parent who blames the umpire on a "bad call" is preventing the child from developing an opportunity to learn to make positive changes himself. These positive changes ultimately will result in the transition from the external to an internal attribution. What actually happens in this unfortunate scenario is that the child relies on the assistance of others to learn the skills that he should develop by practice and trial and error. *The greater the difficulty a child experiences in learning a task, the more likely the child will remember the task and how to perform the task correctly in the future.*

The child who practices his pitching skills with his parent and learns to develop the ability to become a first string pitcher learns that they have the ability to achieve their goals on their own and will develop the self-esteem to take on new challenges in the future. Additionally, the child's internal attribution is further developed by realizing they have the capacity to take control and master athletic skills that are essential to success:

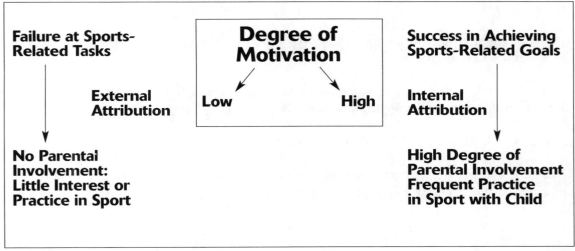

Figure 4a

■ ZONE OF PROXIMAL DEVELOPMENT: KEVIN LEARNS TO RIDE A BICYCLE

One mechanism that has been proven to be highly effective with teaching children the coping mechanisms in a variety of activities (within the classroom as well as outside) is Vygotsky's Zone of Proximal Development (ZPD). The Zone of Proximal Development refers to a theory introduced by Vygotsky (1896–1934), the famous Russian psychologist. Vygotsky introduced a concept referred to as Zone of Proximal Development that incorporates the elements of parental involvement, intrinsic attribution and high levels of motivation among children in sports. The Zone of Proximal Development is described as a philosophy or a style of interaction where problems that may prove too difficult for children to solve independently may be solved with the aid or assistance of a parent or caregiver. Note that the Zone of Proximal Development does not simply provide information to the child while working on a task—the child is engaged in problem solving skills and is gradually provided with minimal input from the adult. The child gradually begins to solve the problem with minimal assistance from the adult—this technique allows the child to see the answer gradually and builds on the relationship with the adult. The Zone of Proximal Development offers several advantages over traditional forms of educational intervention programs. Perhaps most importantly, the ZPD process further enhances and develops the relationship between the child and parent, where the parent asks a series of questions to the child that may help the child solve the problem through insight. Additionally, the ZPD process helps the child feel more confident about future problem-solving situations and develop stronger levels of self-esteem and self-efficacy. Perhaps most importantly, the child is experiencing a positive relationship with his parent and having fun while solving the problem. Many children have overcome the math-fears and anxiety when using the ZPD approach (Karpou & Haywood, 1998). We will now describe the ZPD process with Kevin, a 7 year old child who is learning to ride his bicycle for the first time without training wheels.

Zone of Proximal Development: Learning to Ride a Bicycle

Father: Okay, Kevin, here is your bike . . . Do you feel like trying it out without your training wheels today?

Kevin: (somewhat nervous) I don't think so . . . I don't want to do this right now. Can't we go inside and watch television?

Father: How about if we just try to sit and pedal . . . I'll be here to help you if you have any problems. I promise I won't let anything happen. Now let's get you up on that seat.

Kevin: What do I do now? How am I supposed to stay up without you holding me?

Father: Just keep pedaling, and pretty soon you won't need anybody to hold you up . . . see, now you are pedaling by yourself . . . It's fun, right?

Kevin: Yes, but I'm still a little scared. Don't leave me, okay?

Father: I won't, but look you are doing it on your own! [Father slowly releases his grip on the bicycle—Kevin keeps pedaling and slows down];

Kevin: Your right! This is fun! And it is not that hard! I knew that I could do it!

Father: Good Work Kevin! Now let's slow down and put your foot on the ground. Next time, let's see if you pedal by yourself and steer. Remember, always put your helmet on and tell me before you decide to ride your bicycle.

Kevin: I knew it—next time, I want to try to pedal longer without you holding me, okay?

Father: Okay, great. Now let's go play catch with your ball.

Note how the elements and fundamentals of ZPD were incorporated in this brief vignette describing how a father teaches his son to ride a bicycle. Before each step was mastered by Kevin, the father encouraged him and gave him instructions how to correctly incorporate each step that leads to successful bicycle riding: a) Sitting on bicycle seat; b) Pedaling the pedals; c) Steering while pedaling; d) Braking to slow down to avoid obstacles; and e) Exiting the bicycle safely. The father gently provided information as each step was mastered—and Kevin's self-confidence and self-esteem gradually improved as he incorporated his father's suggestions. This experience was perceived as high positive by both father and Kevin, and this positive experience will help Kevin learn the coordination skills for future tasks.

■■ ERIKSON'S PSYCHOSOCIAL STAGES OF DEVELOPMENT AND PERSONALITY: TEACHING CONCEPTS OF SPORTS:

Erik Erikson (1902–1994) was an incredibly gifted scholar and teacher of psychology that focused on early childhood relationships with parents as formative influences on the development of the personality. Erikson was an incredibly insightful writer who seemed to always maintain a pleasant demeanor with students and faculty. Erikson writes in a very logical and analytical style that provides his theory with a simple approach that is easily understood by students. Perhaps his most compelling points in his theory refer to the fact that all of us must engage in some form of a personal crisis for true personality development to occur. Erikson does have some influence from Freud in his early work—he felt that the role of the parents (especially the attachment and bonding process with the mother from birth to about age five to six) was critical in terms of shaping the personality of the child. Note also that Freud describes that the personality of the adult is complete in its development at about age six. Erikson describes the child's personality as being entirely developed from the quality of the relationship and interaction with the caregivers that the infant is dependent on. Each of the eight stages of psychosocial development describes a process where the individual develops a role or responsibility they must take on in society. Furthermore, Erikson argues that each stage of development necessarily involves some form of a crisis or problem that can either build the character of the individual or result in dependency and malformation. As the child matures and develops, new responsibilities must be met and addressed appropriately; if for some reason the child or adolescent is incapable of meeting these demands and responsibilities, the personality suffers from development and insight and is prevented from becoming an authentic, unique and creative human being. We live in a technologically advanced era where machines do more for us than ever before. Our society is constructed on the idea that ease and comfort are priorities to strive for, and that somehow work or a "crisis" are negative concepts to be avoided at all cost. The easier something is to achieve the better it is. Why exercise when we can purchase a mechanical device placed on the stomach that does sit-ups for us? If we do not complete our homework, then quickly print out an article on the internet and turn it in as our own work. Why bother working through problems in a marriage or relationships when divorce or breaking up and finding someone new via internet chat rooms is only a "mouseclick away"? The problem with these scenarios is that our lives are seemingly becoming easier by the insulation provided by technology. According to Erikson, all people progress through eight psychosocial stages of development, each associated with critical periods of psychological and social development that we need to experience ourselves. In many cases where people experience problems, they have not been afforded the opportunity to learn from their mistakes. For example, a parent completes his child's homework while he watches television; an adolescent is arrested for drunk driving, but his father "fixes" the ticket because he knows the judge; or a young couple encounter difficulties in their marriage and file for divorce rather than pursue counseling. According to Erikson, we *need* to encounter difficulties in various stages of our lives in order to grow from these experiences and encounter interpersonal growth. However, in order for us to benefit, grow and maximize our knowledge, we need to experience difficulties so that we may gain insight and development. If things are done for us and we do not learn, then our likelihood of engaging in a similar problem is very strong. We will now describe each of the eight stages of psychosocial development as they relate to the world of sports and health.

a. *Trust versus Mistrust (birth–one year):* In the traditional sense, Erikson describes the first stage of development as a key component in future interactions with adults in terms of trust and dependency. From birth to about one year, Erikson argues that the infant makes his or her first impression in the world, and whether or not that impression is positive or favorable depends on the quality of the interaction with the primary caregivers. Stated very simply, if the infant is loved and provided with positive and loving interactions, he or she will in turn be able to reciprocate with love and trust. If the child is loved and trusted by his parents, then (and only then) they will be able to love and trust others as adults. Conversely, if the child is neglected, abused or raised in a very inconsistent environment where the infant does not know what to expect on a daily basis, they will grow and develop with a highly suspicious and critical nature.

   Trust versus mistrust and the ramifications in sport psychology. Although the infant is very young and cannot participate in sports or athletic activity, they are beginning to learn the fundamental skills and personality characteristics that will play a fundamental role in their ability to play in a variety of sports later in adult life. For example, imagine the consequences of an individual who was raised in an environment that lacked in trust and attention, where every need that the infant had was left unanswered and neglected. Of course this neglectful type of environment would have a profound negative impact in future team or collective styles of interaction. The child who was neglected and lacked the ability to trust others clearly will now have problems in his or her ability to trust others in team sports. They may feel compelled to have control over events that surround their athletic world, and may lack the ability to trust and confide in their team mates. Erikson would explain the psychological phenomena as the child saying: "If I cannot trust my parents to provide me with the basic things that I need, such as trust and love, how then can I trust others (such as team mates) in critical and important events in my life?" The child must decide whether or not the world is a loving and trustworthy place, and if provided with the love and attention necessary at this first stage of psychosocial development, they will be able to face future dilemmas effectively and positively. An additional factor to consider is the importance of trusting your coach and teammates. The ability to develop trust and share trust in our relationships with other people is critical in how we interact and relate to people. Without trust, our ability to develop our skills, formulate relationships, and create a safe environment for all people becomes severely limited. Trust can only be developed when we are provided with trust as infants. The first psychosocial stage of development and the first "crisis" that Erikson discusses in his research is the importance of providing infants with consistent and reliable parenting skills. When children are hungry, they need food. When they are lonely, they need attention and nurturing. A child cannot display trust if he or she has not been given the things that they need in early development. Athletes that cannot trust others as they develop and mature will have significant difficulty in understanding the dynamics of team sports. Team sports inherently involve the ability to trust and build interdependence; without interdependence, the team will lack the ability to play as a single unit. We will discuss in the next several stages how the development of trust is the foundation upon which the following stages are built upon.

b. *Autonomy versus Shame & Doubt (Age one year to about three years).* At this second stage of development, the child now learns to approach tasks independently and autonomously, or they feel shameful and doubt their ability to learn new tasks due to their relationship with their caregivers. The child is beginning to develop the skills and abilities to master certain activities, such as walking and crawling, as well as feeding himself or herself. A healthy sign of development is when the child wants to learn these skills independent of parental assistance. This is a critical period of time for the child to learn skills in trial and error to see what athletic skills they can develop with the assistance and interaction of the parent or the caregiver. Common tasks that are developed during this period of time include toilet training and sensorimotor skills, such as gross motor skills (i.e., throwing and catching a large ball). If children are successful n learning these tasks, they become further motivated to learn new tasks that are sports related in the future. The more autonomous the child is in learning new skills relative to their development, the more likely they will learn sports and athletic skills and play with other children.

Conversely, if the child is unsuccessful in learning the task, or if the child's parents are too controlling or dominating in allowing the child to learn tasks independently, their ability to develop skills necessary in sports will be delayed. Additionally, the child will doubt their own competence and ability because parents (however well-intentioned) are frequently interfering with the child's ability to execute tasks. The child interprets this as a sign that he or she is inadequate in skills and aptitude development and thus may experience shame about themselves and doubt their ability to perform well in future tasks. Thus, according to Erikson, parents must decide when to intervene if a task is overwhelming (or dangerous) or when to allow the child to try and learn from his or her mistakes. Finally, it should be noted that Erikson places much emphasis on how quickly children learn these skills on the relationship with parents.

Autonomy versus Shame and Doubt: Ramifications in Sport Psychology. Given the fact that this stage is critical in the child becoming an independent (autonomous) worker with others, parents need to teach children the skills to maintain persistence and determination when attempting a variety of athletic tasks involving coordination. Invariably all children will fail at some task, and parents need to cooperatively work with children in showing them how to achieve success and master the skill (see Vygotsky's Zone of Proximal Development in chapter 3). There are a variety of things that parents can do to facilitate autonomy, but perhaps the most important task is in showing the child that they have the power to control the events that occur in their lives. For example, parents can show a child how to catch a ball by putting their hands together as the ball is thrown, or how to kick a ball in a specific direction. Parents need to allow children to learn by trial and error and more importantly let the child learn from his errors. During this second stage of psychosocial development, children are also learning the skills to play and coordinate activities with others, such as cooperative play and learning to form relationships. Hopefully they have the capacity to trust others, and now in stage two they begin to show independence in selecting tasks and sports where they are showing independent skills and aptitudes essential for sport.

c. *Initiative versus Guilt (3 to 5 years).* If we were to explore styles of behavior among 3, 4, and 5 year old children, we would see groups of children who want to display their knowledge and engage or initiate activities with other children. According to Erikson, children between the ages of 3 and 5 years need to begin and initiate a variety of activities with other children. Playing team sports, such as basketball and football will allow them to develop a variety of skills that are used in sport activity. When children have been provided with nurturing and love and support in a trusting environment they develop the capacity and ability to trust others while playing in a variety of activities. It should be noted that the ages from 3 to 5 years are critical in teaching children the basic skills necessary to be competent and successful in a variety of activities. A child capable of trying to learn skills, such as playing catch with a ball, climbing, running and throwing skills combines eye-hand coordination and gross motor skills to be more competent in future activities. Children at this stage with a strong sense of autonomy will initiate beginning tasks and learn from their experiences (both positive and negative).

A child with a healthy sense of self and ego will want to initiate tasks and learn a variety of skills with other children because they are not afraid of failure. They are not afraid of failure due to the unconditional support that they have received from their parents and caregivers during this third stage of development. Furthermore, the child who feels confident in learning new skills and initiates a variety of activities creates a highly supportive learning environment rich with future learning potential. For example, the 4 year old child who is learning to run, kick a ball and control the direction of the ball is incorporating several skills simultaneously: Coordination of gross motor skills and balance. The child who engages in these activities is learning to coordinate their physical movements and also the ability to coordinate decisions with other children who are playing sports with them. The more active they become in this activity, the more potential to learn and become competent and thus the greater the likelihood to initiate future activities the result in learning. Thus, a healthy reciprocal relationship develops with the child who is provided with a supportive, loving and trusting environment: The more they learn to initiate a variety of activities the more confident they become to face new challenges in their life (see figure 3c).

Initiative Versus Guilt (Ages 3–5 years)
Positive Interaction
Supportive and Loving Environment (Trust)

Throws Ball to Friends (success) » **Child Increases Self-Confidence**

☺ **To Initiate Future Activities**
Child wants to play with others

Result: Child has fun and develops the motivation to face new sport challenges (throw ball further, play catch with friends, develops positive motivation)—Child feels more confident in learning new tasks and wants to engage in other activities with children.

Initiative Versus Guilt (Ages 3–5 years)
Negative Interaction
Critical and Rejecting Environment (No Trust)

Child Attempts to
Play with Friends (no success) » **Child lacks in self-confidence; Fails to initi-**
☹ ate future activities with friends. Feels inad-
equate to play with others; Feels rejected

Result: Child feels inadequate and guilt from lack of success. Likelihood to engage in future athletic and sport activities minimal due to perception of inadequacy and guilt in not feeling "good enough" with the other children playing. Child withdraws from future interaction with children—skills and aptitudes become dormant.

Figure 4b

The child at this stage of development is constantly learning and developing new skills by interacting with others. If the child at this stage lacks in initiative and the ego strength to begin new health and sport activities, guilt and a sense of inadequacy may develop. This concept is what Adler referred to as the "inferiority complex" where the sense of being inadequate served as the incentive and motive to strive harder to achieve our goals. Children will initiate activities and work to their full potential if provided with love and support in earlier stages.

d. *Industry versus Inferiority (6–12 years).* In the fourth stage of psychosocial stage of development, Erikson describes learning really as a matter of self-esteem and how feelings of self-worth influence the likelihood of children beginning constructive tasks. If the child has not been provided with love and support where they feel that they can trust others in their community, they will not feel capable of beginning tasks due to feelings of inferiority and a lack of self-worth. What does it really mean to be industrious? An industrious person is defined as an individual who is hardworking and diligent—someone who does not shy away from challenges. These are incredibly important characteristics in the world of development. More importantly, these characteristics are in fact capable of being taught to children and student athletes. A good coach is someone who has the ability to make people feel that they have something to contribute to the group or the team. An excellent coach makes athletes perform to their "personal best" and realize goals that they themselves did not think were attainable. An outstanding coach combines both of these characteristics in such a manner to the student athlete where they want to contribute to the team because of the pride they feel about being part of a team.

What are the mechanisms that allow parents to teach children to work independently and to set realistic and challenging goals for themselves? Perhaps more importantly, how can we teach children perseverance and determination, to keep working in the face of initial failure? How can parents raise their children to be more industrious in their everyday challenges of life? These are very important questions, and Erikson answers these questions by telling parents and coaches to offer unconditional support and trust to the child. When the child feels that they have support from the most important people in their life (their parents), they feel that it is okay to take chances and fail. The critical factor, however, is in the parent's response to the child when he or she occasionally does fail. Earlier in this chapter we discussed Vygotsky's theory of the zone of proximal development, where parents provide key information to children during the course of learning a new project—note the parent does not simply give the answer to the child, but allows the child to discover the answers and solutions himself. When working with children and fostering an industrious child, the parent still offers support and insight to the child, but encourages the child to continue working to complete the task even after initial failure. Parents who simply allow their children to "give up" and go on to some other activity are not allowing the child to learn from his or her mistakes. More importantly, the child now develops the concept that he or she is "inferior" and cannot complete the task.

For example, assume that Sara is an 8 year old child trying to understand the basic concepts of fractions and mathematics in general. She just cannot seem to grasp the concepts of how fractions function—how can one half and one half actually equal one? What does one-third actually look like? Sara is very confused, but she is trying very hard. If her teacher offers her support and works with her by asking a series of questions and providing visual examples, Sara will understand that one half of an orange plus the other half of the orange will give her one total orange. Sara sees the orange, sees the two halves, and then sees how they are put back together again. She visualizes this concept and now understands the concept. The teacher has provided her with an actual visual image that will allow her to pursue more complicated tasks in fractions and math problems. Most importantly, Sara wants to solve more complicated fraction and math problems because of her positive interaction with her teacher. Conversely, parents and coaches can limit the perception of industriousness when they offer conditional support and love. Let's use the classic example of Little League Baseball and "Tim." Tim has been trying to hit the baseball in his game for weeks. When he is at practice, he is less nervous, and he is capable of coordinating his eye-hand movements in a way where the ball is hit almost every time. However, during the game, his mother and father and siblings are all watching, and he gets very nervous—they are cheering him on (thinking that they are helping him) and he is only getting more nervous because he knows that he is the center of attention). When he gets to the plate, He "feels all jittery . . . and almost sick to my stomach." To make matters worse, Tim's father tells him to "get up there [the plate] and make us proud of you!" Of course, the father is trying to motivate Tim, but Tim already is in a very high state of arousal—now negative arousal. Tim strikes out the third time, and his father just turns at the end of the game and says nothing. This form or style of interaction actually depletes industriousness and motivation—because now Tim feels that he cannot play up to his father's expectations.

This form of a relationship between family members and the child athlete is usually described as *conditional love / positive attention,* where the child compares success in sport with more love and attention from his family. Things are fine when Tim hits a home run, however, if performance drops, he feels ignored and unloved. Children at this stage of psychosocial development thus begin feelings of inadequacy and inferiority if they compare success (such as hitting a home run in a baseball game) with self-worth. The more home runs they hit, the more attention they receive from the family which in turn makes the child feel special and important. However, when the athletic performance drops (as it inevitably will), the sense of self declines and self-esteem also plunges. When we base our self worth on either physical appearance or successful performance, we eventually risk a healthy balance of self-esteem and self-worth. The child should be taught that feelings of self-worth and self-esteem come from facing challenges and working to the best of their ability—not in the outcome of success or failure. How we feel about ourselves is a matter of intrinsic worth, not external success or accomplishments. This is very important for the child to learn at this stage, because a child who has enough self-worth with an industrious attitude will feel positive about himself or herself, regardless of the outcome. If the child is not provided with the love and support that they need to become industrious and to take on new challenges, a sense of inferiority develops that will impact how the child faces new challenges and demands throughout his or her life. How can we overcome this very common problem among parents and their children or coaches and their athletes? Create an *unconditionally* positive and supportive environment where children will feel your support even in light of occasional failure. When the child feels this type of support, they will feel more confident to begin new challenges and activities in the future. The more support you provide as a coach or parent, the more motivated and industrious the child will be to try new activities.

■ ADLER'S THEORY OF INFERIORITY

Perhaps a brief word should be included here about Alfred Adler's theory of the creative power and inferiority. If you remember from chapter one, Adler argued that all persons are born with a sense of inadequacy and low-self-esteem. This low self-esteem is translated as inferiority, and all individuals feel compelled to compensate and develop these perceived physical and/or intellectual inadequacies. The sense of "not being good enough" serves as a highly effective motivator to become more diligent and successful in the very activities that we initially have difficulty with. For example, the young child who has difficulty in running, coordination and physical agilities (as was the case with Adler himself as a child) will train especially hard and condition himself to overcome these physical challenges. Thus, the industriousness that Erikson describes at stage four of psychosocial development is comparable to Adler's theory of inferiority, where in both cases the child is working through his or her perceived physical or psychological challenges and ultimately becoming stronger and most competent as an adult. The child learns to take on new challenges because of the self-esteem and confidence he is achieving about himself at this stage and as Adler notes the child is physically overcoming his perceived area of inferiority. The two theories are positively correlated with each other, and the common link for both Adler and Erikson is through an *unconditional support system* the child will eventually achieve his physical goals by overcoming the perception of inferiority.

e. *Identity versus Role Confusion (adolescence).* Often I am surprised how often people comment how "difficult" it is being a teen-ager and how often many young people are faced with difficult choices in the lives. What people are referring to are the numerous changes adolescents are experiencing in their life—the psychological, emotional, and physical changes that are occurring each day. Additionally, as adults we often have unrealistic expectations of the adolescent—in some cases we tell them to "act like an adult and make the right choices for themselves" and in other cases, parents and relatives may place demands on the adolescent and literally treat them as a child. This is very confusing for the adolescent and places them in a difficult position in knowing exactly how to act or behave most of the time. The world of the adolescent is changing constantly—and the crisis that Erikson describes that faces most teen-agers is the decision that will affect their future and their career. Commonly asked questions during this period of development include: "What am I going to do with my life?" or "What am I going to do after high school? Do I go to college like most of my friends . . . or do I try to find a full-time job, or should I just stay home and watch television all day?"

Our society in general is becoming increasingly complicated and competitive—high school students are faced with "AP" (advanced placement) courses, requirements for entrance to colleges and universities are becoming more stringent, and the demands made upon adolescents seem to be increasing on a daily basis. Decisions and choices that are made today have greater impact on the future of adolescents, and many adolescents are feeling pressure to select a career or identity prematurely. According to Erikson, the major crisis or problem to resolve during this period of time is in deciding what career is appropriate for them. Think of the tremendous ramifications when you discuss with people what your interests are in a career. Additionally, think of how people react (usually to stereotypes that have become associated with various professions) to you when you discuss your career interests. *Quite literally Erikson describes that the career you have chosen becomes your identity and defines your sense of self.* Think about various social situations you have been exposed to with people that you have just met. Of course they ask your name and where you go to school, and if you are older, they ask *"what do you do."* If you declare yourself to be studying to be a doctor, attorney, or some other professional, you are presumed to be serious, mature and perhaps even have your career and life plan designated. In fact, in some cultures, even your spouse is "pre-selected" for you.

Identity versus Role Confusion: Ramifications in Sport Psychology. In terms of athletics and sport competition, the sport activity itself may define the identity for the individual. The athlete "jock" in high school who plays a variety of sports assumes the identity of the football player, the basketball player or baseball player. The adolescent who engages in a sport activity defines his or her identity as the athlete, just as the computer "geek" defines their personality as an intellectual. The fifth stage of psychosocial development according to Erikson is critical in terms of achieving an individual identity and providing a sense of direction to the adolescent's life. For example, at this point in the adolescent's life, the crisis develops between achieving an identity (i.e., such as in a career in sports) or remaining in a state of confusion and lack of direction. For many adolescents, choosing a sport is more than just an athletic activity to pass the time during high school. The sport that the serious teen-ager selects during adolescence becomes his or her current identity as well as their future identity (i.e., what college to attend and receiving an athletic scholarship). Thus, during this critical period of time, the selection of sport activity often serves as the adolescent's own identity and future goals.

Identity versus Role Confusion: Role Confusion May Lead to Tragedy. As a final note, the adolescent who feels that they cannot "fit in" to any of the groups that will serve as their identity may lose their identity entirely and feel displaced in society. A common reaction to rejection is aggression, and when adolescents feel that they cannot find a suitable identity that connects them into society, frustration and aggression may result. A tragic example of this is the Columbine incident—two young high school students in search of their own identity became enraged at the ridicule and scorn that they received from their peers. They were unable to adapt to or find an identity of their own despite numerous efforts to belong with various campus groups (computer, sports etc.). The faculty failure to recognize the trauma and obvious signs of frustration experienced among these two teen-agers should serve as a signal to all of us of the importance in understanding the role of identity in adolescence.

f.   *Intimacy versus Isolation (young adulthood).* During this period of time the "crisis" or the problem that the individual faces is in how to trust and share intimacy with another person. Intimacy may be described as a form of psychological vulnerability where trust and communication are vital. Remember earlier in the beginning of this section describing Erikson's theory, each stage is characterized as a form of a "crisis" that is typically associated with various stages of development. While we may not typically regard a crisis as something positive or desirable, Erikson reminds us that a crisis allows growth and insight to develop if we are willing to learn from the experience. Thus, each of these stages represents an opportunity for inner growth and development of the self. This inner growth process of trust and communication may be manifested through a variety of team sport and athletic activities.

Team Sports, Intimacy, & The Need For Trust. Imagine playing basketball or football and not being able to count on your guard to pass the ball to you because he or she wants the opportunity to make the basket themselves and "look good for the camera." Imagine that you are playing football and you are relying on your tackle to block the middle linebacker who is "blitzing" (making a direct attempt to tackle the quarterback) and the tackle fails the block. You are hit very hard, knocked down and you question your lineman's ability to protect you in the future. Team sports require an ability to trust and rely on your teammates to work to their full potential and not play selfishly. Thus, the connection in this sixth stage of psychosocial development according to Erikson is the ability to allow yourself to trust others in a community where groups of individuals comprise a team. You become vulnerable and rely on others to perform their job, and others rely on you to do your job. If this is achieved, team work is the result. However, note the inherent connection between stages one (trust versus mistrust) and stage six (intimacy versus isolation). If the athlete has not been afforded the opportunity to grow and develop within a loving and trusting environment that we discussed in stage one, then he or she will not have the capacity to trust others in vital or critical game situations. Rather than trusting others, the individual plays like an individual and the team represents more of a group of self-serving and egoistic individuals. Balls will not be passed to other team mates, blocks will not be made to protect the quarterback, and so on. Trust will be replaced by greed and a sense of entitlement. Clearly, this sense of entitlement and lack of trust and intimacy was displayed by the Los Angeles Lakers during the 2004 season. Most sports critics agreed that the Lakers had the potential to be a national championship team, but in-fighting, conflict, a lack of unity and communication prevailed that ultimately destroyed their career. In sum, the inability for the players to trust each other and communicate with each other resulted in a group of individuals who became psychologically isolated rather than a cohesive team.

g. *Generativity versus Stagnation.* In this seventh stage of psychosocial development, the crisis among middle-aged adults is to maintain and continue to find meaning in their life. Specifically, the "crisis" in our lives at this stage of development is to find some form of a meaningful activity that provides validation and affirmation to our existence. We need to generate meaning by the development and cultivation of relationships in our lives and contributing to society. According to Erikson, during this stage, we need to give back to society the kinds of things that have created and shaped our identity and contributed to the passion that we experience. The problem with many individuals today, according to Erikson, is that we place too much emphasis on the material possessions and physical appearance of people. The only way that we can achieve meaning in our lives is by appreciating experiences and the relationships that we have with a variety of people that have somehow touched our lives. Erikson notes that as adults we have benefited from the sacrifices of others, and now we need to give back to the community where we live. We generate meaning in our lives by helping others and providing assistance to those who need intervention in our society. Individuals need to look beyond things like money, physical appearance (i.e., cosmetic surgery) and fancy cars and learn to establish meaningful relationships with others. Erikson notes that meaning is also achieved by making sacrifices in the community and seeing how others benefit from our contributions.

Generativity versus Stagnation: Ramifications in Sport Psychology. When we revisit the issue of generativity and finding meaning in our lives, clearly activities such as sports and athletics may provide meaning for us. For example, if you learned the basic skills of baseball from your father as a child, you need to teach those skills to other children who may lack a significant male role model in their lives. If you were taught how to participate in any activity, such as basketball and soccer, the skills that you learned may now be taught to other children who need guidance and direction. The instruction, guidance and support that you provide may not only help a child excel in sports and become happier, but you may also help the community by re-directing young people to engage in a very positive and healthy activity. Furthermore, as Erikson notes, the relationship between giving and receiving is a reciprocal one. In other words, the children that you helped by serving as a volunteer coach or mentor also have helped you in achieving a sense of identity and purpose in your life. These things simply cannot be bought or bartered—they can only be achieved by making personal sacrifices to help improve the lives of young people in your community. These activities through sport participation create a meaningful and purposeful existence and prevent stagnation in middle adulthood.

h. *Ego Integrity versus Despair* (Late Adulthood). This final stage of psychosocial development addresses a time of reflection and evaluation of life experiences—has our life been meaningful? Have we achieved meaning in our lives? Do we have a sense of completion and purpose in our lives that contributes to integrity? Or do we feel lonely, despair, and bitterness because we feel that life has been unfair to us? The grandfather who taught his son the game of baseball now plays and teaches his grandson the concepts of baseball. Understanding our role in life and how we have impacted the world around us are central or core themes in this final stage of the life cycle. Perhaps the ability to see your work, your efforts and love in your relationships with others may combine to form a sense of purpose and meaning that is unique to your experiences with your loved ones.

■ ERIKSON AND PSYCHOSOCIAL DEVELOPMENT

Erikson describes eight psychosocial stages of development:

a. *Trust versus Mistrust* (birth to one year). At this stage of development, either the child learns to trust others in his or her environment, or they mistrust others because of neglect as an infant. If a child is provided with love and stimulation, and they are provided with the necessary items for survival (i.e., food, warmth and stimulation) they begin their lives with the capacity to trust others. However, if they are chronically neglected (as if in a substance abuse environment where no one can provide them with the necessary items for survival) they develop with a very skeptical and mistrusting nature. This personality type is what Bowlby refers to as the "affectionless character."

b. *Autonomy versus shame and doubt* (1–3 years). At this stage of development, the child learns to become autonomous and independent, and the child's efforts to learn skills are welcomed by the parent (i.e., if a child wants to pour a cup of milk, the parent encourages him to do so, even if that means cleaning up spilled milk with the child). If the child is not provided with an opportunity to learn these skills, they begin to doubt their ability to perform skills and feel shameful about their performance;

c. *Initiative versus guilt* (3–5 years). At this stage of development, the child continues with developing skills and develops the ability to start and complete tasks on his own. Children now are feeling confident of their ability to draw, color, put their clothes away or clean their room. They want to "be just like grownups" and the developmentally healthy child feels that they can accomplish these tasks. Children who are not provided with an opportunity to develop these skills begin to feel inadequate and guilty about their ability, and thus self-esteem and self-confidence also may suffer;

d. *Industry versus inferiority* (5–11). At this stage of development, children begin taking on more tasks and responsibility—for example, many children begin the first grade by ages 5 or 6, and now the industrious child welcomes the new responsibilities (such as homework) because they can be more like older siblings. Conversely, if children feel inferior about their potential aptitude in completing tasks, they tend to shy away from challenges because of what Adler refers to as the "inferiority complex";

e. *Identity versus Role Confusion (adolescence).* At this stage of development, it is normal for teen-agers to questions who they are and in what direction is their life headed. Many adolescents go through various stages of experiments in determining what kinds of activities and possible career choices give them the most happiness. In colleges and universities, many undergraduates go through several phases of "declaring majors" which in a sense is declaring your identity—it means what you intend to do with your life. Young people who have a clear mission and sense of identity seem to progress through this stage relatively smoothly, conversely, others seem to frequently question their career choices and often make changes regarding career choices;

f. *Intimacy versus Isolation (Young adulthood)*. During this phase of development, we need the ability to trust other people in order to experience a meaningful and intimate loving relationship. Without the capacity to trust others, achieving intimacy and love would virtually be impossible. An important link should be drawn between stage 1 (trust versus mistrust) and stage 6 (intimacy versus isolation), as infants who cannot trust develop into young adults who cannot love and become intimate. Thus, individuals isolate themselves and prevent themselves from becoming involved in close relationships of any type with other people;

g. *Generativity versus Stagnation (Middle Adulthood)*. At this stage of development, adults now are continually generating meaning in their lives by "giving back" to the community and teaching their skills and knowledge to younger people. Either we continually find meaning at this stage by volunteering and working with others within the community, or we tend to "stagnate" and rely too much on "things" rather than our relationships with others. Often, the common "midlife crisis" develops here, where adults question their careers, their spouses, and their lives in general in terms of meaning. They ask: "Have I made the right decision" and usually this stage can cause tremendous life changes if not addressed in therapy. For example, the president of a successful company may suddenly quit his or her job, a person seemingly happily married may have a torrid romance with a much younger partner, or simply just take an extended vacation to the Bahamas for no apparent reason.

h. *Ego Integrity versus Despair (Late Adulthood)*. At this final stage of psychosocial development, the mature adult questions their life—what is meaningful to them, what relationships still exist with family members, and are they generally content with their lives. Adults often are capable of looking back, acknowledging successes as well as failures, and generally can conclude that they have had a meaningful and successful life. If the mature adult cannot do this, then we live in despair, relying on money to buy relationships with people and loneliness usually engulfs them.

Erik Erikson's Psychosocial Stages and Characteristics of Sport Psychology

a. **Trust versus Mistrust—Individual and Team Sports:** Trust as a necessary factor in all forms of athletic competition. The ability to trust others is learned in infancy through the quality of parenting and providing infants with things vital to physical and psychological survival: Food, love and nurturing. If the infant has had problems in attaining a loving and trusting relationship with his or her primary caregiver, then they will be at a disadvantage in trusting all other people in their relationships with others. Team sports require communication, practice with each other and above all trusting one another. Individuals who have been exposed to inconsistent parenting skills will have difficulty in establishing a cooperative relationship with others. Erikson noted that among all of the stages of psychosocial development, the first (trust versus mistrust) is most critical and vital in the development of personality skills. In many ways, a coach takes the place of the parent and must provide a compatible and communicative relationship with his players—similarly, if the players on the team do not trust the capabilities of the coach, little direction and growth will result; In order for team sports to become effective, trust and communication among players and coaches are vital.

b. **Autonomy versus Shame & Doubt—** Developing your skills and working independently. Parents need to allow children to learn from their mistakes. The autonomous child has a positive relationship with the caregiver who provides direction and support for the child to learn. The child raised in a highly supportive environment has enough ego strength to learn from his mistakes—and this autonomous behavior continues throughout his or her life. Athletes who begin to learn new tasks are autonomous in the sense that they experiment and learn what works best for them and are not afraid of failure.

c. **Initiative versus Guilt.** During this stage of development (3–5 years), it is critical for the child to receive unconditional support when learning new tasks. The child at this stage begins or initiates activities that promotes learning in a variety of environments. For example, a five year old child will form relationships and friendships that will allow activities to develop. Cooperative relationships, team work and compatibility are key components that are necessary in playing team sports as the child gets older. If the parents are placing high expectations on the child to excel at this stage and the child does not perform up to the unrealistic expectations of the parents, he or she will develop a sense of inadequacy and ultimately guilt. This age is critical for parents to provide a highly supportive relationship with their child that the child perceives as unconditional.

d. **Industry versus Inferiority.** Children are now engaging in a variety of activities and developing skills that are necessary to participate in exercise programs and team sports. Now the 5–11 year old child should feel competent and as though they can contribute to the team or sport that they are playing. An industrious child at this stage of psychosocial development faces new challenges and has the ego strength to persevere despite initial failure—this perseverance only manifests itself from a healthy, supportive, and nurturing relationship that parents should have with children. Children at this stage should now be actively seeking out those specific sport activities and exercises that they find exciting, fun and rewarding.

e. **Identity versus Role Confusion.** Adolescents now are experimenting with a variety of critical themes and experiences relative to their psychosocial and physical development. For example, Erikson describes this stage as a process where teen-agers are struggling with an identity of their own, something that is inspirational to them and provides a passion for them to pursue. The teen-ager that has a healthy ego and strong sense of self does not shy away from experimenting and trying a variety of identities. High school and collegiate athletics now not only serve as a recreational activity, but now may serve as the identity itself. We are all familiar with the "high school jock" or the athlete who incorporates sport and athletics now as part of his or her identity. More importantly, the attainment of sports as an identity serves to promote healthy activities that help in the transfer to higher education (colleges and universities) and avoid negative activities such as gangs, drug activity, and so on;

f. **Intimacy versus Isolation.** The development of sport activities during young adulthood helps to facilitate intimate and psychologically close relationships with family members and loved ones. When family members all participate in healthy exercise programs, a psychological bond develops that facilitates closeness and intimacy;

g. **Generativity versus Stagnation.** The key factor associated with middle adulthood is to somehow keep finding meaning in our lives—often the middle-aged adult experiences the "midlife crisis" where we place too much emphasis on materialistic possessions ("conspicuous consumption") and physical appearance. Relying too much on possessions can lead us to a sense of alienation and a classic midlife crisis. However, when we train and exercise for intrinsic reasons (i.e., exercise to feel good and relieve stress), we find meaning and purpose in our lives. The 45 year old man who rows daily 10,000 meters or the 60 year old woman who runs the marathon each year does so because the sport provides a sense of meaning and purpose for them. Training and exercise may also relieve stress, anxiety, and help athletes to structure their daily schedules. At this stage, we exercise to continually generate happiness and balance in our life;

h. **Ego-Integrity versus Despair.** In this final stage of development, individuals need to find some form of closure and a sense of purpose. In late adulthood, individuals need to reflect and evaluate the quality and impact of their lives. Either we look back and feel good about our lives (i.e., we can see our accomplishments) or we feel a sense of despair and bitterness over lost relationships and a sense of alienation from loved ones. While sport and exercise activity may be limited at this final stage of development, incorporating some limited some of exercise may help individuals experience integrity and pride in their lives and engage in social activities with friends.

■ CHAPTER 4 QUESTION & REVIEW

1. Describe the attribution theory and how attribution may influence sport performance;

2. Describe the differences between the internal and external attribution in sport performance;

3. Describe the Zone of Proximal Development and how this may be incorporated into sport activity;

4. Describe Erikson's 8 psychosocial stages of psychosocial development and the ramifications in sport activity;

5. Describe Adler's theory of inferiority and how this influences sport activity and performance.

Chapter 5:
Modern Society & Obesity:
Changing Your Style of Living to One
that is Exercise Friendly

"Fit or Fat? . . . 58% of adults in society are considered overweight, and 23% of adults are considered obese". . ."They can't do it alone . . . getting the whole family involved is crucial in helping obese children to lose weight. Maria Cruz bustles around her kitchen . . . keeping one eye on a simmering pot of salsa verde and the other eye on her 8-year-old son Abel. Abel is 4 feet 7 inches and weighs in just under 200 lbs."

—(*The Daily News*, Thursday, December 9, 2004).

This chapter will address the important topic of obesity and changing your lifestyle to improve physical health. Living healthy and eating a sensible diet have become very important topics today, especially considering the magnitude of people suffering from obesity. The American Academy of Pediatrics reports that children today are significantly heavier than children just 20 years ago, and that over 30% of America's school-age children are now overweight (American Academy of Pediatrics, "Prevention of Pediatric Overweight and Obesity," August, 2003). Consider the following: Humans evolved as primates over 100,000 years ago primarily designed to continuously wander and search for food. In an interesting article from *The Daily News*, Daniel Lieberman from Harvard University commented that Humans have evolved specifically for the purposes of running and walking: "Take the distinctive bulge of the buttocks, at the back of the human silhouette . . . The muscles connect the femur, to the trunk and keep the body from over-balancing in each step . . . the stiff arch of the human foot allows a runner to push off the ground more efficiently and utilize the ligaments on the bottom of the foot as springs (*The Daily News*, November 18, 2004). This research presented supports the hypothesis that humans have evolved not only to be nomadic and moving from location to location in search of food and adequate habitat, but also that humans need to have an active lifestyle to maintain adequate levels of physical health. A leading contributor to obesity is not necessarily the content of our food, but rather the sedentary lifestyles that have permeated our lives: Computer work, watching television, driving, office work, and changing lifestyles all have contributed to obesity in our society today.

One of the primary reasons we began writing this text was to address the dynamic relationship between psychology and physical health. After several years of working with individuals in the health industry, I began to notice a trend among those individuals who were motivated to come to the gym to train and exercise and feel good about themselves. These individuals were not celebrities or famous people, but rather just people who wanted to make a positive change in their lives. Some of these people knew that it would be difficult, and they did not hesitate to ask for help and others were more autonomous in their training. After working with many individuals who were interested in physical training and exercise, I noticed that the successful individuals were the ones that were able to adhere to a training schedule and were very committed to their program. More importantly, however, was the fact that they were intrinsically motivated and that this form of motivation played an important role in the consistency in training. But the commitment aspect of the program was only a part of their solution for success—the other portion of the successful ingredient to health was the simple fact that they were enjoying what they were doing and having fun in the process. They tended to change their routine occasionally, and they seemed to know what their body needed at the time of exercise. Some individuals stretched and chatted on the mat and floor for their routine, others immediately began work on the treadmill, and still others would simply come to the gym, sign in, and chat for 20 or 30 minutes before beginning their exercise routine. Each individual who reported to the gym on a consistent basis had one thing in common: They enjoyed coming to the gym because it made them physically healthier, they felt better because they knew they were doing something positive for themselves as well as their family, and they were enjoying the experience. We will now explore specific issues that contribute to a successful and happy experience in exercise and health training.

■■ MOTIVATIONAL FACTORS IN EXERCISE PARTICIPATION: FOCUS ON ACTIVITIES THAT ARE FUN, CHALLENGING AND CONSISTENT

When you get up each morning, perhaps your routine goes something like this:

a. Wake up at 6:00 am—shower and dress for work or school;
b. Eat a bagel and have a cup of coffee walking out the door or en route to work or school;
c. Hit traffic—get stressed and begin thinking of all of the things you need to do or have not done yet. You look at your watch and (incredibly) it is almost noon and you haven't really accomplished much!

The point of this brief scenario is that most of the points mentioned you probably do without really giving much thought. We get up, brush our teeth, take a shower and so on. But why is it when we try to incorporate healthy exercise as part of our daily routine, suddenly "problems" develop? Why can we not view health training and exercise as simply as important as getting up and brushing our teeth in the morning? The group of successful individuals that I mentioned earlier do just this—they have incorporated training and exercise as part of their daily routine and they truly enjoy this necessary component of their life. More importantly, they do not ask themselves: "Do I really have time to go all the way to the gym [actually the gym is in the office building] . . . get dressed and be 'all sweaty' or should I just stay seated here and keep working myself while I eat another donut?" Unfortunately, the result is that the person who questions himself or herself as to whether they "really have the time" to exercise has already answered their own question—they probably will not report to the gym. If we truly have made a commitment to a positive exercise program we do not ask ourselves questions if we should. To coin a popular phrase, we "just do it."

So what exactly are the "motivational factors" that contribute to a healthy training and exercise program? While different people use different motivational strategies, there are some key components that we should incorporate into our own personal training program: A new program that has had tremendous results is the program that first sets realistic goals, works with a trainer for monitoring and encouragement; allows individuals to earn their goals by focusing on intrinsic motivational programs; activating change to avoid "burn out" and training hard and having fun (SWEAT):

SWEat Program:
Set Realistic Goals!
Work With Skilled Trainers!
Earn Your Goals!
Activate Goals!
Train Hard & Have Fun!

a. *Set realistic goals.* If you wish to lose weight, select a target zone that is realistic and one that you can adapt to—remember, the faster you lose the weight, the more likely that you will put the weight back on; conversely, the slower and more consistent you drop weight, the greater the likelihood that you will keep it off. Realistic goals might include coming to the gym and working with your trainer three or four times a week for approximately 45 minutes to one hour. The goals should be challenging and realistic, if you wish to try to drop just three or four pounds a month—this would be a good target goal. Do not make your program unrealistic—have fun, enjoy the process and be systematic in your approach. Record your attendance, log your activities, and perhaps make notes in terms of what you did that was particularly effective in training and what was perhaps not effective.

b. *Work with a trainer that you trust and be open to listening and incorporating the information they give you.* For example, many people want to get started right away when they report to the gym—sometimes without proper preparation. If your trainer suggests that you spend a paltry 15 minutes on the mat to stretch and become more flexible prior to exercise, perhaps we should heed this advice. Your relationship with your trainer is critical to your success in your program. Trust in what your trainer provides for you in terms of information, and more importantly create a collaborative and communicative relationship; tell him or her what you feel confident in doing as well as any doubts. When you have a positive and supportive working relationship with your trainer, they can provide insight to help you achieve your goals most effectively.

c. *Earn your goals.* Remember the "intrinsic motivational" factors that we discussed earlier? In order to achieve our goals, focus on the experience of exercise and how it makes you feel *from the inside out—not from the outside in.* What that means is begin your training program in a way that makes you feel good about yourself and take control of your life. Remember—you are doing this for yourself—not for your doctor, your spouse or significant other. Train and earn your goals because they are making you a stronger, more dynamic and healthier person who will achieve your goals!

d. *Activate change in your exercise routines.* Perhaps the most common problem among athletes who exercise regularly is the problem of mental fatigue, commonly called "burn out." Mental fatigue or burn out occurs when athletes remain structured to the point where change is limited and routines become fixed. Frequently athletes continue their programs with little creativity or change in their routine, and this lack of flexibility may result in exercise boredom that usually results in inefficient training. Try mixing up your work-out schedule, work out with a partner who knows your physical training goals, or switch exercise programs entirely. For example, if you are a weight lifter, why not switch to aerobic or cardio training? I think the change in the routine will be a nice mental break and will help your overall training.

e. *Train hard and have fun!* The human body physically adapts to the many stressors that we place on it—our bodies are incredibly resilient and resist the demands we place on it. While we are placing exercise as an important factor in improving the quality of your life, the reasons why you are exercising is to improve your quality of living and to feel better. Be healthy and train hard and have fun in the process. Remember—training hard and having fun are not mutually exclusive concepts. Therefore, it is critical to place demands on our system relative to the capacity of our cardiovascular system. We may determine this method by utilizing the "Karvonen Formula":

1. First determine your maximum heart rate (MHR): 220–age;
2. Subtract your resting heart rate (RHR) from this number—this number is now called the heart rate reserve (HRR);
3. Multiply the HRR by 55% to 85% to get the low and high end of your training level;
4. For example, Jim is a 40 year old with a resting heart rate of 65 bpm. His Karvonen would be calculated as:
   220–40 = 180;
   180–65 = 115;
   115 × .55 = 63 and 115 × .85 = 97. Thus, the training rate for Jim is between 63 and 97 for approximately 30–45 minutes. For a more intense training program, Jim would exercise for 45 minutes at a heart rate of 97.

An important topic today regarding health, exercise and training is obesity and how to control weight factors. Many people may comment that they have "inherited" genetic characteristics that may put them at risk for weight gain. This certainly may be true, as with other heritable characteristics, such as athletic skills, hair and eye color and so forth. However, a central thesis of this chapter is to remind individuals who in fact may have inherited such predispositions to weight is that they are just that—in inherited condition that we have some control over. ***Thus, the important rule in health and weight control is this: We inherit genetic conditions that partially determine our weight, but ultimately our body weight is determined by our diets and levels of activity. If you consume more calories than you burn, you gradually will gain weight, conversely, if you burn more calories than you consume, then you will lose weight—period.*** The greatest risk to our health today regarding weight gain is sedentary activities combined with unhealthy diets. An increasing problem in society that we have been discussing is the lack of activity and decreasing opportunities for exercise that results in more of a sedentary lifestyle. Our society has become increasingly more sedate as we embrace and incorporate technological advances. Now, rather than going for a walk to shop for food at a supermarket, we simply "log on" and have the computer do our work for us. Children today now opt to stay indoors and utilize their computers and video games that simulate exercise and sport activity rather than actually engaging in the activity themselves. Baseball, football, soccer, and a variety of other activities have now become incorporated into electronic technology. Children and adolescents seem to prefer with growing popularity to stay indoors and let "the computers do the work." The problem is that *"the computer"* now does the mental and physical work that we have historically done and should be doing now. Routine calculations by adding machines as well as simulated sports activities have made *in vivo* human participation almost obsolete. Concern over weight and body image is also impacting adolescents and even younger children at alarming rates. Even six year old girls have reported about becoming "fat" and a recent survey suggests that over 40% of nine and ten year old children have at some point incorporated a "diet" in their lifestyle to lose weight (Schreiber and colleagues, 1996). The answer is clear to this growing problem—increases in sedentary lifestyles combined with an unrealistic portrayal of "thinness" creates a problem for young people. We are portraying an unrealistic body image based in a culture that is highly sedentary and saturated with unhealthy foods. This combination may lead to younger and younger children (even pre-teens) beginning unhealthy eating habits and even eating disorders.

Another important measure in determining a healthy weight as opposed to being overweight is the concept of "body mass index" (BMI). The BMI is a more accurate measure of identifying a healthy weight that is associated with height. According to the Mayo Clinic, an ideal BMI score is between 18 to 24.9. A reading of 25 to 29.9 is overweight, and any BMI that exceeds 30 is considered to be obese. The concept BMI refers to a persons overall percentage of body weight compared to their height. The body weight is further is determined between body fat and lean muscle mass. In order to calculate your BMI multiply your body weight (in pounds) by the number 705, and then divide the result by your height in inches, then divide that by your height in inches again (see figure 5a):

BMI **Height**	**Healthy** **18.5–24.9**	**Overweight** **25–29.9** Weight in lbs.	**Obese** **30>**
5'0"	127	128–152	153 or more
5'4"	144 or less	145–173	174 or more
5'8"	163 or less	164–196	197 or more
5'11"	178 or less	179–214	215 or more
6'2"	193 or less	194–232	233 or more
6'3"	199 or less	200–239	240 or more

Figure 5a   The Body Mass Index

■■■ "THE BIG FIVE": FACTORS COMMONLY ASSOCIATED WITH OBESITY

There are several theories that contribute to the growing problem of obesity today in our society, and lack of activity and increases in sedentary behavior perhaps are the primary cause. Obesity is currently defined as any body weight that is above 20% the recommended height and weight levels. The current problem of obesity among children is growing at an alarming rate, where obesity among children between ages 6 and 11 has increased over 54% (Lamb, 1984). However, other causes of obesity have been identified as:

a. Observational Theory and Poor Eating Habits: Children learn what to eat by watching poor role models (i.e., their parents);

b. Taste Sensitivity;

c. Technological Advances;

d. Reductions in physical Training Programs in Primary and Secondary schools; and

e. Changes in the food content and ecology of the development of food.

a. *The first theory regarding increases in obesity addresses simply observational theory and poor eating habits.* Children who watch their parents eating poor foods or engaging in poor eating habits are most at risk to engage in poor eating habits themselves. The classic research described earlier by Bandura (1991) states that children and adolescents tend to imitate the types of behaviors that they are exposed to, especially if those models they are watching are portrayed as positive role models by the media and if the models are physically attractive. Furthermore, when the media portrays the models as being rewarded for demonstrating a particular type or form of behavior, eating a certain type of food, or wearing a particular type of clothing, those behaviors are also rewarded. If the media portrays healthy eating habits in a positive way, such as including more fruits and vegetables in children's diets, children are more likely to incorporate them into their own diets. Additionally, when parents and older siblings eat the healthier foods during meal times and snacks, as preschool children develop and mature they will be significantly more likely to maintain healthier diets.

b. *The second theory that describes the increases in obesity is taste sensitivity.* According to a recent *Daily News* newspaper report, researchers at Rutgers University study found that women who had a significantly more sensitive taste capacity tended to have less body fat and were 20 percent thinner than their female counterparts with less sensitive taste buds. There are numerous suggestions and interpretations for these results, however, the most logical seems to be that people (both men and women) who are more sensitive to tastes eat less fatty food, less sweeter foods, and less spicy foods. Perhaps, those of us with less sensitive taste buds use more condiments to season foods, as well as prefer foods with more taste, which is what fat does to meats when cooking. The "super-tasters" as the researchers called them, tended to have significantly less overall body fat, with a body-mass index (BMI) total of 23.5; Medium tasters had an average of 26.6 BMI, and the non-tasters had a BMI of nearly 30. The lead researcher at Rutgers University, Professor Beverly Tepper, also discovered that approximately 50% of Americans are what she called "medium tasters" and about 25% are either "super tasters" or "non-tasters." To summarize these important findings, the more sensitive we are to taste, the less likely we are to overeat certain foods (such as sweet and fatty foods) as well as prefer eating healthier foods (i.e., broccoli).

c. *Technological advances.* We have briefly mentioned the important role of technology in our lives. Television, computers, automobiles, and many other devices have undoubtedly played a role in facilitating our lives and helping us manage our lifestyles. However, the problem that we are now seeing is that the role that technology once played is having a negative backlash impact—not only does the technology we crave break down more often, but much of the work that we once did played an important role in our physical health. More and more we are relying on automated devices to do what we once did. Shopping on line, recreational activities now on video programs, even talking to one another in person has been replaced by cell phones. The result is a more sedate, inactive and pasty society. Diets have become increasingly higher in saturated fats, and more and more families are relying on the "fast food" service to replace more nutritious (and in my opinion more delicious) home-cooked meals. In general, school age children (ages 6–15) tend to engage in very little physical exercise and overall are not considered to be physically fit (Wolf and colleagues, 1993. Wolf, A.M., Gortmaker, S. L., Cheung, L. & Gray, H., Activity, inactivity, and obesity: Racial, ethnic, and age differences among school girls. American Journal of Public Health, 83, 1625–1627). For example, in a recent survey, about 40% of boys between the ages of 6 and 12 are unable to do more than one pull-up, and about 25% cannot do any pull-ups! Furthermore, according to Ungrady (1992) and Murray (1996), both groups of boys and girls (between ages 6–18 years) are significantly reducing levels of physical activity by 24 % and 36%. Earlier in the first section we discussed how observational learning plays an important role in weight management and modeling—if we portray positive role models as being healthy and fit and participating in regular aerobic exercise, children tend to imitate this. However, there exists a problem with watching television—children who watch television tend to eat unhealthy snacks, and television itself is a highly sedentary activity in itself. Furthermore, the commercials themselves that are advertised during television viewing usually advertise snacks and unhealthy foods that only compound the problem.

d. *Reductions in physical training and exercise programs for children.* Due to many budget cutbacks and reductions in the availability of funds for schools and education, the first programs to be cut usually involve physical education and theatre arts or drama. Due to the lack of available activity programs, children and teen-agers are the first to suffer the negative consequences that are typically associated with obesity. Children who are raised in lower socioeconomic areas may be also deprived of physical activities due to safety issues and crime, where too many risk factors exist that would prevent children to play even in a public park or recreational area. A greater emphasis on modern technology and less emphasis on physical activity have created a sedentary-friendly environment where children are putting on more weight that ever before. There simply is no incentive for children to increase activity, especially if they see their primary role models as sedentary. The irony of schools that have de-emphasized the importance of physical activities based on economic problems is that most physical activity programs may be developed relatively quickly and inexpensively with fast results. For example, many teachers, coaches and parents simply emphasize the fun and exciting component of exercise as an efficient way to involve students in more exercise and sport programs. When teachers and coaches de-emphasize the competitive nature of exercise and build up the fun and social components, children will participate on a more regular and enthusiastic basis. Some other suggestions to make exercise fun for students and young people include:

✓ Create a program where students can coordinate their gross motor skills and physical prowess with a game (i.e., kickball) or activity program—all of the children should be able to participate in the activity, and this contributes more for an exciting and inclusive experience—Remember, children also learn from each other;

✓ Teachers, coaches and parents should also participate—By exhibiting positive role model skills, as well as teaching children the positive characteristics and components of sports, children will be significantly more likely to participate in activity programs in the future;

✓ As the teacher or coach, you should select how the teams become paired and grouped. Select teams that have relative equal balance and skills among participants, and intervene if children become critical or begin to ridicule a less competent child. Select teams that are gender-equal with relative equal skills among participants;

✓ Perhaps most importantly, begin at a level that is appropriate for all children—begin at a level that is comfortable for all children and encourage them to have fun and to enjoy the activity. Do not critique or create a hostile or competitive environment—try to create games without winners or losers.

e. *Changes in the food content and ecology of the development of food.* The advertisements in our media today emphasize time-saving techniques and ways to improve time efficiency. We are told how much busier we are and therefore create a lifestyle that is always "on the go." For example, consider the impact and importance of time and how we relate to each other—the most valuable commodity that we can provide for someone is our time spent with them. As Bruno (2000) describes in *Perceptions of Time Management,* our society is becoming increasingly impacted with different types of stimuli and we have access to more and more different forms of technological programs (i.e., the internet) which is impacting our time availability spent with our family members. Washing machines save time on laundering our clothes, computers are processing information at increasingly faster paces, and even our food is prepared in a time-saving manner (i.e., the microwave). As Bruno illustrates, we are impacting more and more activities and condensing them into shorter and shorter periods of time. The cost of this is inadequate relationships with people and poor communication skills relative to how we relate to each other.

Given the fact that Americans are working more and more hours and spending less time at home, Americans are purchasing foods that are pre-prepared (such as pre-cut foods, frozen foods, etc.) and even prepared to be consumed while in transit (i.e., while driving). Foods are not only purchased at fast-food restaurants, but now the restaurant chains have realized that there is a market for foods that may be eaten literally with one hand while driving with the other free hand. Foods that are purchased from fast-food restaurants are significantly higher in saturated fats and thus contribute to obesity. School districts now have vending machines for students to purchase sodas or high sugar content drinks. The structures of newer buildings accommodate purchasing unhealthy foods while banning individuals from bringing their own healthier foods—even drinking fountains are practically non-existent in newer facilities, but of course purchasing "bottled water" at a premium price is always available. The ecology and psychology of eating has dramatically changed, where not only the types of foods have changed in terms of higher fat-content, but also the manner and style in which we eat has changed as well. Waffles are now created to be eaten "while on the run" with prepackaged syrup packets, specially prepared burritos are prepared to be eaten while driving, and even our social environment and how we relate to people is conducted over foods. In conclusion, the role that food plays has taken on important changes, not only in terms of what we eat, but how and when the food is eaten. Foods in general today are higher in fat content, more expensive, and prepared for people to eat while driving in traffic. Children are not receiving proper and nutritious foods, and the typical ten year old child today is 10 lbs. heavier today than ten years ago (USDA, 1999).

■ OTHER PROBLEMS ASSOCIATED WITH OBESITY: DISCRIMINATION IN THE WORKPLACE

While many of the topics in this text have addressed the physical and health problems that are associated with obesity, we should also focus on other disadvantages that are connected to obesity in our society. While overweight individuals have indicated for years that they have been the victimized by discrimination in the work environment and hostility among strangers in public places, empirical data verifying this phenomena has been lacking until recently. Prior to the year 2000, most research primarily was anecdotal and reports by obese individuals as being targets of hostility and discrimination in a very weight-conscious society. In a very insightful and illuminating article addressing three problem areas that have been associated with obesity, Rebecca Puhl and Kelly Brownell (2001) argue that discrimination is a very real problem in our society, and as they authors state: "obese persons are the last acceptable targets of discrimination" (page 788). The authors cite three clear areas of discrimination regarding obesity: Employment areas, education and health care. To illustrate the blatant and very mean spirited comments that are commonly directed toward the obese, the authors quoted several independent surveys with the following responses: Twenty eight percent of teachers in one survey said that "becoming obese was the worst thing that could happen to a person" and 24% of nurses in a different survey indicated that they were "repulsed" by obese persons, and even parents of normal weight and obese children tend to offer more support to the normal weight offspring.

Numerous studies and reports support the idea that the obese are routinely discriminated against in a variety of environments, but especially in the work place environment. Several employers in a study by Roehling (1999) were found to have highly negative stereotypes of overweight and obese employees. For example, Roehling found that the typical views and stereotypes of obese employees included laziness, a less conscientious work ethic, and sloppy and disagreeable personalities. Obese employees were also perceived to be emotionally unstable and more disagreeable with other employees. Additionally, in a study by Klassen (1993) researchers discovered that managers of a business routinely selected non-obese or normal weight prospective applicants for an employment opportunity position that was advertised among nine hypothetical vignettes. The vignettes that depicted the applicant as being overweight were routinely bypassed for normal weight applicants. Furthermore, the study indicated that overweight women were perceived to be more likely to possess negative characteristics, including low supervisory potential, low self-discipline, and poor personal hygiene and appearance. Obese individuals who work in specific environments may be especially prone to bias and discrimination. For example, imagine an overweight health instructor or physical education instructor who applies for a position at a school or fitness facility with other applicants who are physically healthy and in good physical condition—who do you think will receive the job? Furthermore, consider an obese physical education instructor who is much more educated, knowledgeable and well-trained for a position in health and fitness and compare this person with a non-obese person who is applying for the same position. The chances are very good that the non-obese individual would be awarded with the job. These are examples of discrimination against the obese and are clearly illegal procedures, but unfortunately they occur all of the time.

The problem appears to be that most individuals respond to inaccurate stereotypes and biases that are associated with the obese. When people continually see movies, videos, commercials and newspaper ads that associate obese persons with inefficiency, non-desirable forms of behaviors (i.e., laziness and lack of motivation) and in general an unkempt appearance, they begin to form these illusory correlations and stereotypes that are very difficult to correct or change. Ask any one that you may know that is overweight and they will probably agree, and these stereotypes and biased opinions that people have are very hard to change. Most obese persons are aware of these biases, and thus are very reluctant to interact with others where body image and physical features may be factors that influence opinions regarding employment ability or educational skills. Not-so-subtle stares by children and teen-agers, caustic and insensitive comments by employers and family members who do not understand the etiology and causal factors impacting obesity can only further exacerbate the self-conscious feelings that play a negative role in the obese person's life. Employers, family members and friends of the obese are encouraged to provide a supportive and informed relationship with the obese to provide positive and healthy changes in their lifestyle. For example, employers are encouraged (and required by law) to provide a fair and unbiased evaluation of all job applicant and their abilities without being negatively influenced by features such as weight. In fact, if more individuals evaluated the skills and abilities that we are capable of providing in a variety of environments and were less influenced by our own personal biases, we clearly would be more successful in communicating and interacting with all people.

■■■ THE MEDICAL ENVIRONMENT: "PROFESSIONAL" BIAS AGAINST THE OBESE

At first glance, an individual may think that of all of the different forms of employment bias and discrimination, the obese would be the safest from discrimination in an environment of educated, trained health care providers, such as nurses, doctors and certified health specialists. However, Puhl and Brownell (2001) and Maddox and Liederman (1969) have identified a vast source of discrimination and outright hostility and rejection toward the obese during routine check-ups and health evaluations. Over one-third (34%) of the physicians interviewed responded that obesity was one of the most common conditions where they experienced the most negative reaction to treating patients. In another study that explored the negative reaction of the health community toward the personality and general characteristics of the obese, over 87% of the health care professionals reported that they felt the obese were "indulgent", lacked willpower (32%) felt that the tendency to become overweight or obese was due to a lack of "love or attention." Even those individuals who were not yet employed in the health field (i.e., medical students, nursing school students, etc.) were found to have a highly negative perspective of the obese and a bias regarding the personality characteristics of the obese (Blumberg & Mellis, 1980). Some of the terms that the students associated with the obese included: "worthless, bad, ugly, awkward, unsuccessful and unpleasant." The evidence thus far presented strongly supports that there is a clear bias and prejudice against the overweight and obese. These findings are especially significant in light of the fact that many of these individuals are actually working in the health field and have direct contact with the obese. If many individuals actually do harbor negative characteristics and opinions regarding the obese and are working in the health field, these biases may in fact influence their professional judgment and relations with these particular types of patients. This is disturbing, as the quality and care of health care management may be decided by physical characteristics and prevent those individuals from receiving the services that they need most.

■■ THE OBESE AND THE EDUCATIONAL ENVIRONMENT: PEER REJECTION

We are all aware of the problem of critical peer relationships, physical appearance and rejection. Many times children may say things that are very hurtful to others without fully realizing the negative impact of their harsh words. Peer rejection of the overweight and the obese child is a very serious issue, and may have very serious ramifications. Children who are obese and who have been the target of cruel jokes and ridicule are most prone to suffer from depression, low self-esteem and in some cases even suicide (Solovay, 1999). In a now classic (albeit outdated) study by Richardson and colleagues (1961), several hundred children in a public school (n = 600) ranked other children in a series of pictures and were asked: "Who would you like to have most as a friend?" Several of the pictures included disabled children, children missing limbs, and even facial disfigurement. The children in the study overwhelmingly selected all of the other "non-desirable" characteristics first selected the obese child as the last person that they would select to develop a friendship with. A more recent study that revisited childhood peer rejection among the obese unfortunately discovered similar results (Latner, 2001) who also found rejection of the obese among 4th and 5th grade children. In summary, these results strongly suggest that overweight children are clearly at risk among rejection among their peers and are more likely to suffer from low self-esteem. Adult obese individuals are more likely to suffer from a wide range of discrimination from a variety of potential employers, and even the health care industry are more likely to engage in discrimination against the obese. The three primary areas thus described (health care, education and the employment sector) offer ample evidence that discrimination is endemic among the obese, and that the need to engage in healthy and consistent programs to reduce the obesity epidemic is vital to our society.

■■ OVERWEIGHT PEOPLE—OVERWEIGHT PETS?

Perhaps a final note to the complex problem of obesity in our society addresses not only the health of individual people, but also the pets that they own. In a recent U.C. Irvine study as reported by Science Today (January 11, 2005), researchers discovered a positive correlation between the caloric intake and obesity among pet owners and the weight of their pets. Typically when we think of pets, we think of domesticated animals, such as cats and dogs. However in the current study, researchers discovered even *horses* tended to become overweight due to inactivity and high caloric diets. The crux of the research suggested that when people tend to become overweight due to inactivity and high saturated fat diets, our pets tend to become overweight as well. It seems logical that pet owners who are more active will have more time to take their pets for walks and other cardiovascular activities, allowing their pets to enjoy the benefits of exercise as well as their owners. The next several chapters will now discuss how we may incorporate sport and exercise activity as an important intervention device to counter the trend toward obesity.

■■ BE AWARE OF GIMMICKS: "LOSE WEIGHT BY FIDGETING OR BRUSHING YOUR TEETH"

As a final note in concluding our discussion of weight control and psychological factors associated with weight loss, individuals need to be very much aware of misleading advertisements. For example, recently published in a newspaper (Daily News, February 16, 2005), an article published in the Opinions Section stated that individuals who tend to "fidget more . . . people who drum their fingers, wiggle their feet or pace around a lot are more likely to be leaner that those who do not fidget." Additionally, the same author cited how a study in Japan by Dr. Takashi Wada of Jikei University in Tokyo interviewed over 14,000 people whose average age was in the mid-forty range were trimmer when they brushed their teeth after every meal. The reason why we cite this study is to demonstrate how easily someone can be misled into thinking all they have to do is "fidget" more or brush their teeth more often and they automatically lose weight. It is specifically these types of advertisements that create frustration and problems among individuals who are seriously interested in losing weight. After numerous attempts to lose weight by false claims such as these, the danger is that the overweight individual eventually believes that his or her condition is hopeless, and they eventually give up home on themselves. Devices that strap onto your midsection that buzz purportedly being the equivalent of 5000 sit-ups, brushing your teeth and losing weight, or fidgeting more to lose weight are simply advertising gimmicks that catch the public's attention. The authors of the study need to clarify to the public the distinction between correlation and causation—in other words, there may be individuals who in fact brush their teeth after every meal and they indeed may be leaner than those who do not brush after every meal. But those same people who brush their teeth after every meal may also be driving a convertible car as well—does driving a particular type of car also result in losing weight? Of course not—a correlation simply means two variables may be linked or correlated with each other, but not causally linked. The researchers in the study should have clarified these points further—that fidgeting people may also be leaner than those who do not fidget, but the lean body mass and fidgeting (as with brushing teeth) are correlated to each other, but not having causal relationship. We need to be much more skeptical of these claims by researchers and definitely read the fine print. Weight loss means only one thing: No gimmicks—fewer calories consumed and more calories burned means you lose the weight, and more calories consumed than burned means you gain the weight. Simple and end of story.

■■ CHAPTER 5 QUESTION & REVIEW

1. Describe why obesity has become such a widespread problem in our society. What is the "SWEAT" program and describe each stage;

2. Describe the Karvonen formula—determine your ideal training rate and level of exercise intensity;

3. Describe the 5 factors that have contributed to obesity;

4. Describe how obesity becomes problematic in the workplace environment, education, and health industry.

Chapter 6:
Team Sports and Individual Sports:
Cultural Values Defining
The Importance of Sport

"Character is what you really are . . . reputation is merely what you are perceived to be."
—John Wooden

We have been discussing the importance of sport and exercise in our lives, and how a consistent and active program can enhance and improve the quality of living and enhance our professional lifestyles. When people incorporate a consistent and regular program of exercise into their lives, research demonstrates that the benefits are numerous: People are happier, healthier, more active, sleep better, lowered blood pressure and in general fewer physical complaints. Most importantly, people who exercise regularly often comment that they "just feel better about myself and my relationships with others." Individuals who exercise regularly have significantly higher levels of self-esteem and are less likely to suffer from depression. Furthermore, exercise and health programs have been used as effective measures in mental health programs and have been useful tools in the treatment of several psychiatric disorders, such as schizophrenia (Tkachuk & Martin, 1999). Research has traditionally supported the psychologically positive effects of exercise, and many theorists suggest that this may be due to the impact of neurotransmitter release (i.e., epinephrine and norepinephrine). More importantly, regular participation in exercise helps individuals socially and interpersonally by creating new ways to interact with others, and also helps increase self-efficacy. We have also discussed the negative ramifications of a lifestyle that does not incorporate a healthy activity exercise program. Obesity, depression, and low self-esteem were discussed in the previous chapter as consequences of a sedentary lifestyle that does not embrace exercise and a healthy diet. We will now look at other important factors that influence how teams participate and interact with each other, and how cultural values may also influence athletic performance.

■ THE BOSTON RED SOX: CHAMPIONS PLAYING "LIKE A GROUP OF IDIOTS"

An example of how sports and exercise plays an important role in society addresses a recent article that was written about the 2004 Major League Baseball World Championship Series involving the Boston Red Sox and St. Louis Cardinals. Boston won an incredible pennant series against the New York Yankees and overcame a 3–0 deficit to win the pennant 4–3. This phenomenon had never before occurred in any major league sport. When a professional team was down three games to zero, the odds of them coming back to win four consecutive games was incredible—but this in fact is exactly what happened. Boston went on to win the world series with a 4–0 sweep against St. Louis—and when asked how could this have happened, the players responded like a team and commented that they "all played together [like a bunch of 'idiots'] we communicated and knew how to put things together as a team." This very humorous and humble demeanor about playing as an effective team, as well as the comment "playing like idiots" is the key to winning games—a group of very talented individuals putting their skills together to create what was then an unstoppable force. The tongue-in-cheek comment "playing like idiots" perhaps needs clarification. One can speculate what the team players were really referring to was that they were a group of naïve but very talented players who had no idea of what they were actually getting into—they played just like a group of talented athletes against another team, and they did not subject themselves to pride and arrogance, nor was their style of play selfish or characterized with a sense of entitlement or aggrandizement. They perhaps also realized that while each of them was good, very good in fact—they were still significantly much better when playing as a team. This is the essence of the concept "team": Groups of individuals working together for a mutual goal whose strengths are based from and dependent on each other's contributions. In truth—the 2004 Boston Red Sox team was anything but a group of "idiots"—they were genuine and true athletes who played like champions and they deserved the title of being called the best ball club of 2004.

What makes this win truly unique was that the Boston Red Sox had not won any world series since 1918! The games were exciting, people were happy, and the baseball game allowed people to temporarily forget the war on terror and other world problems. Sport provides us with a temporary reprieve of the world problems involving the economy, global warming, and the latest threats from Osama Bin Laden and terrorism. The article was written by author John Wisdom Dancer (Daily News, Sports Section, November 1, 2004) who commented on the numerous strengths and advantages of sports and how people relate with each other in society. The author commented that major league baseball was an important contributor to integrating athletes of different ethnicity and religions and played a role in assimilation. Dancer also argues that the development of modern sport in the 1932 Olympiad helped defeat the prejudicial and discriminatory views of Hitler when Jesse Owens soundly defeated the German athletes in track and field. Sports bring us together, regardless of the ethnicity of the team, and regardless of the ethnic make-up of the audience. We cheer for winners, regardless of their religion or ethnicity. In this manner, exercise and sport programs play an important role in bringing groups of people together in a positive activity and helps us focus on our strengths and to compete in a healthy forum. How can people be encouraged to compete in a healthy way and in a forum that brings out the best in each of us? The answer to this question lies in the culture in which we learn sport. In the next section of this chapter, we will explore how different cultural values that are taught to children influence how teams participate with each member and why we place special value on winning.

■ THE COLLECTIVISTIC AND INDIVIDUALISTIC CULTURE: PLAYING FOR YOURSELF OR PLAYING FOR THE TEAM?

Perhaps what makes the 2004 Boston Red Sox World Series championship game most successful wasn't necessarily their style of play (they actually committed several errors during the innings of each game) or their "glamorous" appearance (some actually looked like they could stand to lose a few pounds themselves). I submit that the true and exceptional image that we need to acknowledge and understand in what made this team world champions was their display of sportsmanship, team value and unselfish style of play. These virtues in modern sport are extremely difficult to see in competition—regardless of individual or team sports. Our culture today emphasizes winning—and winning at all cost to enhance your self image. The individualistic cultures that permeate the Western hemisphere are replete with examples of how egoism and greed have determined the outcome of sport and athletic competition. Earlier in this text we discussed the importance of one's culture in shaping and defining the personality, attitudes and values that characterize our behavior. The United States has long held a reputation as being fiercely independent and very competitive—perhaps too competitive according to some historians and educators. The form of cultural influence embraces all of the values that are associated with individualism: Autonomy, freedom and typically a highly competitive nature. Furthermore, the individualistic culture that is typical of America can produce more emphasis on individual success (as compared to team success) and performance and just plain *winning*. Very different from this cultural value is the collectivistic culture. The collectivistic culture is one that has a profound influence on the group, where the group is the center and the focus of attention and responsibility. The "group" may be close-knit, such as the family, or larger, such as the company where an employee works. The collectivistic culture is most profound in Asian families and African cultures, where the individual is expected to work for the needs of the group, and in turn the group will provide for the needs of those individuals who comprise the group. Thus, the relationship is reciprocal, where individuals who make sacrifices for the group are praised and even honored.

The problem with American culture and sports is that we as a society do not typically teach, value nor do we appreciate the inherent benefits of the collectivistic culture. Now, perhaps more importantly than ever, we need to illustrate and teach how collectivism is important, no only in terms of how we relate to others from an athletic perspective, but perhaps in our community relationships and international relationships. Kitayama and colleagues (1997) argued that in the West we typically do not teach our children the value of group effort, cooperative work and team work, but rather emphasize the importance of individual success, winning, and "conspicuous consumption": The more we own, the higher the value of the property, the more our independent value and perceived self-worth increases. The irony of this philosophy is that only through understanding and appreciating the value of teamwork and trust can we truly achieve our inner strength and what I refer to as our "absolute potential."

■ THE COLLECTIVISTIC CULTURE AND THE AWARENESS OF OUR ABSOLUTE POTENTIAL

The absolute potential refers to the highest achievement an individual can make regarding his or her athletic, career or intellectual goals. The absolute potential is only possible through the cooperation of supportive individuals who have helped you achieve your goals gradually and systematically. Parents, coaches and significant others in our lives who have made tremendous personal sacrifices in their own lives to help you achieve your goals can emphasize the importance of the collectivistic philosophy: We can only become stronger and ultimately reach our goals by the sacrifices that our family and friends have made for us. When we realize the sacrifices that others have made for us in our effort to achieve our goals, we begin to understand that the relationship is truly reciprocal and we typically feel compelled to "give back" to those who have sacrificed so much for us. This insight and true awareness becomes the motivating factor that ultimately allows us to reach our goals in sport activity and athletic endeavors through team competition. The ability to function as a team hinges on the ability of the individual athlete to sacrifice his own needs and to think and function as a group dynamic. Furthermore, this insight is the antithesis of greed, ego, and self-entitlement that we unfortunately see so often in professional sports. In sum—our ability to reach our absolute potential is based on an unconditional form of loving, support and acceptance that is typified in the collectivistic culture. The reciprocal relationship that is inherent in the collectivistic culture is further described in Erikson's psychosocial theory. If you recall from earlier chapters, the relationship between the child and parent is based on love, trust and mutual support. In the first stage of trust versus mistrust, the child only becomes capable of trusting others in his environment if he has been provided with love, trust and unconditional support. What was given to him or her in the early phase of the relationship with parents will be reciprocal as they are provided with the capacity to love and trust others in future relationships.

When individuals are provided with unconditional love and support, they are more concerned with opportunities of self-improvement, constructive self-criticism and they typically want to improve their relationships with others. They take the opportunity to become proactive in creating a more supportive environment and show initiative in improving relationships with others. They are supportive of others, supportive of their coaches, and supportive of the institutions that have become the vehicle for their success and financial development. Conversely, in the individualistic culture, the athlete typically becomes critical of others, and emphasizes their own importance and value often at the expense of the team. Furthermore, in the individualistic culture, athletes focus more on how the group can serve their needs, whereas in the collectivistic culture the athlete will focus on how he can serve the needs of the group. The self is sacrificed for the betterment of the team, whereas in the individualistic culture the team becomes sacrificed for the betterment and the advancement of the individual. The example of the Los Angeles 2004 Laker professional basketball team again serves as a good example of how exceptional talent may become wasted due to the greed exacerbated by an individualistic culture that is compounded by blatant egoism and an inability of individual players to think like a team:

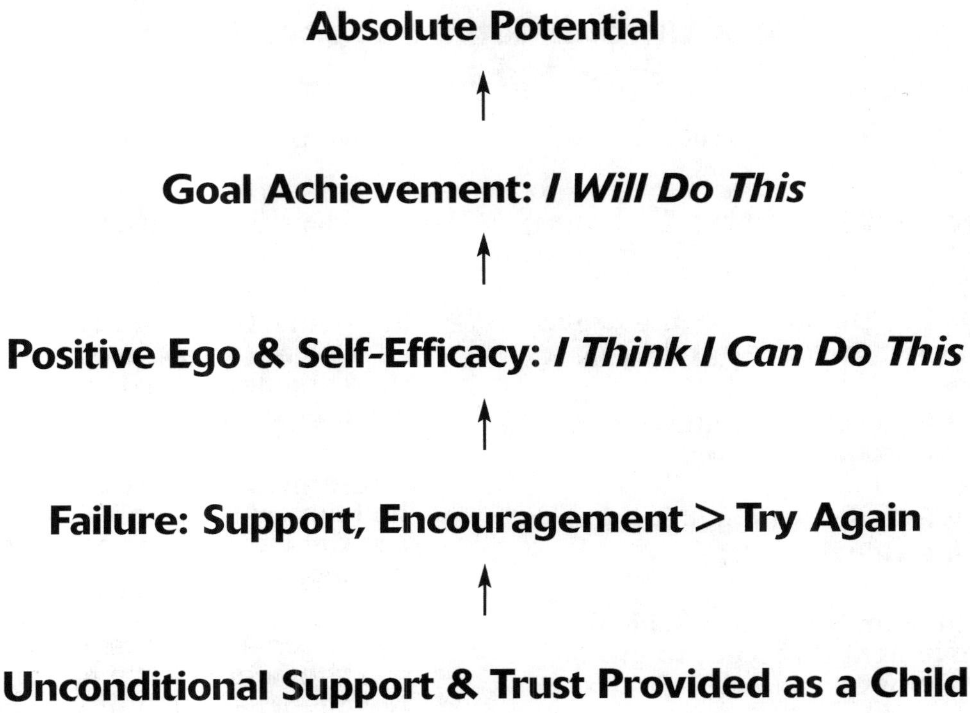

Absolute Potential

↑

Goal Achievement: *I Will Do This*

↑

Positive Ego & Self-Efficacy: *I Think I Can Do This*

↑

Failure: Support, Encouragement > Try Again

↑

Unconditional Support & Trust Provided as a Child

Figure 6a   The Influence of the Collectivistic Philosophy in Sport Achievement

Unrecognized Potential / Blame

↑

Failure of Goal Achievement: *I Shouldn't Have to Do This—They Should Do This*

↑

Inflated Ego & Self-Importance: *I Think I Should Do This*

↑

Failure: Conditional Support > Why Bother Trying Again?

↑

Lack of Unconditional Support & Trust Provided as a Child

Figure 6b   The Influence of the Individualistic Philosophy in Sport Achievement

Collectivistic Sports Culture:

➢ Emphasize the needs of the group » What can I do for the group?

➢ Honor to serve the group and to make personal sacrifices;

➢ Needs of the group take priority over individual needs;

➢ Self-criticism leads to individual improvement that leads to group improvement:

➢ I represent the group, when I contribute to the group, we all benefit.

Individualistic Sports Culture:

➢ Emphasize the needs of the individual » What can the group do for me? What should I be getting from the group or team?

➢ Resentment at serving the needs of the team » "Why do I always have to pass the ball to him and he gets all of the glory / points?

➢ My personal needs take priority over the needs of the group—"I'm a free agent"—What can you pay me? I have to 'look out for number one';

➢ Criticize the performance of others: If you hadn't screwed up—we could have one the game;

➢ The group represents me and I benefit from what others do for me.

Figure 6c   The Mentality of Two Diametrically Opposed Cultures

■ THE EVOLUTION OF THE GROUP IDENTITY IN TEAM SPORTS

This chapter has been focusing on the differences between the collectivistic and individualistic cultures, and how these differences have influenced how individuals relate and interact with one another. The individualistic culture has shaped people to behave more competitively and to focus on their individual needs. Here in the United States, we encourage and teach our children to compete and to win, often at the cost of good sportsmanship. Conversely, the collectivistic cultures have taught individuals that the true strength and virtue within people's behaviors come from working together and focusing on a common goal. Furthermore, individuals who have been raised within the collectivistic cultures focus on placing their individual needs behind the needs of the group, and that making sacrifices towards the group is a key component to success for everyone. Through group success, all individuals who comprise the group succeed. Within the collectivistic culture (such as Asia), many individuals define themselves within the context of the group itself. The question that is posed as: "Who am I?" is rephrased as: "Who are we?" Furthermore, those individuals who are raised and exposed to the collectivistic culture define themselves and their identity by meeting the needs of others (usually parents and authority figures), whereas the individualistic culture defines individual identity without regard to the group. Indeed, often the individualistic culture encourages individuals to "pursue their dreams without regard to group concerns." Self-enhancement and self-improvement are just two examples of concepts where individuals are encouraged to advance themselves often at the cost of the community, where the individual from the collectivistic environment often makes personal sacrifices to advance the well-being of the group.

In reality, most societies and communities have a relative balance of those individuals who make up either the individualistic and collective identity, in fact, each of us personally have a combination of the traits and qualities that comprise the individualistic and collectivistic identity. Many would classify this distinction as "givers and takers" within society, however, too many individuals that comprise the individualistic identity may eventually tip the scales of balance in society where teamwork and individual self-sacrifice are rare events. In terms of the development of the team (collectivistic) identity, an important goal for educators, teachers and parents is to teach children the importance and value of the group, and how important sacrifice and sharing is to how we relate with each other. Teaching young athletes to focus on the contributions of other team mates, or to focus and reflect on the skills of others is a good place to start. Building team work begins with each athlete understanding the value and respect needed for all players who comprise the team. Coaches need to encourage young athletes to emphasize what each member can contribute to the team, and how success and winning is not an individual effort, but rather a collective and group effort.

■ THE COLLECTIVE GROUP AS A TEAM

The collective philosophy should emphasize the importance of the group, and that all teams need to understand how the processes of communication and contribution are essential for success. The collective identity makes the distinction between a team as an interactive and dynamic force that shares a common goal as compared to simply a collection of individuals who are more concerned about individual success rather than team unity and cohesion. We can see how the values and cultures clash between individual success and maintaining a group identity that we may classify as a "team." Tuckman (1965) in earlier research was the first to describe several distinct stages that most groups experience when meeting together. Tuckman argued that all groups go through a formation period, a "storming" period where conflict emerges, a "norming" period where feelings of unity develop in working towards their goal, a "performing" stage where the group accomplishes the task and cooperation is established, and finally an "adjourning" stage where the group experiences remorse at the end of the process. We will now discuss how each successful team in sports experiences the process of successful group identity.

The Evolution of The Group Identity in Team Sports

a. *The Recruitment Phase: Putting On Our Best Behaviors.* In this first stage of team development, individual athletes meet each other for the first time and begin to interact on a superficial level. Introductions are made, and people are generally very civil and friendly to one another. The athletes are happy that they have at least made the team and for now the pressure is off. They get to know one another, and begin to form professional and personal relationships. People typically get along well during this first stage as they are beginning to determine and understand their role and status on the team. Athletes communicate their concerns and worries with each other and do not view each other as "a competitor." On the contrary, athletes at this first stage of group development are friendly and supportive of each other and are not competing with each other. The development of the "status hierarchy" or "who's the boss" has not quite yet begun;

b. *Rivalry: Teammates Competing Against Each Other for 1st String.* According to the second stage of group identity in team sports, there are a limited number of available positions for members of the team. This automatically creates a highly competitive situation where team mates now experience conflict with each other. Individual team members may feel that they are the best choice for the position and want to make first string. The previous discussion regarding collectivistic and individualistic philosophies is especially important here. If the individual has been exposed to a collectivistic culture, he or she may not necessarily be disappointed in not representing their team as a "first-string" position if they feel that this is in the team's best interest. However, typically individuals who have not been selected as a "first-string" choice and have been exposed to the individualistic culture may blame the coach or feel that they have been somehow wronged or "cheated." In the rivalry stage, conflict may develop not only among players who are competing for the same position, but also through the chain of command in player-coaching relationships. For example, players may not agree with coaching strategies or the general philosophy of the coach, and ultimately conflicts may develop in how decisions are being made. This situation is especially true if the coaching staff is young and inexperienced. Players who are seasoned veterans may seize this as an opportunity to control the direction of the team and control and manipulate team morale. Furthermore, veteran players who are unhappy with coaching decisions may play a very detrimental in morale by influencing negative behaviors among other team mates, thereby causing internal conflict and even "team mutiny" (i.e., 2004 Los Angeles Lakers and the Kobe Bryant / Shaquille O'Neille conflict, which later evolved into the Kobe Bryant / Karl Malone conflict);

c. *Role Attainment & Status.* In this third stage of group identity in team sports, decisions have been made regarding the roles and positions of players. This is a very difficult position for the coaching staff, as often several players are competing for the same position and are highly qualified. Tempers flare but the anger subsides into acceptance. Roles have been achieved and determined based on the judgment of the coaching staff, and now the status of each player is determined. Here the collectivistic philosophy is critical, as individual team members now must play cohesively and support one another, even if they feel that they should have been awarded the 1st string position. In true team development that is characteristic of the collectivistic philosophy, members are now highly supportive of each other and the team has taken on a single unifying theme. The "second string" players now support the team and help all players to play up to their full potential. They are also looking forward to an opportunity to contribute to the development of the team as competition advances;

d. *Team Competition: The Season Begins.* In this fourth stage of team development, all individuals who comprise the team now combine in a cohesive force that represents their unity. The relationships with each other, as well as with the coach, have become stabilized and merge toward a unifying force. The team itself executes plays and competes to their full potential—the maneuvers and the skills that were learned during the practice phase are now put into action on the court or in the field. Most importantly, there is a form of interdependency that is unique and inherent in the collectivistic identity that contributes to the overall positive style of play. When players realize that they are dependent upon each other, and that their goals are mutually shared, and most importantly winning is dependent on mutual cooperation, the usually the ideal team performance is the result. Most importantly, players who have attained the group or team identity have realized that they could not have achieved success without the success of each other, and that the combined force of individual players creates a force much more powerful than individual performance. Furthermore, successful teams show their support for each other during the good times as well as the difficult times and acknowledge their support for each throughout the season. This period of time during competition is one of affirmation of individuals working collaboratively for a mutual goal—The Championship. This is the essence of the word *team*.

e. *The Collective Identity.* In the final phase of the development of the team identity, team mates recognize and value the accomplishments of each other and make their departures. This is also a very difficult time for most individuals who comprise the team, as team mates recognize the value and effort that each has contributed to the team. Team mates now recognize that they have grown and learned as a team and have gained valuable experiences with each other. Their identity has changed from a collection of individuals from the beginning of the season to a collective singular unit that has progressed cohesively through the end of the season. With most teams, the end of the season brings regret as members realized that they could not have achieved success without the unselfish contributions of each other. In successful team formations in sports, athletes have made the sacrifices necessary with each other to achieve something that is very rare: Team unity and a unique identity. Members typically report that they have discovered strengths and characteristics within themselves that they previously were not aware of. Most importantly, successful teams have realized that goal achievement was not possible until they changed their individual identity into the team identity (see figure 6d).

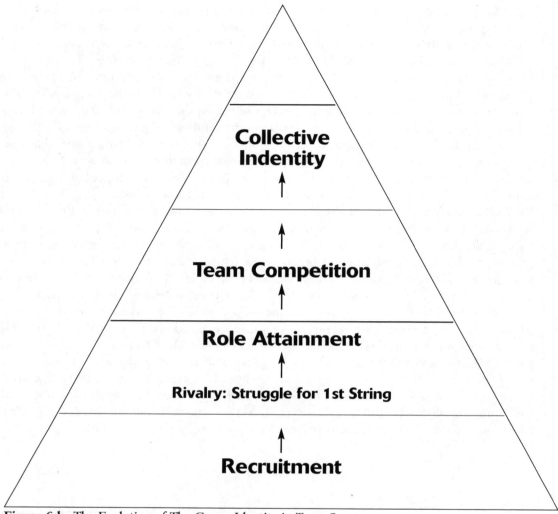

Figure 6d The Evolution of The Group Identity in Team Sports

■■ CHAPTER 6 QUESTION & REVIEW

1. Describe the terms "collective" and "individualistic" culture and how these terms may relate to individual and team sports;

2. In your own opinion, explain how an individualistic culture (such as ours) may improve the way team sports are conducted today—what can coaches do for athletes to help them play more as a *team* rather than a group of individuals?

3. In your opinion, what are some of the things that parents can do to improve the quality of team sports among younger children? Do we place too much of an emphasis on winning in our culture and not enough emphasis on the style of play and overall enjoyment? Justify your reasoning;

4. Briefly explain the five stages of the evolution of the group identity in team sports;

5. Provide one example of an experience that you have had working with a group of individuals— How was the experience? Was the group capable of achieving the goals necessary? How did you relate with your group members? Did your group work cooperatively as a team? How did your group members communicate with each other?

Chapter 7:
Controlling Aggression in Sport Activity

Aggression and hostility have become very serious and important issues within our society as more activities among groups of people may encounter hostile or aggressive activity. This section of the text will now focus on various themes of aggression and describe how they influence sport activity. Interesting topics will include aggression in the world of sport activity, spectator or fan aggression, and even aggression while driving (commonly referred to as "road rage"). Even as this section was being written, one of the most violent and aggressive actions was displayed during an NBA Detroit Pistons and Pacers game which in fines and suspensions among the players and possible jail time for some of the spectators. The topics of aggression in modern sport activity have recently become serious issues not only in sport psychology, but in society in general. According to a recent survey involving individuals who drive their automobiles on public highways, at least 10% of the drivers who were surveyed admitted to intentionally cutting off other motorists, and one in twenty five drivers actually carry some form of a weapon in their car for protection against others on the road. In a variety of different sport activities, as the competitive levels increase dramatically among athletes, so does the likelihood of aggressive contact. Furthermore, the overall style of play in athletic competition typically will become extremely intense. There are several reasons for the significant increase in aggression in sport, and this chapter will explore what aggression exactly is from a traditional psychological perspective and how it manifests itself. We will also explore how and why sport provides a forum or a unique environment for aggression to manifest itself, and a third focus of the chapter will look at aggression from the other perspective—fan and spectator aggression. An interesting component of spectator influence and aggression would include the dynamics of what people view and why they find particular types of aggressive sport and athletics particularly rewarding. We will also compare this significant increase in interest in aggressive style of play (i.e., wrestling, ultimate fighting programs) with the increases in reality television programs.

■ TRADITIONAL PSYCHOLOGY AND VIEWS IN AGGRESSION

Before we can describe aggression in modern sport, we first must describe the term aggression itself and how it is used in psychology and sport psychology. The term aggression is commonly used among coaches, educators and the general public, but unfortunately how this term is used can often be very misleading. Aggression defined refers to the use of force to intentionally inflict harm on other people or even one's self. Aggression may be manifested in a variety of forms, but most typically aggression is exhibited in either overt form (i.e., physical force) or forms of psychological / relational aggression (intentional verbal assault or manipulation of others to alienate the targeted victim).

Some research recently suggests that gender differences may exist in terms of how the aggression is displayed. For example, girls and adolescent females are more likely to use relational forms of aggression where boys and adolescent males use overt or physical aggression.

Typically in sport psychology we see overt aggression where players inflict physical force on others. Sports should be regarded as an important activity that allows athletes to play physically and assertively without using physical aggression. Often coaches, parents, and newscasters actually misuse the term by describing an athlete's style of play as being "highly aggressive" or "the football player made an aggressive tackle." The use of the adjective phrase "aggressive" of course is misused in this example, and we need to clarify differences between "assertive" (a forceful form of behavior designed to achieve one's goals) as opposed to "aggressive" (intention to inflict injury on another). There are several theories that explain why aggression has existed in human behavior for literally millions of years, and we will explain the traditional theories regarding aggression and the more current viewpoints. The explanations involving aggression will be described from the sport psychologist's perspective—how certain physical and contact sports may make individuals prone to become the aggressor or the victim of aggression. The following views will be addressed: Evolutionary psychology, Freudian psychoanalytic theory, social learning theory, frustration-aggression theory, displaced aggression, road rage (hostile attribution bias), personality bias as indicators of aggression (Types A and B), instrumental aggression, environmental aggression, parenting strategies and coaching strategies as indicators of violence in sport and aggression, and finally spectator aggression.

Evolutionary Theory and Aggression: Violence as a (Short Term) Adaptive Mechanism

A recent and interesting theory that explains human behavior from a variety of perspectives involving our evolutionary history is the evolutionary theory of psychology. Evolutionary psychology specifically explains modern human behavior through a variety of situations and styles of interactions that played an adaptive role in our survival. Charles Darwin was the first scientist and naturalist to propose the idea of evolution and natural selection, where genetic variation and diversity played key factors in our survival as a species. On his now famous voyage on the H. M. S. Beagle in December of 1831, Darwin made the ground breaking discovery that the environment and the physical appearances of a variety of species (a term called *phenotypical* appearance) are closely linked and dependent on one another. After five years of meticulous observations, Darwin returned to England in 1836 and began what is now considered to be one of the most influential books written in science: *The Origin of the Species* (1859). Natural selection occurs because all humans possess the capacity to reproduce far more offspring than they can support, a concept referred to as *superfecundity*. Through this natural tendency to reproduce, an enormous variety of physical traits were developed and ultimately became influenced by our environment. Some of these traits are suitable and indeed preferable for existence, and others are not. Those individuals with key or selective physical traits suited for their particular environment are more likely to survive and thus pass those traits to future generations.

Aggression was a key factor that played a role in our survival—especially in competitive environments. Natural selection builds on shaping the psychological traits that have been useful for our survival, and aggression proved to be very useful in environments where resources were limited. Other traits that proved to be central in our role of survival included the balances of key traits that influenced our survival (see Figure 7a):

Aggressive & Egoistic Traits
(Greed)

↓

Benefits Self (Short Term Advantage)
(Isolates Self From Group)

❀❀❀❀❀   ❀❀❀❀❀   ❀❀❀❀

Cooperative & Altruistic Traits
(Sacrificial Behaviors)

↓

Benefits Group (Long Term Advantages)
(Group Interdependency, Protection
& Reproductive Fitness—Group
Protects Offspring)

Figure 7a

Where the aggressive traits increased the overall fitness of the individual *within* the group, cooperative traits increased the *overall* fitness of the group itself. Altruistic traits increased the fitness of the group but compromised the fitness of the individual, and egoistic traits increased the overall fitness of the individual at the cost of the fitness of the group. Thus, according to Darwin, much of human behavior was shaped by a combination of psychological characteristics (i.e., cooperation and altruism) and physical behaviors (aggressive traits and egoistic behaviors). Ultimately, as Trivers (1971), points out, a reciprocal relationship developed between cooperative behaviors and reproductive fitness, where those people who engaged in helping behaviors were more likely also to be recipients of those behaviors. The group protected the individual who made sacrifices and also protected the offspring of the altruist. Evolutionary history has become a complex relationship between the needs of the group and the needs of the individual. All groups in our evolutionary history have necessarily had both "givers" (those who contribute to the integrity of the group) and "takers" (those who take advantage of the group and group resources). Clearly, certain psychological traits (such as aggression) have been critical to our survival. Most researchers would agree that individuals within the group have a vast array of traits and dispositions, and certain environmental characteristics may trigger a wide range of behaviors, ranging from altruism (giving food or some other natural resource) to aggression (taking food or water by force). The key point to note in evolutionary theory is that just as humans had a wide range of physiological traits that were suited for survival under a wide range of conditions, evolutionary theory argues that humans also had a vast array of psychological traits and characteristics that were selected for survival (such as intelligence, language, and the ability to engage in cooperative behaviors where favors were exchanged). Key environmental characteristics would gradually influence phenotypical characteristics (i.e., skin color, eye color) to facilitate survival, but also key environmental characteristics influenced the development and manifestation of psychological traits. For example, in environments lacking in resources (such as food, water, or fertile available females) males who engaged in aggressive behaviors were more likely to secure critical resources that ensured their reproductive fitness.

The evolutionary branch of psychology combines several factors that have played a critical role in our survival in explaining modern human behavior: Genetics, environmental factors, and natural selection are just a few factors that have been formed to describe evolutionary psychology. How was aggression considered to be an adaptive characteristic to our behavior? Aggression clearly may have been a desirable and advantageous characteristic, as early primates used aggression in securing food, protecting themselves and kin from predators, and even selection of mates by force as a means of increasing reproductive fitness (see figure 7b):

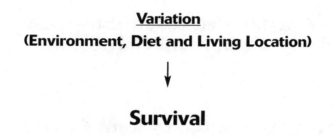

<u>Variation</u>
(Environment, Diet and Living Location)

↓

Survival

<u>Selection</u>
Phenotypical
characteristics:
hair, eye, skin color

<u>Inheritance</u>
Genotypical
characteristics
(DNA, genetics)

Figure 7b

In evolutionary theory, genotypical advantages helped humans evolve and adapt to specific environmental characteristics. In other words, according to Darwin's theory of evolution, the key to survival was genetic variation. The greater variation of phenotypical characteristics (i.e., hair and eye color, skin color) improved chances of survival. Those individuals who possessed phenotypical characteristics that proved favorable to extreme environmental conditions (i.e., dark skin color with warmer climates) had a significantly higher chance of survival and those characteristics were passed on to future generations. The successful male reproduced with as many fertile child-bearing females as possible (superfecundity) that ensured that his genetic lineage was passed on to future generations (a term called "reproductive fitness"—see Robert Trivers article: The Evolution of Reciprocal Altruism, *Quarterly Review of Biology,* 46, 35–57). Competition and aggression were thus very important characteristics that improved reproductive success. The physically stronger male who competed with other males had a significantly higher percentage of reproductive success with a wide range of females. The psychological characteristics of aggression and competition were highly beneficial in terms of survival and were passed on to future generations with increasing populations of offspring. Furthermore, the psychological characteristics of aggression may also have been learned by other members and offspring, thereby increasing the likelihood of aggressive behavior manifested in social environments.

Environments lacking in resources (food, water, living space) may also have played a role in the development of aggression. The greater a given area was lacking in basic essentials for survival, the greater the role that aggression played in securing those resources. The aggressive individual who competed for resources was successful and those skills and styles of behavior were either passed on to future generations through genotypical inheritance or through learned behaviors. The role that aggression played in environments lacking in key resources has been a central issue in the role that aggression plays in competitive environments. Darwin's theory of natural selection seems to support the role of the athlete and aggression—significant characteristics of the environment may trigger aggressive behaviors in some people who are physically more suited to display those behaviors (see figure 7c).

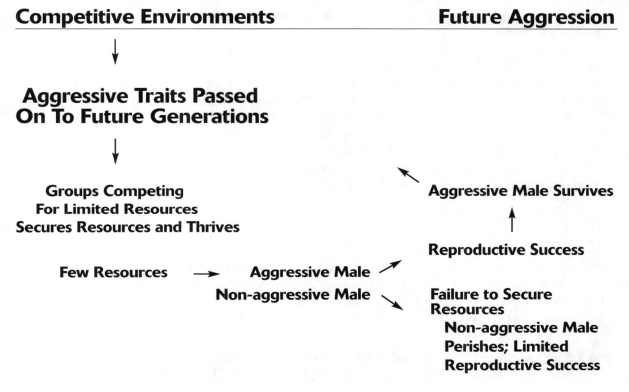

Figure 7c

■ FREUDIAN PSYCHOANALYTIC THEORY & AGGRESSION

The Freudian psychoanalytic theory is very closely linked to the theory of aggression in sports and human aggression in general. Sigmund Freud (1856–1939) arguably has had the most profound influence in psychology for a variety of reasons. Perhaps his greatest contribution to psychology was his work on the unconscious mind and the role of instincts on behavior. Freud's views were revolutionary and highly controversial—he created an uproar in the field of psychology that is still reverberating today. Perhaps one reason why Freud's theory in psychoanalysis and human behavior has become so significant is that his theories are universal and cross-cultural. Additionally, many people were upset with Freud's theory of psychoanalysis because they had violated many taboos involving sexuality, incest and family values.

This chapter will explore how Freud explained how instincts have influenced our behavior and will also address some of Freud's major contributions. Some of these topics will include: Defense mechanisms, theories of personality, psychosexual stages of development, dream analysis, and the role of the unconscious mind. Freud actually began his practice a medical doctor (neurologist) and was impressed with the number of psychogenic (physical disorders with no organic basis) disorders that his patients were suffering from. Literally all of Freud's patients were female, and some of the more common disorders involved paralysis, blindness and neurasthenia (numbness in hands and feet). Given the tremendous influence of sexual repression during this period time, Freud made a huge theoretical leap by hypothesizing that the conditions were more due to sexual repression which was exacerbated by the Victorian era. It seemed plausible to assume that the intense moral and sexual repression that was typical of the Victorian era played a key role in the increases in psychogenic and psychosomatic disorders. It was at this point where Freud developed his landmark theory addressing the role of the unconscious and mental health. Freud's greatest contribution to psychology was his introduction to the unconscious mind and how the contents of the unconscious mind may influence our physical health.

Freud later hypothesized that the reason so many of his clients were suffering from psychosomatic illness was due to repression of the instincts sex and aggression. The urges or instinctual drives were actually forms of energy, and energy repressed eventually required an outlet or release. The greater the amount of anxiety or instinctual drives became repressed, the more damage to the ego of the personality (the id, ego and superego will be addressed in the next section of this chapter which is referred to as the personality theory). According to Freud, the only way repressed sexual drives or instincts may be cured was through psychoanalysis where the content of the unconscious mind becomes understood and interpreted—a process Freud called *insight*. Insight is only possible through one of three mechanisms used to understand the unconscious mind:

a. Dream interpretation;
b. Hypnosis; and
c. Free Association

The key to understanding neurotic behaviors, according to Freud, is through understanding how we repress drives and instincts. We will now explore the three levels of consciousness (consciousness, subconscious, and the unconscious) and the five stages of the psychosexual development as key factors that address behavior and aggression specifically within the athletic environment.

■ LEVELS OF CONSCIOUSNESS, THE TOPOGRAPHIC THEORY AND THE PSYCHOSEXUAL STAGES OF DEVELOPMENT

Closely linked to the evolutionary theory of aggression is the Freudian psychoanalytic theory of aggression. Freud argued that most of our behavior is controlled by the role of instincts, and the two primary instincts responsible for controlling our behavior according to Freud include aggression and sex. Freud challenged the notion that human behavior is controlled by free will and rational choices—instincts drive our behavior and we have little control over those behaviors. Given the fact that much of our behavior is instinctually driven, Freud argued that we strive to seek out environments where we may manifest those aggressive instincts in socially acceptable ways. Thus, according to Freud, the athlete who is attracted to contact sports is relieving or driving out his aggressive instinct by hitting and tackling his opponents. This behavior becomes further amplified by coaches who reward athletes for aggressive behaviors. Freud's general negative view of the human condition was reflected through his theoretical research addressing the personality and what is now referred to as the topographic theory. A topographic map is unique in the sense that it is layered, with mountains that are raised and the levels of the surface that actually match the geographic regions. In Freud's topographic theory, the views of consciousness are layered as well, with the conscious level being relative to a state of awareness or the "here and now"; the subconscious levels are directly underneath consciousness and are made conscious with a little effort, and the unconscious levels are those distinct images and experiences that are kept totally out of conscious thought. Freud argued that consciousness and all forms of mental functions occur at these three distinct and separate levels, and only through psychoanalysis can we uncover the true images and thoughts and feelings that are contained in the unconscious mind. Only by understanding our secret thoughts kept hidden in the unconscious can we ever truly hope to understand the meaning of our behaviors.

According to Freud, the motivating drive of all behavior is to achieve "quiescence", or balance between the two diametrically opposed instinctual forces that drives all of our behaviors: Sexual energy (libidos) and aggression. The universal sex drive is important in Freudian theory as this gave rise to the common forms of maladjustment involving sexual instincts (i.e., repression) during the Victorian era (late 18th century). Due to the inherent conflict between the two opposed instincts (libidos and aggression), individuals are continually in a state of psychological imbalance or neuroticism.

■ UNCONSCIOUS ACTIVITY INFLUENCING SPORT ACTIVITY

The levels of conscious activity and mental activity involving the subconscious and unconscious may be repressed in how a child or adolescent chooses and participates in a sport or exercise. For example, at a conscious level (what the child thinks he or she wants) may be more unconsciously influenced by parents, peers, or the media. The child may select a sport such as football or rugby, and feel that he or she consciously decided this sport, but according to the psychoanalytic theory, there are other reasons why the sport was chosen. For example, at a deeper unconscious level, the child may be identifying with the father (a process referred to as *identification* and this occurs at a psychosexual stage called the *phallic* stage—we will address these topics later in this chapter). The child between the ages of three, four, or five emulates behavior similar to his father (if a boy) or to the mother (if a girl). According to Freud, the child learns how to behave in either a masculine or feminine manner and adopts those behaviors that are associated with masculinity or femininity. Thus, we can also see how Bandura's social learning theory (at least in part) is relative to the process of identification with Freud's psychosexual stages of development. If the parent encourages cooperative efforts with the child an emphasizes the importance in valuing the group when completing activities, then the child adapts these characteristics and behaviors and will be more likely to participate in a team sport that reflects the collective value of sport. Thus, how and why a child selects a particular sport has profound ramification in his relationship with the same-sex parent. The more the child adapts and identifies with the same sex parent during the phallic stage, the more they will select the sport activity of the parent.

■ THE TOPOGRAPHIC THEORY: ID, EGO & SUPEREGO

These three levels of mental activity (consciousness, sub-consciousness and unconsciousness) may be further illustrated by Freud's famous theory of the personality: The id, ego and superego. Perhaps one of Freud's most significant contributions to the field of psychology was his work on the personality. Freud argued that the personality is based on three separate and individual mechanisms that help us function on a daily basis. The names of these three mechanisms or portions of the personality include the ego, id and superego. The ego (commonly referred to as the "executive" or the adult portion of the personality helps run things smoothly on a daily basis. The ego allows us to meet the daily physical and psychological needs that we have, and when we are hungry, for example, the ego allows us to get food and resume work. Stated in psychological terms the ego is that portion of the personality that serves the instinctual needs of the body in a safe, civil and appropriate fashion. The ego works in the conscious level of the "real world" and helps the individual adapt to the needs and stressors commonly facing us in our daily functioning. For example, if an athlete on a basketball team is shooting poorly, his "id" may resort to a more aggressive style of play due to his frustration. The superego (the moral imperative of the personality) criticizes the athlete to train harder and practice more to improve the style of play. The superego is never satisfied and can continually work itself 24 hours daily. Conversely, the id refers to a raw, basic and animalistic drive to satisfy our basic biological and psychological urges. Thus, in the example mentioned earlier with the basketball player, rather than play more aggressively and "foul out" of the game (id induced), the smart basketball player identifies his source of frustration and then allows the ego of the personality to achieve his goals of improved style of play. In other words, the ego resolves the problem and corrects the mistakes being made. The athlete now is capable of achieving his goals most efficiently (see figure 7d):

Styles of Athletic Performance & Topographic Theory

1. **Ego:** Allows athlete to identify problem in sport competition and rationally select appropriate strategies to defeat opponent and improve overall quality of play. The ego allows the athlete to understand different strategies and theories to improve his or her quality of play—athlete feels that they are in control of performance and can change their behaviors to adapt to competitive environment;
2. **Id:** Player becomes frustrated with his or her overall style of play—the id dominates the personality and aggression results due to goals not being reached. Player fouls out or is penalized because the id cannot conform to rules and regulations of society or organized sport activity—The id does not allow for impulse control to change behavior and control emotions when under pressure;
3. **Superego:** Player becomes frustrated with his or her overall style of play and become overly critical of self or team members. The superego is characterized by Freud as being the moral component or the moral conscience of the personality that controls behavior to conform to social norms and rules. In terms of athletic competition, the superego encourages the athlete to try harder, practice longer, and to push himself or herself further than anyone on the team. Excessive guilt may impede performance and the athlete may become too critical on himself or herself or team mates.

Figure 7d

We have reviewed how traditional Freudian psychoanalytic theory has shaped and influenced behavior from the three levels of consciousness and mental activity (unconscious, consciousness, and sub-consciousness) as well as from the theory of the personality (id, ego, and superego). The ego serves to balance the needs of both the id and superego, where the id lacks impulse control to social norms and the rules of society. The id also operates through a concept known as the "pleasure principle" where behavior is governed by the consequences of pleasure and avoids all responsibility or what we commonly think of as work. Conversely, the superego operates form the philosophy to keep working harder to improve one's self and is commonly referred to as the moral conscience and the parent of the personality. Finally, the ego of the personality serves as the adult and rational component of the personality that tries to meet the diametrically opposed needs of the id and superego. The ego operates on the principle known as the "reality principle" where the ego meets the demands of the id and superego in a socially acceptable manner. For example, if you as an athlete are tired and exhausted from practice, the id may encourage you to slow down or simply to stop training. The superego challenges you to push yourself harder and to train harder to be a better athlete. The ego meets the needs of both of these personality components by slowing the pace down somewhat to recuperate but not quit altogether. An interesting illustration and analogy of Freud's traditional psychoanalytical theory of behavior and sport psychoanalytic theory may be offered at this point (see figure 7e):

Freud's Perspective

Superego: The individual engages in moralistic behaviors. Describes behavior as always needing improvement;

Philosophy: Always critical of behavior; moralistic; overly idealistic regarding goals and motivation; Describes human behavior as always in a state of moral decline; It is the inner voice in all of us telling us that we ought to be trying harder, pushing ourselves further, and work longer hours; *Risks:* Neuroses; Difficulty in maintaining relationships and communication with others; depression and frustration with perception of "not feeling good enough"—Hypercritical of performance influences people to have unrealistically high standards of performance that can lead to frustration and depression.

Id: The individual does simply what is pleasing to him or her. Describes behaviors as uncivilized, raw and animalistic. Does not conform to rules, social boundaries or any form of laws associated with decorum of behavior.

Philosophy: Operates from the personal perspective of "if it feels good then just do it, regardless of the impact of your behaviors on others or society." Behaviors are typically unconventional, self-centered and highly egoistic with no sense of remorse based on consequences of actions. *Risks:* Team dissension; lack of conformity to rules, and typically an inability to adhere to any structured training program. These athletes typically foul out or incur several penalties for their individualistic style of play. Finally, these athletes have difficulty in conforming to coaching advice and insight and reject valuable suggestions regarding their style of play.

Ego: The individual engages in behaviors that are socially correct, responsible, and balances the needs of the id and superego.

Philosophy: the ego allows athletes to balance his biological needs with the norms and obligations of society. The individual engages in the capacity to maintain satisfactory relationships with people and balances his or her biological needs while conforming to the rules and norms of society.

Figure 7e

■ SPORT PSYCHOANALYTIC VIEW OF PERSONALITY

Superego: The athlete can never over-train or "try too hard." The athlete that tries the hardest will win over other athletes in competition. The superego in the athlete is the inner voice that tells him or her to "try a little harder . . . push a little further . . . lift one more repetition of weights or drive yourself one step further to outperform your opponent. The sport psychoanalytic view of the superego argues that athletes should continuously be training to improve themselves, and that it is a fallacy to over-train. The athlete who trains in this psychological dimension pushes himself or herself harder, work longer hours, and are more self-critical of their performance. Rest and relaxation are very difficult for them because they begin to feel guilt at their perceived lack of dedication and diligence. The athlete who trains under the influence of the superego runs the risk of injury and a series of psychological problems: Depression, frustration and intolerance of training mistakes. They are compulsive athletes who drive themselves into a training regimen that increasingly becomes more demanding and increasingly impractical to maintain. The athlete who trains under the influence of the superego sets highly unrealistic goals that may lead to self-destruction (example: Larry Byrd, NBA; Lou Gehrig National Baseball League).

Advantage: Extreme drive, passion and determination in achieving goals. Devoted athletes who will train under any circumstance to achieve their unrealistic goals; Usually very successful in achieving goals despite great cost in psychological balance and personal relationships with others; *Disadvantage:* High risk of burn-out; high risk of injury; alienation of those close to him or her as values of sport and winning take top priority. These athletes typically value winning over everything. Prone to psychological maladjustment and need to be encouraged to relax and modify training regimen. Over-training is a frequent problem with athletes that have training schedules that are influenced by the super-ego.

Id: The athlete who trains under the influence of the id is difficult to maintain and to adapt to rules and regulations of the coach, the team, and practice schedules. The athlete who trains under the influence of the id engages in highly self-centered and egoistic behavior—has difficulty in training with others or sharing and communicating with team mates. The athlete who trains under the influence of the id often is described by coaches as "un-coachable"—failure to adapt to the coach's suggestions and ideas, often feels that his or her ideas are superior to others. The athlete lacks an internal discipline that can guide his or her behavior. Often creates disruption on team sports—may provide a negative influence on the attitude and philosophy of younger athletes. A prime (now retired) example of a modern-day sports basketball star who characterizes the "id" in his style of play and personality is Dennis Rodman. Lacking in discipline and respect for team values, this athlete conformed to nothing in terms of regulation styles of play and played according to his own individualistic whims and disregarded the fact that he played on a team.

Advantages: A more relaxed style of play; athlete plays for himself and can be very popular with the media and fans because they "follow their own beat to the drummer" and disregard the needs of others. *Disadvantages:* Alienates self from others on team sports; creates disruption with others and especially coaching staff. Fails to conform to rules, coaching instruction and advice of others. Athlete is typically arrogant, pompous and disregards the needs of others. Athletes playing under the influence of the id of the personality cannot adapt to practice schedules and usually foul out of regulation play with referees and umpires. These athletes admittedly play for themselves and have difficulty with sharing their views and goals with other teammates. Athletes who play and train under the influence of the id can be highly destructive and deteriorate team morale and ultimately destroy a highly competent team.

Ego: The ego allows the athlete to balance their own personal needs with the needs of team mates. The athlete who operates under the influence of the ego can satisfy the mutually exclusive demands of both the superego and id. The athlete at this level can listen to instructions and incorporate change in their style of play; they are responsible and talented and capable of making changes that improve their overall performance. Furthermore, these athletes may typically fluctuate between team and individual sports and can offer advice to others as well as receive constructive criticisms and suggestions. These athletes are observed often to contribute back to society and volunteer their time and effort for charitable and prosocial causes.

Advantages: This athlete is capable of incorporating change in their athletic performance and are capable of communicating effectively with coaches as well as teammates. They are capable of making sacrifices for the team and can conform to practice schedules. They are reliable, determined and successful in achieving their goals in athletic performance. They are capable of meeting the demands of personal life and professional life and set positive examples for the public. Examples of athletes at this personality level would include: Tiger Woods (golf); Michael Jordan (basketball); Lance Armstrong (cycling). *Disadvantages:* None.

In summary, Sigmund Freud's contributions to psychology played a very important role in improving our understanding of human functioning with respect to the unconscious mind. Freud proposed new and revolutionary views that are still discussed today in psychoanalytic circles. Regarding sport activity, perhaps Freud's greatest contributions may be summarized in understanding the aggressive instincts and urges that become manifested during aggressive styles of play. Freud argued that these instincts and drives are a form of energy that requires some form of release—and this release may occur in a healthy way (i.e., positively channeling the aggressive energy through sports or socially approved activities) or unhealthy way (aggressive crimes). As we discussed in the previous section addressing the evolutionary theory, aggression played a key role in how we protected our natural resources, territory, and even how we may have selected mates. The instinctual drive that played a key role in our primitive evolution, according to Freud, still plays a very important role in how we relate to others today. The aggression may become internalized (i.e., repression) that requires some form of a release usually in a behavioral disorder. Freud used the analogy of a pressure-cooker, where the pressure continuously builds until a release is achieved. Sports and athletic activity have traditionally provided an important release for this universal aggressive instinct. We will now explore other leading theorists and their views regarding the role of aggression in modern sport.

■■ SPORT PSYCHOANALYTIC VIEW OF PERSONALITY

In summary, the athlete's personality is often a mix of positive characteristics with other less desirable types of personality characteristics. It would be easy and tempting after reviewing these sport psychoanalytical characteristics to generalize that all athletes (and people) fall only into one or two categories. This is simply not true—often people have a wide range of personality characteristics that make them very unique and genuine. For example, an individual may be typically very responsible in showing up for practice and trains very diligently, and only rarely decide to skip practice. The personality characteristics that make up the ego, id and superego influence our behaviors throughout the life span and change continuously based on a variety of psychodynamic and environmental circumstances.

The Social Learning Theory of Aggression

We have discussed the social learning theory earlier in chapter 3 when discussing how young children may watch adults and other role models engage in a variety of behaviors and imitate those behaviors. Regardless of the actual behavior, what seems to be the critical point is the role and the relationship the model plays in the individual's life. Positive role models have a very strong influence in terms of what young people do, not only in terms of eating behaviors but also the display of cooperative styles of play (such as in team sports) or aggressive styles of play. This theory regarding aggression will review how our relationships with others may trigger behaviors as well as vicarious forms of reinforcement in sports. Much research has recently addressed the role of aggression and specifically whether or not the individual's unique character is responsible for the displays of aggression, or perhaps specific environmental factors (such as watching other successful athletes aggress during sport activity) trigger the aggression. One very interesting study explored the actual physical size of the athlete and found that physically larger athletes were more prone to engage in aggression regardless of the type of (athletic) environment (Lemieux, McKelvie, an Stout, 2004). These researchers discovered through self-reports among athletes and non-athletes that physically larger athletes were significantly more likely to become involved in hostile aggression than non-physically large individuals (athletes or non-athletes).

Research addressing the social learning theory of aggression in sports also identifies reinforcement as key factor in how the aggression is displayed. For example, particularly aggressive athletes were found to have been verbally rewarded (praised, in fact) for playing in an aggressive manner against other athletes. Thus, aggression in sports is not only learned by watching other positive role models play violently, but can be learned by rewarding young children to hit harder and to intimidate other athletes.

Frustration-Aggression Theory & Goal Achievement

Many of the most successful athletes throughout the history of sport achievement have been highly goal-oriented. What this means is that it is critical that the athlete have some form of goal to work towards, so that he or she can monitor and gauge their progression towards their goal. An NFL player may be trying to win the super-bowl championship for years, an elite runner may try to break the four minute mile, or simply a high-school baseball player may want to make "first-string" pitcher during his junior year of high school. Goals are critical factors as a gauge of human happiness as well as frustration and aggression. When we achieve our goals, we typically are ecstatic; we have done something important for ourselves and in some cases perhaps few people have achieved. Typically, the harder the goal, the happier we become if we in fact do achieve these goals. However, when we fail in reaching our goals, many of us respond negatively or aggressively. Classic early research by Neil Miller (1944, 1959) describe clearly how failure to reach goals may result in conflict and aggression.

There exists several different types of conflicts, some positive forms of conflicts (i.e., approach-approach) where we have to choose between two or more positive choices in our lives. For example, an NBA rookie player may be offered generous contracts by two or more teams, and he must decide which team to sign for. A coach may offer a high-school football player his choice to play two highly sought after positions, and so on. The second form of conflict described by Miller includes primarily the opposite phenomena, where an athlete has two different negative choices to make. For example, if the coach wants to improve the training and stamina of his athletes, he may offer them the "choice" of running 5 miles or train bleachers for 45 minutes. Both of the choices involve hard work and leave little room for enjoyment. Finally, Miller describes the third form of conflict as the "approach-avoidant" conflict, where the athlete is faced with a choice with both positive and negative consequences. For example, an athlete may be recruited to the University of Wisconsin from Southern California to play football. He is happy that he has qualified for the scholarship, but the negative aspect is that he is traveling to a much different and colder environment in Wisconsin. These three examples of conflicts explain how athletes may respond under difficult situations or environments, and it should also be noted that when we are faced with choices we can help resolve the conflict somewhat.

Sometimes we may act out aggressively when we are deprived of the very things that we have been working so hard to achieve. In the now famous study done by John Dollard and colleagues (1939), Dollard was able to show that when we cannot obtain certain types of resources, such as food or water, we engage in aggressive behavior. Dollard worked with rats and found that the rats contained in a box behaved increasingly more aggressively with each other as the resources (such as food and water) became increasingly scarce. Additionally, as the number of rats increased within a limited area, so did the likelihood of aggression and even cannibalism. These early results of aggression with rats by Dollard have been also documented with other animals (i.e., primates in captivity) and illustrate the importance of resources in monitoring human behavior. In the next section that addresses aggression, an increasingly popular theory in social psychology is the realistic conflict theory.

Realistic Conflict Theory

In the now popular realistic conflict theory, researchers argue that conflict (usually among different ethnic groups or groups competing for limited resources) argues that conflict is a result of direct competition between various groups over scarce resources. We can see how employment factors, income, and even natural resources (such as land and water) are becoming increasingly valuable resources as human populations continue to grow. Within sport competition, we can see how aggression develops among athletes through the realistic conflict theory. For example, competition may develop among two or three players who are competing for the same position on the team, or on a larger scale collegiate athletes trying to be recruited by a sports team with a limited number of available positions. Team players who compete for the same position on the team now regard each other as "the enemy" or a viable competitor and draw boundaries for themselves in play. In sum, when people view specific goals as limited or scarce, we become highly competitive and even aggressive with each other. Important tools that coaches may use to reduce conflict among athletes who experience realistic conflict theory include increased communication and validation of each player and confirmation of expectations from each player on the team. Further, working together on the team for a mutual goal, referred to as the increased contact hypothesis, has been shown to reduce conflict and stress among players. When players become aware that they are working for mutual goals, interdependency increases and aggression decreases.

Goal Achievement in Sport Activity

Earlier in the beginning of the chapter we discussed the importance of goals in motivating athletic behavior. Goals are very interesting in the sense that they can either motivate the individual's behavior during training and competition, or they can actually hinder performance if the athlete believes that the goals are unattainable. Goals may be tangible (i.e., income or rewards) or psychological (an athlete playing his best performance). Goals provide people with reasons for getting up in the morning and beginning their day. Individuals who select healthy and realistic goals generally are more motivated and happier in the typical daily routines. Most of the successful athletes today have goals that they are continually working towards. In order to better understand how goals motivate behavior, we must first understand the developmental sequence or hierarchy of goals among athletes. The factors that motivate athletes to achieve their goals operate from a basic or primitive level to an advanced level. Most athletes enjoy and prefer working on clear and realistic goals. As the goals are gradually achieved athletes feel more empowered and motivated to continue in their training program. However, goals that are achieved and developed in each athlete's training program originate from a hierarchy. In order for athletes to maximize their individual performance, each goal must systematically be achieved and in systemic order. More importantly, how these goals are achieved are built upon the support and encouragement that the athlete has derived from a loving and supportive environment. Any highly successful or elite athlete will most probably inform you that there has been at least one central figure in his or her life that provided the impetus for them to gradually achieve their goals. The Hoffman Athletic Hierarchy (figure 7f) and The Exercise Actualization Pyramid (figure 7g) provides an illustration of how each goal is only attainable after experiencing specific qualities that are found in the relationships that athletes have with significant and supportive coaches and family members in their lives.

Hoffman's Athletic Hierarchy of Needs®

Peak Performance &
The Fully Maximized Athlete:
Elite Performance in Competitive Sport Environment
Athlete Gives Back To Community Service Programs
Internal & External Positive Belief Systems
Are Offered For Other Adult Athletes & Children

↑

Intrinsic Drive to Excel in Sports
Self-Esteem and Identity Achieved Through
Successful Sport Performance
Internal Psychological Needs & Positive Belief System
Are Provided
For The Athlete

↑

Encouragement & Insight Provided By Others
Through Coaching, Nurturing and
Familial Support Systems
External Psychological Needs &
Unconditional Positive Support
Are Provided
For The Athlete

↑

Basic Training Needs & Physical Environment
Needs Are Met: Courts, Equipment &
Training Skills Are Provided
For The Athlete

↑

Basic Biological Survival Needs:
Food → *Nutrition* ← *Health*
Physical Needs Are Met
For The Athlete

Figure 7f

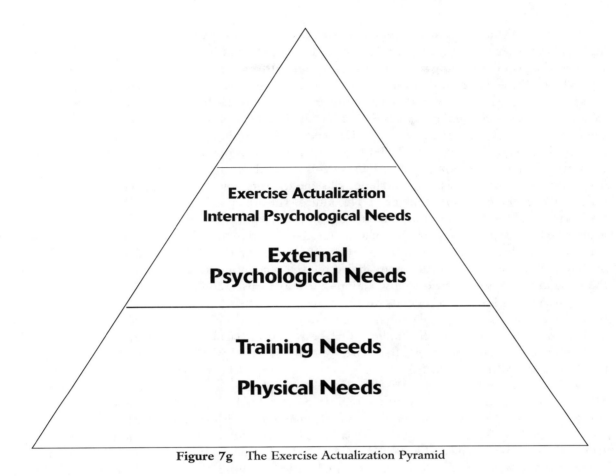

Figure 7g   The Exercise Actualization Pyramid

In the Hoffman hierarchy of athletic needs, we see a gradual progression of motivating factors that influence the progression and development of athletic sport competition. In the bottom stage, the athlete simply needs biological substances to exist and perform in his or her sport. Health, nutrition and foods are provided as the most basic substances that will ultimately provide the athlete with the ability to reach their full potential. Primarily the physical needs must first be taken care of before the athlete can move on to higher goals. Unfortunately, many talented athletes may never progress to higher goals because they cannot receive the financial support or grant that may allow them to train at the level they want to. Thus, they must first take care of primary and biological factors (such as basic food, housing, etc.) and may not be provided with resources to progresses to higher goals and challenges. The second stage of the hierarchy of athletic needs addresses the physical environment where the athlete may be training. Elite and top-level athletes must also be provided with the training equipment and proper environment to train in. For example, football players need specific equipment, such as pads, helmets and training equipment. While many resourceful athletes may find alternative ways to train without fancy or expensive equipment, the fact remains that those athletes who are provided with adequate tracks and weight rooms to train in clearly will have the competitive edge. While resourceful athletes may be able to train and develop sport-related skills with marginal equipment, most athletes excel in their training program with equipment and resources in addition to talent and skills that are best suited for their sport. However, just being provided with the equipment and genetics does not make the superior athlete; athletes must also have guidance, skilled coaching, and direction in using the equipment during practice training.

In the third stage of goal development, athletes are provided with critical supervision, support and guidance in terms of training and exercise. The athlete that has the supportive family, sensitive and knowledgeable coaching staff and encouragement in general clearly has the advantage in training. When athletes are provided with unconditional support and encouragement, they excel despite occasional relapses. *Athletes must know that their coaches and family support systems believe in them— only from this unconditional positive belief system can the athlete begin to believe in himself or herself.* In the fourth stage of the hierarchy of athletic needs is the turning point for the athlete—the athlete now has internalized the positive belief system that has been provided to him by his family, coaching staff and significant others. The athlete at this stage of development now develops a highly positive and realistic view of his or her athletic skills and they are now capable of persisting and achieving their goals despite occasional and inevitable slumps. The athlete competes and participates in sports for intrinsic value of the sport and understands his ability and potential in achieving sport-related goals. The final stage of the hierarchy of athletic needs is where the athlete has achieved the full physical and psychological potential of their athletic skills and abilities. The elite athlete is not only capable of utilizing their skills to maximum ability, but they can influence their mental focus and sharpen their cognitive skills to "tune out" distractions and stay focused and "in the zone." The elite or superior athlete is not influenced by outside environmental factors (such as fans screaming or pressure from the coach) but is typically capable of staying mentally and psychologically focused on their goal and are also capable of controlling their body and physical performance to achieve superior performance. For example, how often have we seen elite basketball player Michael Jordan play in the 4th quarter with less than five seconds left in the game with the score tied, and somehow, suddenly, he can make that "3 point" shot under incredible circumstances? The key to players like Michael Jordan is that they know what circumstances make them play their best and they play their game this way—they are in control of the situation and play with supreme confidence.

A second key characteristic of the elite athlete involves the psychological nature and humanistic attitude of their personality. The superior athlete did not achieve his or her goals overnight; in order to reach and develop their skills to be at the highest level requires an extraordinary amount of practice, dedication, *and most importantly sacrifices made by significant others in their lives.* At this highest level of goal development, the athlete realizes the importance to give back and share with the community the valuable knowledge, skills and experiences that they have obtained. We see, for example, many positive role model professional athletes donate their time and effort in creating exercise and sport facilities for underrepresented youths and children suffering from abuse and neglect. This sense of "giving back" to the community that has provided so much for the athlete becomes a very meaningful way for elite athletes to find and maintain meaning in their lives. Similar to Erikson's 7th stage of psychosocial development, the elite athlete now finds (and generates) meaning, purpose and insight in helping others based on his or her athletic skills and experiences. These very meaningful experiences that are achieved at this level of athletic goal development are in themselves inherently and intrinsically rewarding for the athlete, and transcend far beyond monetary or financial value. In this sense, the overall experiences of the elite athlete have become fully realized and even self-actualized by the altruistic and prosocial work completed within the community. In order to reach the final stage of goal development in the sport hierarchy, athletes must realize that they have become the beneficiaries of other people's efforts, time and experiences that have enabled them to reach their goals. At this level of development, true meaning and insight in each athlete's life experiences are achieved through selfless and sacrificial behaviors given to others to help them also achieve their goals in life.

We have discussed a variety of theories that describe causal factors in the development of aggression in sports, and we should identify some of the key mechanisms in which sport aggression may be reduced.

a. *Improved Communication Between Coach and Athlete.* The first method in reducing sport aggression is in allowing the athlete to understand his or her goals and make progress in the achievement of their goals. Coaches should be aware of the progress that athletes are making and let them know what they need to do to improve performance and achieve their personal goals. As we discussed earlier, in the frustration-aggression theory, when athletes have been continuously deprived of goals, they behave significantly more aggressively, either at their opponents or even their own team members;

b. *Coaches Need to Distinguish Between Absolute Goals Versus Relative Goals.* Many athletes paint a very difficult picture in terms of the criteria for individual success. For example, an athlete may convince himself or herself that they must achieve a triple-double every game to completely achieve their goals. Of course, this goal is highly unlikely to achieve, and the result may be frustration. Further, the goal is considered to be "absolute" meaning that there is only one concrete objective that will satisfy the athlete's perfectionism. On the other end of the spectrum is the term "relative goals." With relative goals, the athlete does not pick a single concrete goal, but simply chooses a more relative or general goal, such as improving overall shooting percentage, rather than saying his or her shooting percentage must be improved by 30%. The advantage of the relative goal is that it provides some flexibility for improvement without stringent criteria that may otherwise discount any improvement;

c. *Creating a Friendlier Term: "Competition":* Many athletes respond very aggressively when they hear the word "competition." A third method to reduce aggression in sports may mean changing the definition of competition to more of a contest to measure athletic skills. The coach or trainer may want to emphasize the distinctions between "competition" which means simply a contest, as opposed to the term "rivalry." When athletes experience rivalry among opposing teams, anger and aggression are common results. For example, USC and UCLA have had a long rivalry with each other, which prompts some aggressive behavior. Communicating to athletes that competition can be friendly and supportive as opposed to being contentious is a key factor here;

d. *Reward Positive & Cooperative Behaviors and Punish Aggressive Behaviors.* Our final recommendation to reduce aggression may appear to be the most obvious. Rewarding positive and cooperative sport behaviors, especially when the members are of opposing teams, is an especially ideal method to reduce aggression because you are teaching the athlete the appropriate form and style of athletic competition. Conversely, punishing inappropriate aggressive behaviors should be used as a last resort, however, punishment can also be very effective in reducing aggression on (or off) the field or court. Fines, less play time, and more "time outs" have been shown to be highly effective in reducing aggression. Ron Artest, the Indiana Pacers basketball player who was involved in one of the worst NBA brawls was fined over 25 thousand dollars and has been suspended for the remainder of the season.

Aggression and values in modern sport have become very important issues in the world of sports today. A very relevant topic that addresses values that are seen in sports today is moral development in sports. The next chapter will focus on teaching the young athlete the importance of values, moral development through sport, and ethics through athletic participation in competitive sport.

■ CHAPTER 7 QUESTION & REVIEW

1. Define the term "aggression" and describe Freud's psychoanalytic view of aggression;
2. Describe how the Evolutionary Theory explains aggression in sport activity;
3. Describe Freud's Topographic Theory of Personality and how this theory may explain the athlete's personality and styles of behavior in competition;
4. Describe the frustration-aggression theory of behavior and why athlete's respond aggressively when goals are not obtained;
5. Describe the realistic conflict theory and how this relates to sports;
6. Describe three methods in addressing and reducing sport aggression.

Chapter 8:
Moral Development and Aggression: Kohlberg's Theory of Moral Development— What Exactly Are We Teaching Our Children Today?

Sport psychology has become a new discipline in psychology that helps individuals achieve their personal and professional goals in improved athletic performance and exercise. Whether the person is interested in simply "losing a few pounds and firming up my waist" or an elite athlete who wants to achieve a personal record, preparation and attitude means everything in order to achieve success. Part of developing a winning or successful attitude is in how we relate to others, how we communicate with our team mates and coaches, and finally how psychologically focused and stable we are. This next section addressing sport activity will focus on a term that you may not necessarily associate with sport activity—moral development.

■ THE INDIANA PACERS AND DETROIT PISTONS: THE WORST NBA BRAWL?

Consider the following scenario: You are playing in the NBA and are considered to be among one of the most elite and professional sport organizations in the world. Two elite and professional teams have been playing without incident (Detroit Pistons and the Indiana Pacers). The date is Friday (11/19/04) and there are only 45.9 seconds left in the game, and the score is 97–82 where the Pacers are leading. Suddenly one of the fans throws a cup of soda at you as you foul one of your opponents during play and a fight breaks out—fans begin running out on to the floor, and mayhem develops. One player jumps up (Ron Artest) into the stands and starts punching fans, and Piston coach Larry Brown comments: "It's the ugliest thing I've ever seen as a coach or a player." After two full minutes of total chaos, police and referees had the situation finally under control. The question for us to ponder as psychology students or individuals interested in improving sport behavior and psychological balance—what causes us to "lose it" when we are being paid very well to act and present ourselves as professionals? More importantly, what can we do as parents and coaches of young athletes to teach ethics and values to athletes so that fair, ethical and healthy styles of play are the norm? Artest (who turns 25 on November 13) has had previous aggressive encounters in the NBA, where he was suspended twice by the NBA during the 2003 season when he elbowed Portland guard Derek Anderson and in a second incident last season left the bench during a brawl between the Pacers and the Boston Celtics. Not including the incident most recently on 11/19/04, Artest has been suspended by the NBA a total of eight times for aggressive or unethical forms of play. In fairness to the player Artest, in several of these incidences he was responding to assist other players who were involved in brawls, and there have been several other players who have been suspended for aggressive play. However, it should be also noted that in this most recent incident the NBA has taken the strictest and most punitive measures in its history and nine players in total were suspended for more than 140 games. Indiana Pacers player Ron Artest himself will lose over 5.3 million dollars because of his aggression not only towards opponent players but also for actually going into the seats and attacking fans. He will remain suspended for the remainder of the season. One must wonder what it takes in the NBA for a player to be fired?

■ TEACHING MORALITY & GOOD SPORTSMANSHIP

As a psychology teacher for several years, I have heard several theories regarding the etiology of a wide range of behaviors—some say we inherit behavior, some say that we learn behavior, and other say that there seems to be a complex interaction between the two fundamental paradigms. I tend to agree—different or changing environments may trigger different behaviors that are based on biological predispositions. The important point that I wish to illustrate is that key and vital behaviors that led to our evolutionary development were based on concepts such as cooperative behaviors, effective communication, prosocial behaviors and moral interaction. We need to teach children and athletes who are involved in sport that morality and good sportsmanship are vital in successful athletic interaction. Without some form of moral regard for our opponent, behavior deteriorates and may even become unethical. As parents, we need to teach our children to respect other children and their style of play, not to ridicule others, and to emphasize the value and skills that all people have to offer in exercise, regardless of their ability or level. We also need to teach children to share their skills with others and to learn to listen to other children to learn and become a more adaptive and proficient athlete. These skills are taught to children and people, and they are not somehow "biologically transmitted" by reproduction. When we teach our children to play unethically and without values, then we begin to see how individualistic cultures (such as ours) begins to flourish with a "win at all cost" mentality. Mutual respect, learning and good sportsmanlike conduct decline and a highly unethical and even aggressive style of play usually results that may result in the brawl that took place in the Auburn Hills, Michigan NBA game. The fact that our culture is devaluing the emphasis of teamwork and a collective philosophy is becoming clear in light of several aggressive outbursts in recent sports: On September 13, 2004, Texas Rangers pitcher threw a chair at a spectator and broke her nose; L.A. Dodger Milton Bradley took off his shirt and challenged fans during a play off series game. However, in fairness to the athletes, the fans are clearly agitating these behaviors: On April 19, 2993, an Oakland Athletics fan threw a cell phone at Texas outfielder Carl Everett and again in April of the same year a man attacked an umpire during a game between the White Sox and the Kansas City Royals. Spectators as well as the athletes of the teams they represent are becoming more explosive and violent. In a December 11, 2004 article from the *Daily News,* writer Richard Cohen argues that the aggressive behavior and response from NBA Pacers player Artest should be understandable given the fact that "he is a rough kid from a rough part of the world with what are known as *anger management* issues" (emphasis mine). So, if we are to understand sports writer Cohen's point, because someone happens to come from a "rough environment" it is now understandable that they attack fans? Cohen titles his piece: "What Is It With Fans? Artest? Understandable, But Why Attack a Pro Athlete?" as if to somehow blame the fan for the outburst. The point of his article is to understand what would prompt a fan to attack a 7 foot athlete "bulked up to the strength of an ox" and that "this form of 'stupidity' rarely found in nature that contradicts Darwin's theory." What the writer fails to address in his piece is the overall moral decline that is evident in society and is perpetuated by media that glorifies (and in this cases seemingly justifies) gratuitous violence. When children are exposed to what they perceive as positive sports role models, and these role models "lose it" and go after fans, children interpret this behavior as justifiable and are thus more likely to emulate this behavior. Children sometimes grow up to be athletes, and children grow up to be fans (Bandura, A, Ross, D. & Ross, S., 1963). This is not rocket science—when we portray negative and aggressive role models (regardless of what environment they come from) as ideal and positive figures we should not be surprised what happens on a basketball court or the fan section. What the media, newspapers and television need to be asking are themselves a few tough questions, such as why so much air time and newspaper space is given to these negative role models. Here are a few other suggestions for the media that portray the aggression in sports and appear to present themselves as not contributing to it:

Tips for the Media in Reducing Sport Aggression

a.   Do not repeatedly play over and over the same sequence of aggression in sports—this repeated exposure becomes misunderstood by children as perhaps part of the legitimate part of the sport and thus more likely to be imitated;

b.   Do not sensationalize the specific acts of aggression in the sport activity. Do not speculate what could have prompted the action and more importantly do not attempt to justify the aggression (as we described in the previous Daily News article);

c.   On the contrary, what networks, sport writers and the media in general should be doing is to focus and elaborate on more cooperative and prosocial styles of athletic competition; a runner, for example stopping and helping an injured athlete or an opposing team member stopping and congratulating other players;

d.   Minimize the "trash talking" that players often engage in and do not justify as simply being "cross town rivalries"—numerous clashes and fights have been started simply by players engaging in this seemingly harmless "trash talk";

e.   Do not inflame the rivalries of professional teams or collegiate teams. A good example would be the media showing a burning effigy of a school mascot just one day before the game; and finally

f.   Offer more exposure to athletes engaging in prosocial and altruistic behaviors in helping other players and helping the community. Emphasize the consequences of fans losing control and focus more on the game and competition itself.

While there are numerous explanations regarding the topic of sport aggression this chapter will now focus on teaching *moral values* to children as they both watch and participate in sports.

This section of the chapter will now focus on techniques and skills that are highly effective in teaching moral value to children (and the adult athlete) during sport activity. The moral philosophy is borrowed from the model of the famous moral psychologist, Lawrence Kohlberg (1969) and is translated into a sport psychology frame where we may teach children how to incorporate moral value into sport activity. Many of the students that I teach at the university or college level describe how children's behavior today "isn't what it used to be . . . children today do not respect their parents, their elders, or even themselves for that matter." In this section we shall discuss the role of ethics, values and morality in a hypothetical sport activity, and that parents and coaches can in fact teach ethical styles of play. We will first describe the classical views of moral development among children and then discuss techniques how parents and coaches can teach children to play more prosocially and with good sportsmanlike conduct.

■ KOHLBERG'S THEORY: PREMORAL, CONVENTIONAL AND PRINCIPLED LEVELS OF MORALITY

a. *Premoral Morality.* In the premoral stage of morality, the individual's behavior is characterized by egoistic and selfish behaviors. Typically, the child or young athlete engages in styles of play directed towards winning with little regard to the style of play. The "ends justifies the means" and as long as winning is the end result, how one wins really becomes irrelevant. The athlete plays out of greed and egoism with little regard for team mates and other players. We would expect, for example, a three year old or four year old to behave somewhat selfishly and have problems with sharing toys and belongings with other people. Furthermore, the young child is highly egocentric by evolutionary design, and not as a form of a personality flaw that we may see in adults. Children need to behave in a somewhat egocentric manner as this improved their chances of survival as we were evolving as a species. Furthermore, infants have little in the way of communication skills, so crying was their only mechanism of displaying some form of a problem, such as not feeling well (fever) or hunger. However, we do see cases of premoral behavior in adults.

A good example of athletic competition at the premoral level would be any athlete who intentionally sabotages the performance of another athlete (or worse yet intentionally injures another athlete) so that they can finish in first place and receive fame, attention, media press and of course, money. In a very tragic example of how real this form of premoral behavior may become, during the figure ice-skating championships the case of Tanya Harding and Nancy Kerrigan comes to mind. Nancy Kerrigan was the reigning champion in women's figure skating and was brutally attacked where an unknown attacker beat her with a club on her ankles and legs. This was done presumably to injure her so that she could not compete in the finals and win the gold medal. After much media hype and controversy, it was determined that a plan was hatched involving Tanya Harding and others to intentionally injure Nancy Kerrigan to prevent her from competing and winning the first place championship. This form of collusion typically represents the most unethical and reprehensible form of behavior in an attempt to advance one's position in the athletic world at the cost (and intentionally-inflicted injury) of another more talented player. This is the reason why Kohlberg does not typically associated ages with levels of moral development, as in some cases even adults behave in a highly egocentric and self-centered manner, where the "ends justifies the means." Tragically, we are seeing more and more of a self-entitlement style of behavior and attitude among powerful or corporate executives who feel privileged to take financial advantage of subordinate workers to the point of bankruptcy. Numerous high ranking ex-officials have recently become indicted due to ultimately what appears to be simple greed. Whether the behavior is from a two year old who is crying because he cannot play with another child's toys, or an adult who takes financial advantage of another person for their own benefit at the cost of someone else, their level of moral reasoning is considered to be premoral.

b. *Conventional Morality.* In the conventional level of morality, children base their behavior or style of play based on rules and regulations provided by teachers, parents, officials and coaches. The child's quality of play in terms of morality is based on his or her adherence to rules and regulations. Note that the sports that allow aggressive styles of contact and aggression in general will encourage children to play more aggressively, and the child The key point to note is that the child (and adult) are interpreting the rules literally and do not allow any interpretation. The more the individual follows the rules, the better player or individual person they become. The rules and only the rules according to the child should determine the outcome of the game or competition. All rules, laws and conventional mores are to be followed without deviation. The individual who lives his or her life at this level of moral reasoning, according to Kohlberg, must obey and follow laws and rules or anarchy may result. Individuals have internalized the rules of society or competition and therefore feel that any deviation is unacceptable. Changing rules is the equivalent of an immoral or unethical act, *regardless of the circumstances*. We cannot simply "pick and choose" our laws that we happen to agree with or select those laws that happen to be convenient for us to follow at the time.

The moral level of development at the conventional stage argues that the essence of a democracy is based on the principle of the "majority rules" concept: The majority of a voting party may determine the rules and laws of any given society. However, as we unfortunately know from past experiences, even the vast majority of individuals may be inherently or morally wrong in their majority decision. Sometimes, we get caught up in the "mob mentality" where we agree with the crowd and thus lose our own individuality in determining the differences between "right and wrong." Nazi Germany under the rule of Hitler during the 1939–1945 era exemplifies this form of mass hysteria where dominant groups of individuals may endorse an inherently unjust and morally reprehensible principle or action. In terms of athletic competition, an athlete may be allowed to participate in a given sport even though he feels that his opponent may be incapacitated to continue, such as through injury or fatigue or exhaustion. The moral dilemma facing the athlete is whether to continue and win the competition, or to stop and provide assistance to the injured athlete.

Postconventional Morality: In the postconventional level of moral development, the individual's behavior is based on his or her own moral ethics and values. As individuals move beyond the conventional level of moral development, they begin to see the "bigger picture" and realize that there is more to life than simply following rules and laws. Furthermore, the individual's behaviors are based on social values and improving the overall community that individuals reside in. It is here at this stage where individuals volunteer behavior their behavior to help others and actually find meaning and value in their actions to improve the community and in general their commitment to the human condition. A very good example of an individual who has achieved the highest level of moral development at the postconventional level of moral reasoning is Mother Theresa, Martin Luther King, and Cesar Chavez. These individuals have committed their lives to improve society by improving the overall quality of living for all persons and changing unjust laws to achieve their goals. Furthermore, these individuals have sacrificed their freedom and in some cases their lives to achieve their goals of improving the lives of others. Kohlberg noted that not (in fact the vast majority of people) never reach this highest level of moral reasoning. We will now discuss how Kohlberg's theory of moral reasoning may be used in understanding how athletes participate and interact within the world of sport and competition.

In the following scenario, we will now discuss how the role of ethics and moral development may be translated into the world of sport and moral behavior. Increasingly we are beginning to see the damaging and destructive impact of egoistic styles of play in athletic competition. Athletes who are entirely motivated by extrinsic factors, such as money and fame may resort to more aggressive and unethical styles of play. We are already beginning to see professional sports changing into a more aggressive and egoistic business where athletes appear to be motivated by extrinsic value that operates in the individualistic culture. We will now describe a hypothetical scenario of two high school football players each competing to be the first string quarterback. In this vignette, there are three choices that one of the characters must make. After reading the Moral Football Dilemma, review how the three levels of moral development (preconventional, conventional and postconventional) are relative to the athlete in sport moral development (enlightened athlete, "play by the rules athlete" and the egoistic athlete).

A Moral Dilemma: Playing Football

Kevin is a 14 year-old football player in high school who has aspirations to play in college. He is currently competing with a good friend of his, Michael (also 14 years old) and both are trying out for the quarterback (QB) position for the school football team. There can only be one first-string position and both Michael and Kevin want this position very much—in fact, they have already begun telling their friends that they are "confident" that the coach will assign them the first-string position. However, after several weeks of intense training and practicing and careful discussion with the other assistant coaches, the head coach gives the first-string position to Michael. Kevin is very upset upon learning that he was not selected as first-string QB, and becomes very jealous of Michael as he begins they continue training for the season. However, midway through the practice season, Michael begins to confuse the plays and scrimmages, causing procedural errors for the team. Michael also begins to confuse the calls and the entire team now is confused and practice becomes disorganized. The coach announces that the first game begins in one month, and if Michael does not learn the play sequences, he will be dropped from first string QB to second string QB, thus making Kevin the new first string QB. Kevin is the only one that can help Michael learn the plays for the game. Michael approaches Kevin one afternoon after practice and asks for his help. Now, for the moment, assume that you are Kevin. You realize that you have three choices, and you must make one choice. Each choice has consequences that are discussed below:

a. *The Enlightened Athlete.* You help Michael review the plays and he will definitely maintain his position as the first string QB, leaving you still at the second string QB position. You realize that you are helping someone who needs your help, and furthermore that you are helping the entire team. This collectivistic and sacrificial form of assistance occurs at a cost to you, but you realize that the entire team benefits from your sacrifice. This choice is typically representative of Kohlberg's third stage of moral reasoning (postconventional), where our choices and behaviors come at a great personal and professional cost to enhance and improve the lives of other people. Perhaps one importance consequence that Kevin may receive in making this altruistic choice is the personal feeling of knowing that he has done something very noble and admirable for other people, and the personal satisfaction in itself is very rewarding (not to mention the attention that he receives from his team mates and coaches feels great too!). The help that you have provided for Michael is authentic and genuine:

The Enlightened Athlete:

Legitimate Help   >   Positive Consequences for the Football Team; (Collective Philosophy) Where Individual Identification is Achieved Through Team Identification & Individual Sacrifices

b. *"Playing By The Rules" Athlete.* You refuse to offer assistance to Michael simply because there is no mandate requiring you to do so. You make no decisions or choices and simply decide to "let fate take its course." You feel you're your behavior is justified because there is no rule or regulation that requires you to intervene and help Michael, and you want to play first string QB. By following the rules exactly, you feel that there is nothing forcing you to intervene and help Michael. There is a cost, however. If Michael does learn the plays without your assistance, your relationship with him will be strained, and at some point in the future you may need his help. The second choice of "Playing By The Rules" philosophy is similar to Kohlberg's Conventional level of moral development, as the individual determines what is morally right or wrong by what the law either allows or disallows. If something is legal, then it is morally acceptable; however, if a particular type or form of behavior is illegal, then the action itself is wrong, regardless of the ramifications or circumstances of the act. In Kevin's example, because there was no rule or regulation requiring him to intervene and assist Michael, he refused.

Playing By The Rules Athlete:

No Help Provided   >   **You neither help Michael to learn the plays, nor do you prevent him from learning the play strategies. You simply wait and see how he learns the play strategies by himself. In this second form of athletic moral development, Kevin simply conforms to the rules by arguing no rule exists that requires him to become involved and help Michael. He avoids the responsibility and the personal consequence of making a difficult decision by not making the decision to intervene and help Michael. In this situation, the team does not benefit from Kevin's lack of intervention and may or may not be harmed by his not helping Michael.**

c. *The Egoistic Athlete—"Dog Eat Dog" Mentality in Playing Sports.* In this third and final choice, you say that you will help Michael, but in reality you intentionally provide him with the wrong plays which ultimately will disqualify him as first string QB. You know that if you do this, you will be placed automatically as first string QB. The benefits and advantages that you achieve by becoming first string QB come at a cost to the team. The consequences of your actions determine whether or not the activity is good or bad; in other words, the ends justifies the means.

The Egoistic Athlete

Intentional Sabotage   >   **In this third choice, Kevin intentionally provides bad or incorrect information to Michael, knowing that he will benefit from this. This activity has direct positive consequences for you (individualistic philosophy) but comes at a cost to the team. You benefit directly but at the cost of several other people who comprise the team. We can see this style or form of individualistic philosophy when athletes play for themselves rather than play with a collectivistic or team philosophy. The athlete who competes at this level plays for a "win at all cost for me" mentality and may often engage in reckless activities often at the cost of the welfare of other people and team mates. Examples of the egoistic style of athletic competition would include players who do not conform to team regulations and cause disruption to the morale of the team, players who do not play to their full potential as a means of showing their dissatisfaction with management or salary disputes, or even individual team players intentionally playing at an inferior level for monetary gain (i.e., the Chicago Black Sox scandal).**

■ TEACHING MORAL VALUES & ETHICAL STANDARDS OF RECREATION TO CHILDREN: HAVE FUN AND RESPECT OTHERS

After describing the various levels of moral development in sport activity, we must ask ourselves what are some of the things that we can do as parents, teachers and educators to improve moral and prosocial behaviors among children during sport activity and behavior in general. The first point to remember is that children often learn by observing and watching. What we do and how we behave as adults has strong ramifications in terms of what children and adolescents do in their recreational styles of play. Children watch what you do (regardless of the activity) and imitate your behavior. This tendency to emulate positive role models increases significantly when the model is a popular athlete or famous movie star. A major theme of the previous chapter addressing aggression in modern sport activity was primarily two-fold: Poor role models that display negative types of behavior and aggression as well as parents lacking the knowledge and information in teaching their children the importance of moral behaviors. Parents who fail to teach their children ethical styles of interaction in sports and recreational activities can produce children who lack ethical values in sport and even become a hazard to other players. The term morality itself refers to a system of values and ethics that we apply to our behavior in determining the differences between what we perceive as "right" or "wrong". As we previously discussed in Kohlberg's level of moral development and the dilemma described in the Hoffman football dilemma, children progress through several stages of moral development and reasoning as they interact and play with other people. How children process and reason through moral dilemmas and justify their behaviors is the key to understanding ethical and moral behavior or egoistic behavior. Parents, coaches and educators are encouraged to incorporate the "Fantastic Five" following recommendations that should serve as a model and moral guide in teaching children the values of sport and recreation: **Enjoy what you do!; Create a Routine & Stick To It!; Teaching Persistence; Share Your Skills & Develop a Teamwork Philosophy; and Goals For The Future: Creating Your Own Identity.**

The "Fantastic Five" Values to Sport and Recreation

a. **Enjoy What You Do!** Teach and encourage your children to play for fun. Often children see their parents and coaches place tremendous emphasis on winning and seem to neglect the real purpose of sport and exercise: Having fun and improving health while exercising. Whether your child is playing softball with other students at school or playing in NCAA football championships, people who participate in sport and exercise should enjoy what they are doing. The key is to experience intrinsic motivation, where the activity itself provides the reward and enjoyment for the athlete. As we have discussed in previous chapters, when athletes change their style of play from intrinsic value to extrinsic value (i.e., money, attention or fame) the overall ethical quality of play begins to deteriorate. De-emphasize points, scoring and winning in the initial phase of the sport activity and teach children to first learn and comprehend the purpose and technique of the sport. For example, when teaching children how to play basketball or baseball, have them first learn the mechanics of dribbling or throwing the baseball—encourage them to first appreciate and value the experience of being outdoors, playing with others, and to value the experiences of learning to cooperate with other players;

b. **Practice the Experience of the Sport.** While it is very important to teach children to appreciate the value of the sport or exercise experience by having fun and playing with team mates, it is also important to communicate to children the importance and value of practice in learning the skills that are associated with the sport. Continue teaching the skills despite inevitable failures. Children learn by watching what you do—everything from what the sport or exercise activity is as well as how often the activity is done. If you as a parent incorporate some healthy activity with your children, such as walking in the morning at the park, bicycling every Sunday morning, or rowing with your child in the morning, your children will be significantly more likely to continue the activity and remain healthy. Perhaps more importantly, is the fact that you as a parent need to help your child to understand and appreciate that the concept of exercising is a lifelong commitment and to enjoy the process of the activity itself. Many times as adults we have forgotten the benefit and the enjoyment of exercise activity, and if children participate with you on a regular basis they will remember the benefits and importance of exercise. Remember—exercise is an end to itself where the participation and activity is the reward for a happier and more fulfilled life experience.

c. **Teaching Persistence: Do Not Give Up!** Often children will want to stop training or practicing upon failure. It becomes vital for the welfare of the child not to give up and to keep trying so he or she may value the experience of persistence and learn that they can achieve their goals. Similar to Vygotsky's Zone of Proximal Development, the coach or parent must be aware exactly of what the child's ability is and provide the tools (and words of encouragement) for them to continue working and practicing until they have mastered the particular skill necessary in the activity. For example, a child may not be able to actually hit a softball with her bat. She comments to you: "I'm tired . . . I want to stop and I don't like doing this anymore." Obviously, the child is becoming frustrated and losing patience. Do you allow her to stop—or do you help her continue? Past research suggests that support and encouragement that is provided for the child, together with showing her what to do will help her achieve her goals. Furthermore, if you as a parent or coach add an incentive (i.e., "If you do this one time, we can stop for awhile and have a snack . . . Now slow your swing down and keep your eye on the ball.") this may motivate the child to continue. The most important point here is that the child has realized that she can achieve her goals by hitting the ball with the bat and that she accomplished this by herself.

d. **Sharing Your Skills.** Remember the section where we discussed the importance of teaching collective philosophies to children while playing sports. If we recall in the previous chapter (chapter 4) we reviewed how Erik Erikson described how various forms of social crises formed to create character and development throughout the lifespan. Of critical importance in terms of "sharing your skills" is Erik Erikson's stage 7: Generativity versus Stagnation. In this stage, Erikson argues that in order for middle aged adults (typically parents of children or individuals who are involved in their careers) to find significant meaning in their lives we need to contribute and give back to our community and society, such as through volunteer work with children or helping the sick in community hospitals. All too often at this stage in our lives it is very easy to lose sight of significant meaning in our lives in how we relate and interact with others in our community. Typically adults may experience the "mid-life crisis" where we realize that our lives lack meaning and depth. Rather than becoming lost in a society of "conspicuous consumption" where people buy things to replace intimacy in their relationships, an effect method of providing meaning in our lives is through establishing relationships through sport activity and exercise. When we share our skills with other people, we are re-connecting lost relationships with other people and providing them with the most valuable gift we have: our time. Our skills may include teaching children how to play organized sports, volunteer coaching, and providing seniors with information on health and active lifestyles. Remember—when we share with others our skills that we have, we provide an important element of meaning to our lives that develops the "inter-relatedness" that our society is lacking in.

e. **Goals For Tomorrow: Creating Your Own Identity.** Teaching children the value of learning the skills that they have acquired today, and to rehearse what they want to achieve and accomplish for tomorrow. When we teach children the values that are associated with team sports and activities, we are providing them with the tools to interact, communicate and form relationships with others. We have discussed the serious problems in modern sport that are associated with the individualistic culture—the NBA brawls, the problems with communication and building trust. When we work with children in team sports, we teach them the values of teamwork, commitment and trust. These vital skills and characteristics that should be learned in early childhood will continue with them as they develop and mature in their personal and professional lives. The two most important individuals who can help teach children these values that are incorporated into an exercise program are the child's primary caregivers or parents. How we as parents communicate and relate to our children often can influence how children relate to each other in sports and exercise. If, for example, a parent is very demanding with children without offering explanations or reasoning, they are described as the authoritarian parent. Conversely, if the parent explains the value and fun that the exercise program offers, children will be much more likely to participate and maintain an active role in their program. Below are listed three common parenting and coaching styles that have profound influences in terms of how children relate and communicate with each other in sport or exercise:

Styles of Parenting

a. *Authoritative Parent:* Parent who explains rules and regulations to the child; An ideal form of parenting that produces a positive relationship with child. The parent rules with strict enforcement, but is also highly compassionate and loving with the child;

b. *Authoritarian Parent:* Parent who orders child to obey with little explanation why the child must obey—cold and distant form of parenting with few displays or signs of compassion and love for child ("children should be seen and not heard");

c. *Permissive Parent:* Parent who fails to provide boundaries or rules for child; Often acts very irresponsible where children complain that they are the one's who serve as the parent; Parent befriends several of the child's friends and tries to "fit in" with the child's peers—very destructive form of parenting.

Styles of Coaching

a. *The Compassionate Coach*—descriptive and communicative coach; Fosters a positive relationship with his or her athletes and earns the respects of his or her players;

b. *The "Enforcer" Coach*—A para-military form of coaching that demands adherence to rules with no explanation to athletes. Coach orders athletes to conform to regulations with little explanations or detail into game playing strategies and practice rules; offers little compassion to athletes and creates a very cold environment;

c. *Flexible Coaching / No Rules Enforced.* This form of coaching lacks structure and boundaries, providing athletes with little direction and insight into their practice routines. Coaches want to be "pals" or friends with their athletes and lack the self-confidence or integrity to enforce rules fairly for all players. Coaches may often confuse the boundaries with players and may often lack control of the behaviors of the athletes on the team. This form of coaching usually does not produce respect among the players, and players tend to lack the self-discipline necessary to complete the season.

■ THE IMPORTANCE OF PLAY IN SPORTS

We do not often describe adult activities with the term "play" but actually exercise is a form of recreation that may described as play. As adults, we are so busy working under stressful environments that we have literally forgotten what it means to relax and play. Often in our busy society we have deadlines and live very hectic schedules. Even when most adults take time out to engage in exercise programs, they do so out of obligation and dread the experience. This negative philosophy is counterproductive because we seldom continue in activities that are not intuitively rewarding for us. The goal of this next section is to discuss the importance of play in sport activity and to re-establish the important of having fun through play and exercise. Children need to stay focused on their goals and to participate in a routine involving exercise activities that are fun and exciting. When children learn that their concept of play may be incorporated into their exercise activity, they are significantly more likely to participate and continue in the activity. When children are asked the reasons why they may participate in a particular sport, such as kickball or baseball, they may typically offer the obvious reply: "Because I like it" or "Because I am good at it." The evolution of sports has provided children with many opportunities to interact with others and to learn to cooperate and follow structured activities with rules. A prerequisite to following rules and participating in structured sport activities is the evolution of the concept "play." Play activities involve imagination and creativity, and exercise activities should also incorporate these skills involved with play.

Living in a highly individualistically-oriented society such as ours, it seems more important than ever to teach children the importance of trusting others, communication with team mates, and valuing interdependency. The term play itself may be defined as any activity designed for children to socialize and interact with each other involving motor skills and imagination. Children have historically engaged in styles of play that reflect a transformation from egocentrism ("my world is paramount and more important than any one else") to a recognition of the needs of others ("let's share this toy"). Several styles of play exist that may be incorporated into an exercise activity for young children:

Styles of Play Relative To Sports

a. **Isolated Play: 2–3 years.** Isolated play may involve throwing a ball or rolling a ball to a specific target. Young children remain isolated and detached while playing by themselves. Often children at this age incorporate imaginary friends to play with them, or they may imagine that their toy doll may actually come to life and engage in a variety of activities. Piaget referred to this concept as "animism" and predicted that many children cross-culturally engage in various forms of isolated play. An additional characteristic of isolated play is what Piaget refers to as the "collective monologues" where children engage in conversations with themselves while playing with their toys. They talk, simulate a variety of activity, and are very content while playing by themselves;

b. **Watching Others Play: 3–4 years.** Watching others play is a stage where children still play by themselves, but now they are aware that others are playing in their near proximity; they appear to watch other children play with great interest, but typically do not interact with the other children. They are no longer oblivious to the existence of other children who may happen to be playing in the near proximity. Children continue to play in the own world and operate under their own rules, but now are cognizant of the existence of other children playing similar games;

c. **Side-by-Side Play: 4–5 years.** Groups of children at this age may typically be seen playing next to each other (side-by-side) with no interaction or communication with each other. Now they are in closer proximity while playing and interacting but still do not incorporate each other and involve each other while playing their game; Children see other children playing next to them and are influenced in their own style of play but do not exchange ideas or typically converse with the other children;

d. **The "buddy system": 5–7 years.** In the buddy system, children are now playing together, but no rules are attributed to the games that the children happen to be playing in. No goals or restrictions exist, and the children appear to be orienting themselves to each other as well as the games that are being played;

e. **Interdependency Play:** 7–14 years. In the interdependency stage of play, the child now engages in interactive and communicative styles of play that incorporate rules and strategies. This is a critical stage for children to be exposed to as they now are beginning to understand that different children have different ideas and strategies to complete games and projects, and that sometimes it is a good thing to depend and rely on one another to get what you want. It is here where children learn to incorporate the principles of the collectivistic style of inter-action that is necessary with team sports. Interdependency, communication, and shared responsibility are the key components and characteristics that are learned at this final stage. Children not exposed to this style of play will have difficulty in sharing and participating in group activities typically seen among team sports.

In conclusion, sports and athletic activities remain very psychologically and physically healthy activities in which children may participate in. Children will have numerous positive experiences (and occasionally some negative experiences) that include development of creativity when playing with others, companionship when playing on a team and learning how to play specific sports, and the development of close friendships as children begin learning new activities.

■■■ CHAPTER 8 QUESTION & REVIEW

1. Explain why morality is important in sports and how sportsmanship and morality may be taught to younger athletes;

2. How does the media influence aggression in sports today? What are some suggestions that may help reduce the negative effects of media and aggression in sports?

3. Identify and describe Kohlberg's three levels of moral development and how moral development may evolve in sports;

4. Identify and describe the "Fantastic 5" values to sport and physical activity;

5. Identify the styles of play and how parents may encourage children to continue playing.

Chapter 9:
Revolutionary Concepts in Women's Sports: Breaking Down Barriers & Achieving Goals

Courtesy of Corbis Images

When asked about his success in coaching the United States National Soccer Team in 1999, coach Tony DiCiccio commented that his athletes had worked together, communicated with each other and excelled as a unifying force. His primary example of a woman athlete who combined physical agility with speed, grace and psychological confidence was Mia Hamm. Hamm commented that coach DiCicccio's strategy with the women athlete's was dynamic and motivating: "Train us like men, but treat us like women." This text has described several theories regarding psychological factors that influence athletic performance and exercise. We have reviewed several theories that have explored the history and development of psychology and how sport psychology has evolved in our society. We have discussed the various theories regarding how athletes learn specific forms of exercise skills, how children learn to adapt to the world of sports, and how diet and nutritional issues can impact sport performance. We have also described how sport psychology has evolved into the discipline that it is today, where the concept of sports has defined how groups of individuals have related and interacted with one another. What we will now discuss is how a particular population or group of athletes (such as female athletes) has overcome tremendous barriers and discrimination in achieving their place in the world of sport.

Today, more than ever, the culture is changing where women are reaching new heights and levels in every professional level. The environment today welcomes women athletes to compete as never before, and encourages them to reach individual goals. On Tuesday, December 7, 2004, the 18th annual Conference on Women and Families held in Long Beach, California celebrated woman as "architects of change" (Long Beach Press Telegram, December 8, 2004). The conference was sponsored by Oprah Winfrey and Maria Shriver and emphasized women as components of change and leaders of the community for the 21st century. Clearly, women today as never before have been afforded opportunities for advancement and growth. Although the "glass ceiling" still exists in the corporate world and other environments, women sports has become the most progressive vehicle of change as women literally breaking world records as never before. In this chapter we will also discuss a true story how a young woman (Lisa) overcomes personal problems that have been associated with her weight and how she achieves a healthy balance between her academic and schoolwork with exercise and training.

Additionally, this chapter will explore how women's sports have experienced three phases of evolution and development: The first phase includes overt discrimination and separation from participating in women's sport. During this era, issues were focused more on justifying women's participation in sports in the pre-18th century era. The second phase of development addresses how the female athlete was faced with creating a new identity in participating in sports and athletic competition during the early 19th and 20th century, where those women who participated in sports had to compete under the title of men's sports and were not afforded their own division and identity to compete with one another. Finally, the third stage of female sport development will address how women in the 21st century have achieved success in creating their own division and dimension in sport and athletic competition, and where the area of women's sports is headed for the future. Interesting issues we will focus on will be developing the "new image" of the modern woman in sports, the continued battle of fighting sexism in sports, and finally we will briefly review the issue of "performance enhancing drugs" and how they specifically address women's sports (more will be discussed with drug use in sports in chapter 10). We will also discuss the challenges and future goals for women in sports within the 21st century.

■ EARLY HISTORY OF WOMEN'S SPORTS

The first stage of sport evolution for women occurred several centuries ago (4000 B.C.) where women engaged in a variety of activities and were considered to be relatively equal with men. Some examples included archery, ice skating and an improvised form of tennis. During the very early time periods between 4000 B.C. and 500 B.C. women actually were able (to a limited degree) to participate with men in some sports and were encouraged to focus on their physical health. In ancient civilizations (exceeding 4000 years ago) women were allowed to participate with men in a variety of different forms of sports during athletic competition, and there were not nearly as many barriers and discrimination against women that we see today. The barriers to women's sports and the discrimination in sport with women became more pronounced during the medieval periods where the church viewed pleasurable activity (such as exercise) as indulgent and sinful. Women became the first to be ostracized and limited in terms of what sport activity they could actually participate in.

Where the Ancient Greeks worshipped Goddesses, the males of Ancient Greek also encouraged women to maintain their health and physical beauty so they to could be glorified. This philosophy of "sound mind—sound body" was especially emphasized to women who were fertile and of childbearing ages. These women were encouraged to stay healthy and fit to produce offspring that were also healthy and fit. Social class and economic standing also influenced how women participated in sports and athletics. Women of nobility and high economic standing often played light athletic activities, such as badminton, tennis and archery to fulfill their free time and also to serve as a social activity as well. However, women not as fortunate as the high SES women of nobility were forced to limit their physical activities to work and domestic chores such as cleaning, working in agriculture and simple housekeeping duties. In some ways, this discrepancy addressing social economic class and participation in sport activity and health activities is still with us today. Women who live in higher SES communities now clearly attend affluent gyms (i.e., Bally's, or L. A. Fitness) while focusing more on eating healthier foods that are lower in fat and high in nutritional value. Women today of lower SES typically do not have access to the elite or fancy health spas, and in some cases actually lack health coverage that prevents them from learning what healthy foods they should be eating. Thus, to some degree, what was true centuries ago involving women and sports still remains true today, where economics and income define the variables that are relative to physical health.

While over 4000 years ago women were allowed to participate (and even encouraged) with males in athletic activity (especially in partnership cultures, such as the Island of Crete), as several centuries passed, the influence of the Vatican as well as repression from the Victorian era started to impinge on the freedoms of women to participate in athletic sport and competition. Women became increasingly pressured to bear children and focus on fertility while reducing physical or strenuous activities. The Victorian era emphasized profound sex differences between men and women, and the rights and freedom between men and women were very different. Men were encouraged to participate in a wide range of activities, both professional and recreational, and sports participation was expected among males. However, women were categorized as primarily domestic and were given the role of child bearers, and participation in sports was thought to somehow threaten a woman's fertility. Thus a woman's ability to engage in a wide range of sports, including track, long distance running, and all other stamina-related sports were discouraged. Conversely, those activities that were perceived to be healthful, fun and pleasurable were also discouraged as being "sinful." Ironically, over 4000 years ago the climate and atmosphere for women to participate in sports with men was much more open and positive for women than the more recent 15th, 16th, and 17th centuries. During this period of time, the major form of political power was controlled by the Vatican in Rome, and women were essentially viewed as being sinful for wanting to participate in sports or any activity that was considered recreational. A "good" and "morally upstanding" woman was encouraged not to pursue these activities. This universal view of female of repression and discrimination of women in general reduced women's participation in sports (as well as other activities) significantly.

Women were faced with changing laws and norms in a society that was essentially patriarchal and limited the development of sport activity and exercise. Women were more glorified by males and were encouraged to focus on ways or methods to improve their physical beauty and were thus not encouraged to participate in sports. This concern is still evident today, as many women may wish to participate in some form of exercise activity (such as swimming, rowing, or weight lifting) but express concerns about becoming "too bulky" or "too muscular." These concerns are exacerbated in modern society where a petite and lean look becomes emphasized by the media and fashion magazines. Consider, for example, an environment where women could not vote, drive a car or in some cases leave their homes after a certain hour. Additionally, the expectation for women was to stay at home and engage in domestic activities—during this period of time, it was assumed that if women had enough energy to want to exercise, then they weren't working hard enough in the home.

The second stage of development among women in sports occurred during the mid-1800's and grew in conjunction with the women's suffrage movement. Women were still discriminated against and now were becoming more actively involved with political rights and focusing on equality with men in a variety of activities. However, women were not challenging these discriminatory practices and were starting to fight for their rights. In the world of sports, women were actually masquerading as males just to compete in a variety of sports. Perhaps one of the most famous pioneering female athletes was Melpomene, a long distance (marathoner) runner. When the first Modern Olympiad was held in Athens in 1896, Melpomene had requested permission from Baron Pierre de Coubertin who was organizing the event. Coubertin flatly denied the request, arguing that he had wanted to model the modern Olympics with the ancient Olympics, and the ancient Olympics had only gender-segregated events. Melpomene was convinced that she could compete with the males and was determined to participate, despite Coubertin's ban on women. Melpomene ran the event despite the objections of race organizers and went on to complete the event in about 4.5 hours—this was witnessed by several cyclists who had accompanied her throughout the entire event.

Women were also becoming more aware of the unfair repression and discrimination that faced them and a growing movement developed to encourage equality in the work place as well as the world of sports. The women who were associated with the Suffrage movement had much to do because their rights were becoming increasingly limited in several dominions. Women during this period of time (Victorian era) were essentially considered as "property" as they were not even considered an individual if they were not married to a man. Additionally, women could not own property and were encouraged to "rest in bed" to protect their fertility and reproduction systems. Women who were living in North America during this period of time also had little time for recreation, as the work of the new colonies was never ending, and women typically had little energy to engage in sports at the end of their work day. Women were primarily working in agriculture, cooking, canning, washing, sewing, raising a family, and basically raised their family as the husband worked in the fields. Despite these highly restrictive periods of time, women were starting to make strides in terms of education and university learning. For example, women's colleges, such as Vassar and Wellesley College (founded 1875) provided a haven and protected environment where women were afforded the opportunity to educate themselves and to also participate in sport activity. During this era, some noteworthy women were changing outdated styles of thinking and attitudes in record form. By 1919 women were voting, and participating in a wider range of activities. Names such as Suzanne Lenglen (tennis), Babe Diedrikson (track and field) and Gertrude Ederle (long distance swimming) were making headlines (Ederle had actually broken the men and women's record by 2 hours in swimming the English Channel)! It was until some 60 years later when another outstanding female long distance swimmer by the name of Lynne Cox broke the English Channel record for the fastest time for men or women. Lynne Cox would go on to become one of the world's foremost swimmers by completing some of the most challenging swims through The Bering Strait, Cape of Good Hope, and Strait of Magellan (arguably the world's most treacherous body of water regarding natural predators and rip currents). Ms. Cox has also endured some of the coldest water any human has ever experienced, braving water as cold as 32 degrees Fahrenheit in Antarctica!* Women today are competing as they have never competed before, and in many cases actually surpassing male competitors. A good example of how female athletes appear to be narrowing the gap among the genders in sport competition is endurance training. For the first time in the Ultramarathon (100 miles of running that has a 48 hour time limit for completion) history, a woman shattered the previous record (Pam Reed) who completed the Death Valley run to the Mt. Whitney Portal in an incredible 27 hours, 56 minutes and 47 seconds.

As late as the 1940's era and the 1950's era women were discriminated against in sports and were denied equal opportunity to engage in long-distance or stamina-related sports, such as long distance running events (the marathon). While the rights and freedom of women to participate in sports has evolved considerably in the last 100 years, many leading female athletes still argue that a divide or double standard exists between men and women, where women receive smaller salaries, less media recognition and less opportunity to advance themselves professionally. The era of the 1960's brought with it many exciting changes and people were beginning to fight for equal rights and civil rights, not only for women, but for ethnic minority rights as well. The decade of the 1960's era was dynamic, as many organizations were developed for women's sports. For example, the Division of Girls and Women's Sports was created (DGWS) and women were becoming more than ever in modern sports. The Olympics were allowing women to compete in more events, and the 800 meters was reintroduced

*Personal communication with the author December 2004

to women. Women's events in swimming were expanding, gymnastics and more stamina sports were beginning to open for women. Somewhat later, in 1971, The Intercollegiate Athletics for Women was introduced (AIAW) which further expedited women's participation in sports.

■ THE REINTRODUCTION OF THE OLYMPIC GAMES IN 1896: WOMEN STILL EXCLUDED

While women were making great strides in participation in sports at women's colleges and universities, the world or global view still tended to restrict equal participation. For example, in Athens, Greece, the first modern Olympic games were introduced with great fanfare, however, the founder of the modern Olympic games, Baron Pierre de Coubertin was adamant about excluding all women from participating, justifying this discrimination by claiming that the original Olympics had also barred women from participating. However, the general view after the first modern Olympiad was that women should be allowed to participate in modern sport, and gradually during the next 15–20 years women had become increasingly more visible in Olympic competition. For example, women were able to participate in archery and gymnastics and gradually became more assimilated as time progressed.

The Industrial era saw more women becoming an essential component to unskilled textile labor, which coincidentally allowed organized sport clubs to develop. After working an eight hour shift women (and men) began playing organized sports such as baseball and basketball. Women who happened to excel in sports were now being paid (albeit a very low wage) and assumed a semiprofessional status, juggling between their work load and sport membership. This increase in visibility for women to participate in sports was an added advantage that helped women to create a more open environment allowing diversity in sports. During the 1940's era the world changed with World War II. As more men were reporting for duty overseas, women began to take on the responsibilities of the work force as well as the national past time: Baseball. The first all women's national baseball league was formed in 1943 by Wrigley to fill the gap left by the men who went off to fight in World War II. However, the advantages that were gained by the creation of the first women's baseball league became tainted by the sexism that was associated with the position. The women baseball players were encouraged to wear make-up, wear short or revealing "uniforms" and really presented themselves as a form of male entertainment. However, notwithstanding these limitations, women were making great strides in sport participation.

The 1950's era and the 1960's era saw tremendous change as well—the 1950's introduced more opportunity for women to participate in yet a wider range of sports in the Olympics, and games such as women's volleyball as well as women's foot races (in track and field) were introduced in the early 1960's. However, an interesting caveat to these advances in women's sport participation occurred when in 1968 the Olympic committee now required female athletes to "prove" that they in fact were biologically female. Now the controversy of steroid use and "performance enhancing drugs" were starting to become major issues and are still considered to be problems in sports today. Marion Jones, Kelli White (track and field stars) and Jason Giambi (MVP player, retired) and Barry Bonds (Major League Baseball players) are just a few examples of how world class elite athletes have been accused of (and in some cases, admitted) using performance enhancing drugs. We will discuss the problem of steroid use and performance enhancing drugs in the next chapter.

■ PROBLEMS FACING THE MODERN FEMALE ATHLETE

The third stage of development in women's sports is occurring now, where women are competing for their own identity in the world of sports. Increasingly today, women's sports are slowly beginning to attain their own individual identity and are no longer represented as a "second category" to men's sports. A good example of this would be the development of the Women's Basketball Association

(WBA) and United States Women's Soccer Team. The world of the modern athlete today faces many problems on a daily basis: Getting funding for various athletic programs, scholarships or grants; creating and developing viable sports program in schools and universities; and staying healthy to maintain optimum standards for performance. However, one problem that we have been addressing is the universal discrimination and double standards that female athletes face in virtually every culture of the world. While discrimination against women has typically surfaced in many formats, including employment, salary raises, and so forth, most people are not aware that the female athlete also faces tremendous challenges in the world of modern sports, often more challenges than the male athlete. For example, the average salary of the male NBA player is significantly higher than the average salary of the female basketball player in the WBA. This discrepancy is probably due to old-fashioned biases that people still hold against top-level female athletes. For example, top women athletes in some sports, such as golf and tennis, have been portrayed by the media as being masculine or "mannish." Thus, top female athletes not only have to address issues relevant to their sport and training, but also how they are perceived by the media as being "overly masculine." The dilemma that faces many female athletes is how to excel in sports previously dominated by males, yet maintain their identity as being feminine. Clearly, top female athletic performance and a feminine identity are not mutually exclusive concepts. Male athletes, for example, have no problem being portrayed as aggressive because sports has traditionally been viewed as a masculine activity. If anything, aggressive behaviors by males in contact sports is encouraged and expected by the public as well as coaches.

The female athlete today is also confronted with the role-conflict problem, where often the media portrays them in an unfavorable light, often with commentators making negative remarks. Penn State basketball coach Rene Portland publicly stated that she "would not allow any lesbians on her team" (Stevens, Osborne & Robbins, 2002). As a result of this role conflict and negative image that has been associated with the female athlete, many young women unfortunately have avoided sport and athletic participation to avoid becoming labeled or stereotyped. This is very unfortunate, as women and sports today are increasingly becoming more popular within the public sector. Viewers for women's tennis now match or exceed men's tennis news coverage. Advertisers are now portraying women is being sexy, feminine and participating in contact sports (such as the Women's U. S. Olympic Soccer Team and Mia Hamm). Now, the terms "athletic" and "sexy" are no longer mutually exclusive. We portray women today in the media as being more aggressive, challenging and yet maintaining their sensual and feminine character. The next section of the chapter addressing women in sports will focus on the evolution in women's sports and how women athletes progress to reach their own individuality in sports. We begin with the development of the justification of women sports, where women had to create a reason simply even to participate in sports (pre 17th century). We will also highlight the issues that are commonly associated with female athletes and to explore ways to improve and enhance athletic performance of the female athlete.

Women Overcoming Obstacles: 3 Stages of Sport Evolution in 3 Centuries

Historically women have become objects of discrimination in employment, relationships, income, and sports. Women and men have typically exercised for similar reasons (i.e., physical health, feeling better, aesthetics and so on), however, women have experienced more barriers (both physical and psychological) to developing an exercise program and their ability to use the program on a consistent and regular basis. We will now describe three stages where women have progressed and advanced through sports and athletic activities from the early 17th Century through the 21st Century in an effort to achieve their own individual sport identity:

    a. *Justifying Sport Participation for Women: What's A Nice Girl Like You Doing In A Place Like This?—(Pre-18th Century):* In this first stage of female sport identity development, women athletes attempted to justify their participation and acceptance by overcoming biases and prejudice directed at them. Women were creating excuses for their interest and participation in sport and exercise programs. Women had to literally hide from participating in sport and typically were ostracized when they were discovered wanting to participate in sport activity. The role of women during the Victorian era (1700–1800 era) primarily was in child bearing and domestic activities. When the few outspoken women rebuked this archaic principle, they were typically humiliated or socially ostracized, and in some cases even imprisoned. Historically, women were excluded from sport participation out of fear that some "irreparable damage" would occur to their reproductive system. Additionally, women were informed that their bodies were inherently weaker than men's bodies, and that they should avoid prolonged exposure to physically demanding sports (Cohen, 1993). This bias that prolonged exercise activity is somehow damaging to a woman's reproductive system has existed for centuries, however, no data supports this bias. Amenorrhea is not a result of training, but typically due to an unhealthy diet or stress. While in some cases amenorrhea may occur with intense marathon training, the regular cycle develops when training resumes normal levels. Ironically, the now the greatest long distance runners (commonly referred to as "ultra marathons") are women, where levels of stamina can far exceed male counterparts. As recently as 1960, women were barred from participating in marathons out of fear of damage to their body (i.e., osteoporosis) and reproduction system. It wasn't until more and more women actually masqueraded as male runners that made race officials allowed women to participate in marathon sports.

b. *Creating The Female Athlete Identity—(19th & 20th Century):* Earlier in this chapter we discussed the double standard that many female athletes are exposed to—participating in physical sports and trying to maintain their feminine image. Several factors play into this double standard—often, the media may portray female athletes in a negative light, suggesting that participating in certain sports may make them more "masculine." These biases may unfortunately prevent many talented young female athletes from participating in basketball, soccer or rugby. Our current cultural definition of women's behavior is now opening and expanding concepts that allow women to participate in a wide range of sports that are free from these biases. Many conservative cultures have portrayed women's participation in sports as being either inappropriate or masculine, however, some advertisers are countering this image by portraying women athletes in a very positive and feminine view. Take for example Nike's advertisement of Mia Hamm during the 2004 Summer Olympics, Martina Hingis who won the women's 1999 Australian Open in tennis, or Janet Guthrie, who became the first woman to race the Indianapolis 500 auto race in 1977. These women are breaking down barriers by maintaining a very popular and successful career in sports and still have maintained their own feminine identity.

c. *Women Achieving Success in Modern Sports—The 21st Century:* Today women are more than ever capable of pursuing careers in professional sports. The modern female athlete has overcome numerous biases and prejudice in participating in sports in our society, and these problems have existed literally for centuries, dating beyond the 15th century. Perhaps the most significant milestone in women's sports is "Title IX." In 1972, Congress passed Title IX in the Educational Amendments Act. In this amendment, gender discrimination is prohibited and allows women to participate in sports in collegiate environments on equal ground with males. Women have also become more integrated in professional sports and the Olympics. Amazingly, the first official Olympic competition that allowed women to run the marathon was held in Los Angeles, 1984, where Joan Benoit won the first "women's marathon" with a highly respectable time of 2 hours, 24 minutes. Today women are free to participate in sports in every sport that men participate in. Thanks to Title IX, women athletes can now have equal opportunity to participate in a wide range of sports with other women. After literally centuries of bias and discrimination, it finally appears as if women are going to be considered on equal ground with men and offered the same opportunities to engage in sport activity. We will now offer a true scenario of a young woman, Lisa (not her real name) who describes her story in attempting to incorporate an effective exercise program into her life with realistic challenges and meaningful rewards. The program is described in sequences or stages that many women experience when first attempting to integrate a healthy exercise program into their personal and professional lifestyle. We can summarize the development of the authentic female athletic personality by reviewing the central concepts and paradigms relative to our daily lives: Socially-related behaviors, Professional behaviors, and Sports-related behaviors (figures 9a and 9b):

The Authentic Female Athlete's Personality

a. **Professional Behaviors: Behaviors Performed in Society for Employment & Work (How we typically like to represent ourselves to the outside world); Superficial and non-intimate relationships with co-workers exists primarily as a means of economic survival to engage in true passion: sports and training;**

b. **Socially-Related Behaviors: How we typically present and project ourselves with trusted friends and acquaintances (How we typically like to represent ourselves to our network of friends and family); An identification with the sport and a more trusted environment than Professional Behaviors;**

c. **Sports-Related Behaviors: How we project ourselves to team mates, coaches and to work-out partners. The Sports-Related Behaviors level is a more trusted level than Socially-Related Behaviors because we rely on our team mates more and our personal and professional careers sometimes depend on them. In this stage, we spend time in practice, training and conditioning that builds relationships with others that is unique and profound; The highest level of trust is built in this framework;**

d. **True Personality: Genuine thoughts and attitudes and characteristics of the self are preserved here. The athlete's most secret and critical views of the self are contained here that comprise the personality. Here the athlete may harbor insecure feelings of performance but typically projects self-confidence and self-esteem. Few individuals are aware of the true personality of the female athlete.**

Figure 9a

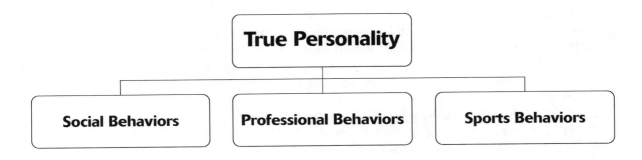

Figure 9b   The Authentic Female Athlete's Personality

The Development of the Modern Female Athletic Persona: Achieving Wellness Through Exercise

Lisa is a 16 year old high school student who is an honor student and is currently thinking about attending college. She has always excelled in academic work and has maintained a 3.8 GPA. She has devoted many hours to reading and studying in her preparation for her schoolwork, however, her physical activity has been relatively sedentary for the past several years. She has wanted to increase her activity level and lose about 10 to 15 lbs., but every time she tried a new diet or some new form of exercise equipment, she lost interest and failed. Throughout high school Lisa would spend most of her free time in the library studying and writing research papers for her classes. While sitting in the library on a spring afternoon she could see other students, some of them she knew, jogging past the library and exercising. Some were riding bicycles, some were throwing Frisbees® and others just were walking and appeared to be enjoying themselves being outside. Some of these student looked like they had been exercising most of their life, and yet others looked like that they were just beginning. Lisa wanted to go outside and participate with them, to tell them she wanted to join them and have fun like they were having fun, but somehow she felt unable to do so. Furthermore, Lisa felt intimidated by the number of other young women her age that seem "to have it all together" and are able to maintain high academic marks in school as well as maintain a physically healthy body—"Why is it so easy for them to look beautiful and I have to struggle just to lose a few pounds?" Lisa wanted to make more friends with other students, but always felt intimidated by other more popular girls in her class. She often felt "invisible" when in the presence of other students and felt as though people never noticed her or appreciated her for the real person that she was. She always felt that people tended to notice superficial things about people, but typically lacked the ability to perceive the integrity and truth that exists deep inside many people. She had always felt more comfortable in environments where she could excel, such as the classroom, and felt very intimidated when participating in the physical education course at her school. She was self-conscious about her physical appearance and felt that she had little control over her ability to make positive changes or improvements in her physical appearance. It had always seemed so easy for others to run, swim, play basketball or to simply even throw or catch a ball—these things scared her. They intimidated her not because they were inherently difficult, but because she had lacked the self-esteem to try and master them.

In the past, Lisa had tried dieting, exercising, yoga, and even once contacted a personal trainer, but nothing seemed to work. She would typically begin her exercises for a few weeks, and then would lose interest and would discontinue her training. Lisa was beginning to feel that her body was physically unable to meet her demands and that she was destined to remain over-weight. She was becoming increasingly frustrated, and when she felt angry or frustrated she did the one thing that compounded the problem further—she continued to eat unhealthy foods. As a way to compensate for her perceived inability to lose her weight as she wanted, she devoted more time to her academic work because this was the one thing that Lisa felt she had control over. When she didn't understand a concept, such as in algebra or chemistry, she focused harder on the text and consulted a trained expert in the discipline (her teachers). What Lisa didn't understand was that physical training and exercise really work the same way as her academic work: Persistence, work and consulting advice and support from other trained experts was the way to achieve her goals.

Lisa had thought that she was able to accomplish just about anything, for example, her academic work was something that she felt proud of and it came relatively easy for her. Her teachers praised her work, and encouraged her to apply to several universities. She often wondered why she could not control her body through exercising the way that she was able to focus her mind while studying. In fact, whenever she began a program to improve her physical health she became intimidated by all of the "super models" that just seemed to have everything together.

Lisa wanted more balance in her life and actually felt that if she was able to incorporate a higher degree of physical activity in her life, then she would feel better about her physical appearance and actually may be able to achieve her desirable weight. Lisa has decided to begin a health program and is determined to reach her goals. She now realizes that if she can achieve her academic goals by utilizing outside help from her teachers, then she should be able to reach her goals by utilizing help from a certified health trainer. She had decided to make a commitment to herself to achieve her goals and will continue working until she is successful.

Lisa already feels better now because she has made the commitment to make positive changes in her life that will make her feel better physically and improve her appearance. She realizes that if she applies herself to the physical goals of exercise and training with the same intensity as she applies to her academic work, then she will be successful. For example, she tells herself the time last year when she actually failed her physics exam because of a difficult concept involving a quadratic equation. She had been intimidated by quadratic equations, but once she put her mind to the problem and consulted a tutor at school, it suddenly came to her in a flash and she understood the concepts. Lisa told herself that exercise training must work in a similar way—that she should keep working and consulting a trainer to help her focus on her goals of weight loss and improved fitness. Just because we have had initial problems with something, regardless if it is a cognitive problem (such as physics) or a physical and health issue (such as weight loss and exercise), we should be able to understand the problem and improve our situation. When she understood the concepts in physics (with a tutor) her overall grade point average improved as did her self-confidence. She now realized that the only way to achieve her goals in health and fitness is to make a commitment to reach her goals with a trainer. She resolved herself to focus and commit herself to a structured and routine exercise program. Her plan included the following:

Lisa's Health Training Program: The Evolution of a New Body

a. *Making The Psychological and Physical Commitment:* Lisa had procrastinated in making a decision to improve her health over several years. She was nervous about the possibility about trying to improve her health by exercising and not being successful. Achieving high grades in her school work had been easy, and she always seemed to know what to do. However, her self-confidence regarding her self-esteem and physical body image seemed to drop entirely. She seemed to have problems in transferring her positive self-confidence in academics to her physical appearance and health. However, she has given this situation much thought and has decided to apply herself with as much drive to improve her physical health as she does with her academic work. Actually, she already feels better about making the decision to make positive changes in her physical health—the ambiguity and lack of conviction in making a decision was difficult for her. She has now made a commitment, and she has promised herself to follow through with the commitment. Part of the reason Lisa was experiencing problems in deciding to commit to a health and exercise program was the amount of pressure that she was placing on herself to achieve her goals. Her parents had raised her with the internal attribution concept that describes our goals are within our grasp and that we are in control of the important events that occur in our lives. Everything that she had done in school was perfect—perfect attendance, perfect academic performance, and perfect behavioral performance that met the standards of her instructors. Failure was never an option, and she wasn't quite ready to commit herself to a program where she could fail. Health and physical training were very intimidating to her, as she felt that she could never reach her goals in exercise to make her happy. As a result, she conveniently created schedule conflicts and study programs for her school work that prevented her from participating in an exercise program. Lisa needed control and structure in her world, and the prospect of developing a new program involving health and exercise was very intimidating to her. However, all that has changed now, as Lisa has made the psychological commitment and the verbal agreement with herself to follow through a program and ultimately to reach her goals. Most importantly, she has become determined to allow herself to enjoy the process and to discover what types of activities are relaxing and will improve her self-esteem and self-confidence. She is hopeful with guarded optimism—even excited!

b. *Creating the Training Program.* Lisa wanted to create a sensible and realistic exercise training program, one that she could really stay with and enjoy. Lisa would wake up in the morning at 7:00 am and would report to the gym. She had called previously and spoke with a health trainer (Mary) and had made the appointment for an orientation seminar to the gym. When Lisa first reported to the gym, she was pleasantly surprised at what she saw. Many different types of people, some in good physical condition, others in not-so-good condition, but they all seemed to have one thing in common: They appeared to really enjoy what they were doing. She could tell this by what she saw and what she heard: "That's it . . . keep going, you've almost got it!" or "Great work out Jim . . . you've just finished rowing over 5000 meters at a super pace! . . . How do you feel now?" She noticed that the people who were working with other people (something Mary called the 'Buddy System') were very supportive of each other and encouraged each other to keep trying. "This isn't what I had all imagined" Lisa confided to Mary, "I mean, the television advertisement typically shows these 'super model' types wearing skimpy outfits and exercising while looking fantastic. These people who are now working out look just like regular people." "That's because they are regular people" Mary had commented to Lisa. Mary was now Lisa's personal trainer. She was vibrant, friendly and highly supportive. Lisa felt very positive about Mary as being her personal health trainer and the two women toured the facility. "The basic key to training is finding something that you love . . . call it a passion, call it your destiny, but the only way people maintain a healthy and active exercise program is through identifying a series of activities that is challenging, healthful, and makes you feel good. The most important point in exercise training is finding the balance between what you think you can do and what you want to do. Mary explained to Lisa the key components in health training: "Come to the gym not necessarily to change your appearance, but rather to change how you feel—how you feel about yourself and how you feel about your world around you." Exercise is about feeling better about yourself first, something that I call the 'intrinsic drive in exercise' then all of the other nice things will follow, such as losing weight, improved self-esteem, and so on." Additionally, Mary explained to Lisa the four primary characteristics and ingredients that are necessary to successful training (see figure 9c):

1. Intensity;
2. Consistency;
3. Flexibility; and
4. Goals For The Future.

✓ *Intensity.* Mary explained each of the successful ingredients as being necessary to achieve Lisa's goals of health and fitness. Intensity is necessary to avoid complacency—Humans typically are creatures of habit—we tend to fall into routines and keep those routines. The problem is, the body adapts well to these routines and we should be continuously changing sequences, repetitions, and types of exercises to maintain the intensity of the workout. A good goal to strive for is in keeping your heart rate at 60–80% of maximum capacity for approximately 20–30 minutes about every other day (3 or 4 days a week). Mary explained also that many women may be at risk for osteoporosis, so the aerobic capacity training should be done with low impact training, such as rowing, swimming or cycling.

✓ *Consistency.* Mary also explained to Lisa the importance maintaining the program, or the "stick-to-it" factor. "Some days it will just feel bad to get out of bed to come to the gym—but I promise, once you do make it to the gym, you will feel better already and will be glad that you did it." Mary also helped Lisa to write up an informal contract that will serve to remind Lisa of the importance of her commitment and that she is making a contract with herself. If Lisa successfully completes her contract, then she is entitled to treat herself to a reward, such as a vacation or going to the movies with friends. Mary also commented that the contracts have been highly successful with her previous clients, and someone by the name of "Ted" successfully completed his contract with her. Furthermore, Mary informed Lisa that a continued approach to exercise that was consistent helped to build self-esteem, and that the best way to be consistent in an exercise program was to incorporate it as a daily required function, just as bathing and brushing one's teeth. Finally, Mary explained to Mary that the program consistency should be viewed as seriously as her academic study schedule. For example, Lisa had always studied for two hours after classes in the library Monday through Friday. Mary explained to Lisa that her program needs to be structured in a similar format, that after her studying she could incorporate her exercise program for about 45 minutes.

✓ *Flexibility.* "Flexibility is a key component to training—just as important as consistency and intensity is to your program" explained Mary. Flexibility refers to the psychological ability to change variables in your program and to maintain the willingness to try different things. Flexibility means not becoming upset if your machine that you typically use every day is being used by someone else, and flexibility also means the ability to make positive changes in your routine. Sometimes it is healthy to switch from aerobic training to weights, and then to incorporate swimming or some other light exercise to loosen up. For example, Mary explained that perhaps one day Lisa's schedule may become very hectic and disorganized. So, as a means of being flexible, Mary suggested that Lisa reschedule her training program. Flexibility, whether it means keeping an open mind in incorporating new training strategies or training on a different time schedule, is essential in maintaining a successful program. The point is that we need to remain flexible in our exercise routines to incorporate new ideas, new strategies that may improve wellness and physical conditioning;

✓ *Goals for the Future.* "Perhaps most importantly, we need to have goals that drive our behavior in the future" explained Mary. Goals are absolutely vital because they are the things that cause us to get up every morning to begin our training and work out. Without goals, we have no direction or criteria that we can gauge our improvement in. Furthermore, goals need to be realistic, such as stretching exercises for about 15 minutes each morning, and aerobic and cardiovascular training between 15–20 minutes, preferably performed at a "conversational pace." "What are your goals, Mary?" asked Lisa. Mary informed Lisa that her goals as a health trainer was in helping her clients (such as Ted and Lisa) to successfully reach their exercise goals and to maintain a level of intensity that is compatible with their training program for the long run. "More importantly, I think the most important and rewarding goal for me is to see the self-realization of my clients that they are in fact capable of making healthy changes in their life and improving the overall quality of life for them. This is only done when clients, such as yourself, come into the gym looking for help and realize that their dynamic psychological power exists within themselves, and I am here only to help them discover that power."

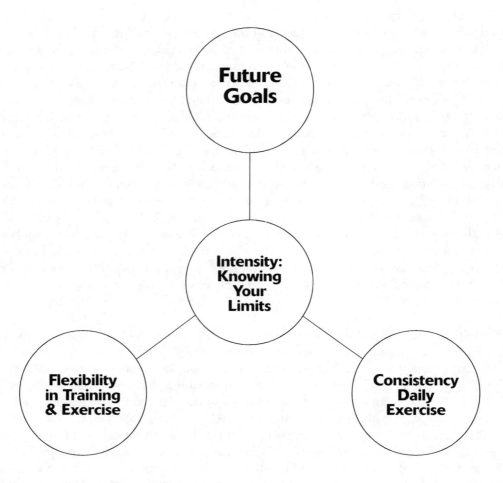

Figure 9c   Lisa's Training Exercise Philosophy

Mary also explained to Lisa that people are happiest when they achieve three key things in their training program. People are most successful when they are:

a.   Aware of their goals;

b.   When they feel that they are in control of achieving their goals;

c.   When they see successful performance and a gradual progression in the achievement of their goals. In fact, Mary explained to Lisa that many top-level athletes prefer the process of achieving their goals as they enjoy and excel in environments where they can quantify and measure gradual, consistent performance. A cycle develops where women athletes first become aware of their goals, then feel that they are in control of achieving their goals, and finally women actually achieve their goals—this process is referred to as "Women's Cycle of Success" (see figure 9d):

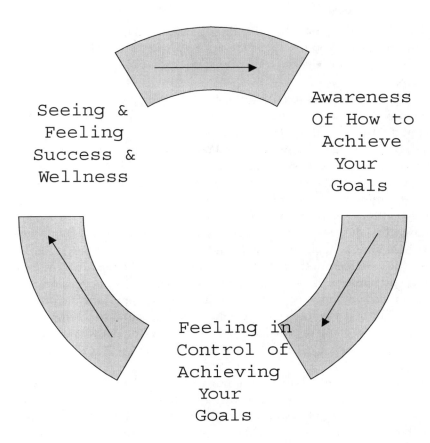

Figure 9d   Women Athlete's "Cycle of Success"

After several weeks of experimentation and orientation, Lisa discovered her training schedule and is currently maintaining her work out program. Her schedule looks something like this:

Lisa's Training Schedule:
Not A Temporary Program, but a Way of Life

a. *Monday–Wednesday–Friday:* Up at 7:00 a.m. and begin stretching (15 minutes); Rowing 5000 meters (under 20 minutes); 15 minutes of light weightlifting (3 light repetitions of weights followed by sets of 3 more sets of slightly heavier weight); 10 minutes of warm-down stretches. Total time: 60 minutes—one hour;

b. *Tuesday–Thursday:* Up at 7:00 am and begin stretching and flexibility exercises (15 minutes). 30 minute run or aerobic activity, followed by a warm-down exercise (15 minutes). Total training time: 60 minutes—one hour;

c. *Saturday–Sunday:* Relaxed activity program. Lisa was encouraged to begin participating in an activity program with friends and family, such as walking, cycling or stretching. She was also encouraged by Mary to increase flexibility and stretching. The key point here is that Lisa is re-learning her definition of exercise, where exercise is a dynamic and fun activity that has tremendous benefit for her physical and psychological health. Lisa is also beginning to incorporate exercise with fun and social activities with her friends. Before beginning her exercise program, Lisa felt that exercise and training was boring work, something that she had avoided.

However, now Lisa combines bicycle riding, power walking, jogging and volleyball on the weekends with her friends. Lisa has already noticed positive improvements in her outlook on her self, and she feels more confident in social situations. Most importantly, Lisa feels more confident about herself.

In terms of foods and nutrition, Lisa is following a common sense and basic approach to eating: Foods that are low in saturated fat, increases in fruits and vegetables, and perhaps most importantly—drinking more water. Mary informed Lisa that the increases in water help with digestion and flush out toxins in the body. Interestingly, Lisa has noticed that the healthier diets are also less expensive and more economical. Lisa made a few changes in her routine in the kitchen that allowed her more time to prepare her foods. Now, when Lisa woke up in the morning she first stretched and exercised for about 45 minutes to one hour. She prepares healthier meals and plans her meals out, identifying the meals ahead of time at the beginning of each week. Prior to her health and exercise program, when Lisa suddenly became hungry at school, she would run to the vending machines and buy a candy bar or chips, or she would go to the school cafeteria and eat the meatloaf. Mary informed her that just a little preparation ahead of times will save Lisa hundreds of calories. For example, now when Lisa wakes up in the morning, after her exercise program she prepares herself a lunch with fresh fruit and vegetables—not only more appealing than chips, but also less expensive. When Lisa is going to class, she puts a few bags of celery sticks and carrot sticks with tomatoes in her backpack. This way, when the "hunger bug" strikes, she can eat quickly and healthy.

Mary had informed Lisa that the most successful health programs are the one's that combine increased exercise activity with a healthy diet that has reduced fat intake. Mary also indicated to Lisa that the more "radical" or rapid her weight loss program is, the greater the likelihood that the weight would be replaced. Conversely, the slower the weight is lost, the less likely the weight will be put back on again. Lisa is convinced that a gradual, consistent and dynamic approach is the best way to achieve success. She is in control of a program that provides enormous satisfaction to her, and this is something that she has done to improve her life. She is now beginning to transform all of the negative self-belief systems about herself, and is instead changing them with positive mental statements about herself. Lisa called them "positive pep-talks":

Positive Pep Talks

a. "I can do this for myself . . . it is difficult, but I am progressing to a goal that will improve my health;

b. "I am a dynamic and powerful person who is capable of incorporating positive change in my life;

c. "The changes that I make in my life are going to be long-term and permanent . . . A 'relapse' may occur, but I can continue on the right track";

d. "I am in control of the events that occur in my life and am successful in achieving my goals";

e. "I am a valuable person and can achieve my goals in a consistent exercise program";

f. "I am worth the time that I am taking for myself for exercising and improving my health."

g. "I am a dynamic person who is in control of the events of my life. I am making positive changes that I have incorporated into my personal and professional lifestyle."

h. "Every day brings me a little closer to my goals of increased health and well-being."

Often, the biggest obstacles to our health and well-being are misperceptions of how things really are. For example, Lisa thought that the health spa where she would be training would be intimidating and competitive, and she found that the gym had many supportive and sensitive people who were invested and committed to helping her achieve her goals. Furthermore, she made a number friends in the gym and discovered that there were several people (men and women) who had experienced the same fears that she had. Being an introspective and analytical person, she realized that many women actually experience a motivational hierarchy prior to engaging in a training program. The hierarchy looks something like this:

Women's Motivational Hierarchy of Exercise

Women have also experienced the "double standard" in training where they are expected to have highly unrealistic body physiques as well as maintain other domestic responsibilities. As a result, women may engage in an exercise program for reasons other than intrinsic health, but rather for extrinsic reasons such as physical beauty and fitness. This model explains a motivational hierarchy regarding women's participation in an exercise and health program. Factors relevant to self-esteem, self-efficacy, (**Extrinsic Factors:** "Can I achieve my goals in losing weight and improving my physical appearance? Will I be accepted more by others if I look more physically desirable?") and different types of motivation (**Intrinsic Factors:** "I will participate in an exercise/sport program not because of what others think, but because of how the activity makes me feel about myself."). We will now discuss the five stages of the women's exercise motivation hierarchy and identify individual characteristics that are associated with each stage. Note that as each stage increases in development, women are training from a perception of how other's will think of them critically to how they feel about themselves during training. When women base their self-perception and self-esteem upon other people's (typically male) critical evaluations of their physical appearance and performance, dissatisfaction and depression usually is the result, especially as women enter their fourth and fifth decade. We will now describe the typical development of the motivational responses from women who participate in a sport/exercise program and explain each stage of development. Note that the stages develop from a transition from fear (virtually no training program) or insecurity of physical training and an inherent negative belief system of an inability to achieve their goals to a stage of training for psychological and physical balance, happiness, and intrinsic satisfaction with their lives. At this final stage of motivational development in exercise, women are have fully incorporated exercise and training into their lifestyles and enjoy the process of physical training and the psychological and physical benefits they receive from it. As a result of achieving this final stage of motivational development in exercise, women are more empowered and stronger where they are capable of a happy interaction with family and friends in society. Women who have reached the highest level of motivational development in exercise often make contributions to society through their volunteer efforts and report more satisfied and happier lifestyles. The stages of exercise motivation will address the following stages: Fear of changes, External affirmation (exercising for the wrong reasons); Discovering your needs and understanding your body; Transitioning stage: External to internal attribution; and Exercise actualization: Achieving holistic balance (see figure 9d). We will conclude our discussion of women in sports by addressing how women's team sports undergo an evolution of change as well: Introduction, Conflict; Agreement; Putting Everything Together; and Group Conclusion—Friendship Cohesion.

- *Fear of Change: The Need to Realize That Change Is Possible!* At this beginning level of the motivational hierarchy of exercise, women tend to procrastinate and harbor fears that are associated with exercise and well-being. For example, Lisa compensated her free time and energy with other school-related activities that served as an adequate excuse preventing her from participating in an exercise program. Lisa also experienced low self-esteem, and an external locus of control where Lisa felt that she was incapable of making positive changes for herself and was controlled by outside events (external locus of control). The term external locus of control is especially appropriate in this first level of exercise motivation, as many people feel that they are unable to incorporate positive changes in the lives, and that outside (uncontrollable) factors control their destiny or fate. A very dangerous side effect results from the external locus of control, term that is referred to as "learned helplessness" (Seligman, 1976). In psychology, the term learned helplessness exists as a means to explain why people do not enact positive forms of change in their lives when confronted with a variety of problems. For example, in the case of domestic abuse, where the wife is constantly physically and emotionally abused, you may say to your client "just leave the situation." However, for individuals who are actually experiencing the problem, it just isn't that easy. Another example would include Lisa and her difficulty in making the commitment to begin a sport and exercise program. She knows, for example, that the first thing that she needs to do is to improve her quality of life and to incorporate some form of activity or exercise program. What is important to note here is that it isn't what we know what should be done, but rather what the individual who is suffering needs to know. The key as a health trainer is to provide the client with the tools so they may discover that change is possible, and provide them with support and information how to incorporate that change as effortlessly as possible. The trainer serves as the role model, the inspiration, communication, lifeline and the support system that so many people at this first stage need. For example, Lisa may first attend a health orientation seminar at the gym that specifically has programs for overweight individuals and those persons who wish to start a program with light flexibility and aerobic exercises. The term learned helplessness is very important here because many, many individuals who have fear or insecurity about starting an exercise program may have convince themselves for years that they in fact were not capable of participating in a successful weight management and exercise program, so why bother? The fundamental rule at this first stage of exercise motivation is to establish a relationship of trust with the individual beginning the program, and change the negative belief system from "I can't" to "I can and will." Once the client has realized this fundamental principle that they have the power to achieve their goals, success will be achieved, and you have made a friend for life;

- *Exercising For All of The Wrong Reasons:* Conforming to Male Expectations. At this second level of exercise motivation, women engage in a health and exercise program for external validation, affirmation and reinforcement. At this stage, women rely on male affirmation that determines how they feel about themselves. Women participate in a variety of training and exercise programs not because they experience satisfaction and intrinsic motivation, but rather because of the praise and reinforcement they get from the dominant male society. Hence, women engage in a form of self-sacrifice where they sacrifice their needs to satisfy the demands of others in their lives (boyfriends, husbands). Women at this stage typically engage in "cosmetic" surgery, such as breast augmentation and liposuction to enhance their physical appearance. The practice of relying on other people's evaluation of your physical appearance as a means of enhancing your own self-esteem can lead to depression and highly self-critical evaluations. This may be referred to as the "Marilyn Monroe" phenomenon, where self-esteem is determined by qualities of physical beauty. Marilyn Monroe was regarded as America's sex symbol for a number of years and based her popularity, her sex appeal, and her success primarily on physical attributes and sexual attraction. This worked for some time, however, eventually, even the most attractive people's body change, and we need to still feel positive about our physique when theses inevitable changes come about. When we base our identity, our ego and self-esteem entirely on critical evaluations of others, we become dependent on them to feel good about ourselves. This practice can only lead to dangerous levels of low self-esteem and suicidal behaviors;

- *Discovering Your Needs & Understanding Your Body.* Understanding how your body responds to diet and exercise is essential in improving wellness and physical and psychological levels of health. Establishing trust with your health trainer and experiencing a wide range of activities to learn what your body responds to is a key factor in identifying the exercise program that is right for you. At this level, women begin to incorporate a health and exercise program as a means of improving the quality of their life and begin to understand their emotional well-being is achieved by the combination of physical and psychological balance. In other words, individual women begin to discover what works best for them physically, and that they are unique individuals with unique needs. Some women prefer forms of psychological meditation and Yoga, whereas other women prefer a stretching and flexibility program; still others may prefer a high aerobic capacity program. The point is, at this stage of exercise motivation, women are discovering the activities that their bodies physically respond to in a positive way. Rather than comparing themselves to others as a gauge of well-being and attraction, women begin to reflect on their own sense of achievement and physical well-being. In a word, women at this stage feel good about being themselves physically and have achieved a form of psychological balance that enhances their overall exercise program.

- *Transition From External Attributions to Internal Attributions.* This fourth level of exercise motivation addresses the fact that women participate in sport to feel better for themselves, not for others. Most important at this fourth level of exercise motivation is that women are training for intrinsic purposes—the best way to continue a training program is to create a program that is enjoyable, challenging and rewarding. Here women have discovered the process of physical exercise and aerobic training is essential for physical and psychological balance. They have moved beyond the negative stereotypes that they cannot achieve their goals and have moved beyond training for the wrong reasons—here, women know their bodies physically and are affording themselves the opportunity to maximize the benefits. Women also engage in exercise to improve their wellness and health and understand that both the physical and psychological needs are necessary to achieve maximum overall health. Most importantly, at this level women exercise for intrinsic benefits and health rather than solely physical appearance or extrinsic factors. Women are training primarily because of the physical rewards and psychological comfort that comes with a healthy training program. Women at this fourth stage of exercise motivation now exercise for the things that make them feel good about their bodies and do not rely on someone else's criteria or opinion to influence their own levels of self-esteem;

- *Exercise Actualization—Achieving Psychological & Physical Harmony & Balance.* At this fifth and final level of exercise motivation, women have achieved the balance between their physical needs (i.e., diet and nutrition), emotional, and psychological needs. They are participating in a program that provides a sense of well-being for them and inner peace and happiness. Furthermore, women who have reached the fifth and final level of exercise motivation now typically want to share and volunteer their experiences with other people to assist them in reaching their physical and health-related goals. The practice of helping and assisting others in exercise training provides the incentive and motivation for them to continue in their own program. Women at this fifth stage of inner balance have self-actualized themselves in the world of exercise training, and typically find meaning in their daily activities either through exercise and training or volunteering their time to others. Their exercise program adds to their life, but they are not controlled by their training program, either. The women who have achieved this level of the exercise motivation hierarchy are highly inspirational and positive role models that find meaning in their lives by contributing to others in society. They are also motivated to help others who are in training and exercise and share their skills and information so others may also be able to achieve their health-related goals. The process of maximizing their exercise program now provides women with the incentives and drives to continue in their own program and to simultaneously assist others who may have experienced problems in achieving their exercise goals.

Figure 9e   Women's Motivational Hierarchy of Exercise

Women's Exercise Survey Test (WEST)

On a scale of "1" through "5", where a score of 1 means absolutely not true, and a score of "5" means absolutely true, please answer the following:

I exercise: Rarely (less than 3 times a month);

Occasionally (8 times a month);

Frequently (12 times a month);

Very Often (16 times a month or more)

1. I exercise to make me feel better physically;
2. I exercise to make me feel better psychologically;
3. I exercise so people will notice me more;
4. It is more important that I look healthy and fit for others than for myself;
5. I do not like to sweat while working out;
6. I think women should look presentable to others while working out (nice workout clothes, hair in place, etc.);
7. My workouts and my appearance would be different if I worked out in a gym with all women;
8. When I exercise, I like to socialize with other people at the gym;
9. If I don't get a chance to work our often (at least once a day) I get frustrated with myself;
10. I think all people should work out more often;
11. People who say the are "too busy" to exercise are really creating excuses for themselves not to exercise;
12. The most important thing about exercise is how it makes me look;
13. I think that it is more difficult for women to exercise regularly due to the double standards in our society;
14. I think that women athletes should serve as positive role models and have an obligation to contribute to our society.
15. I think that I will be more popular with my peers by participating in an exercise program.

■ SUMMARY & RESULTS OF THE WEST

In an informal survey conducted at a local community college and state university, over 100 women were randomly selected and administered the Women's Exercise Survey Test (WEST) and the following results strongly suggest that as women mature, their reasons for participating in an exercise and health program change. For example, the women in the younger age group (18–25 years) responded with an average score of 2.6 out of a maximum point value of 5 to statement #4 ("It is more important that I look healthy and fit for others rather than myself"), whereas the women in the category from ages 40 and older indicated that their reasons for participating in an exercise program were more for aesthetic and intrinsic reasons (average score of 1.8 question #4). Similarly, in responding to question #12: "The most important thing about exercise is how it makes me look" the women in the age group of 40 and over had significantly lower scores (1.8) as compared to the younger respondents (3.0).

In summarizing these informal results, we can tentatively conclude that as women mature they engage in a meaningful sport or exercise activity for different reasons, progressing from a form of "self-sacrifice" exercise where exercise is done for physical appearance to please others, to a more intrinsic experience where exercise provides meaning, insight and balance to one's physical and psychological being. One statement on the survey that all groups of women had agreed on was statement #13: "I think that is more difficult for women to exercise regularly due to the double standards in our society." Apparently, women of all age groups feel that women have a higher standard to aspire to while exercising or working at home or the office when compared to males. According to the respondents, males have more freedom and flexibility to participate in a variety of exercise programs, where women are limited due to domestic responsibilities.

■■ CHAPTER 9 QUESTION & REVIEW

1. Explain how women's sports have faced numerous obstacles and unique problems in developing equity with men's sports.

2. Explain the three stages of sport evolution for women in the past three centuries.

3. Identify and describe the four components of the female athlete's personality.

4. Describe and elaborate the women's "cycle of success"—how are each of the components related to each other?

5. Identify and describe each stage of the women's motivational Hierarchy of Exercise.

6. Conduct your own informal survey of the WEST test among different age groups of female athletes. Score each survey and determine if age is a variable in how women approach sport and exercise.

Chapter 10:
The Olympic Problem of Elite Athletes: Steroids

Perhaps no other topic today has become more controversial in modern sports than the use of drugs. It seems every day when we pick up a newspaper or watch the news on television, some sports star is being accused of illicit drug use, such as steroids. Steroids have been in the world of sports for several years, but only recently have they become more evident as the techniques in hiding their use are more sophisticated. Many sports celebrities and coaches use the euphemism "performance enhancing drugs" to describe drug use in competitive sports. Today, more than ever, drugs have become evident in both amateur and professional sports. Consider the events that are currently unfolding today in track and field with Marion Jones and Kelli White, or the events in National League Baseball with Barry Bonds and New York Yankees Jason Giambi. Drugs have become more controversial even in the name that we use to identify them—should drugs be labeled "performance enhancing drugs" or simply anabolic steroids? We will now review the current controversy regarding drug use and determine what possible solutions exist regarding this serious problem in modern sports. On Friday, December 3, 2004, *The Daily News* broke a key story that shed light on allegations that numerous athletes have been using drugs as a means to improve sport performance. These reports were further substantiated by a leading Bay area lab founder (BALCO) Victor Conte who reported that several leading athletes were using a variety of banned substances in sports, even calling Olympic medalist Marion Jones "a cheat" and that he had personally witnessed Marion Jones use the banned drugs (on Wednesday, 12/15/04, Jones filed a 25 million dollar lawsuit against Mr. Conte for defamation of character as a result of this interview. How his ultimately will work through the courts remains to be seen). Furthermore, Conte incriminated Barry Bonds by claiming that Bonds had used two banned substances and Jason Giambi had admitted using the drugs for several years. Victor Conte, BALCO executive James Valente and track coach Remi Korchemny were indicted in San Francisco in federal court ten months ago and court judge Susan Illston commented that a trial may develop as early as spring of 2005. On a recent national television broadcast, Conte indicated that he gave steroids to several athletes in track and field and baseball ("20/20" news documentary). Conte commented that he gave Marion Jones a human growth hormone and has given baseball players a steroid called "the clear" or "the cream" which is a testosterone-based cream.

The question arises whether or not athletes should be using drugs at all. At one end of the spectrum several sports experts have commented that the problem of drug use in sports is endemic, and given the difficult nature in identifying the authenticity of the drug that all drug use should be permitted. On the other end of the spectrum is the belief that all drugs should be banned in sport competition, and that only "natural training methods" should be made available to athletes. Part of the problem also arises with even the classification of the term "drug" itself. How do we distinguish certain foods and supplements (such as protein powders) from the term drugs? Other more contentious issues develop with drug use, such as asking the question is it fair to compare records broken in a "drug free era" (i.e., the Babe Ruth records) to an era where drug use is rampant?

■ STEROID USE IN SOCIETY: ARE THEY REALLY WORTH THE RISK?

We have discussed the increases in drug use in competitive and professional sports, but we have yet to discuss what some of the causes are. Perhaps the number one cause of rampant drug use in professional sports today is the payoff—money, attention, media, and endorsements all add up to millions of dollars. The public isn't interested in a "second place" athlete—we are focused on the champion and how the champion excels in competition. We assume that the champion excels and wins for the very reason this book is being written—understanding the link between physical and psychological performance. The reality is that as more and more money is being paid out to professional athletes and professional teams, the greater the likelihood that some of those athletes have exposed themselves to illicit (and in some cases illegal) drugs that can improve strength and stamina during the short run, however, in the long run there typically is damage to the overall physical health of the athlete. As a society, if we continue to inflate the salaries of professional athletes and pay exorbitant amounts of money to players who continually win, we can expect the use of illegal substances to continue. Perhaps one suggestion in addressing this problem is if we as a culture de-emphasize winning from the individualistic culture (i.e., winning at all cost) and emphasize more on the sportsmanship and style of play in sports, the use of illegal drugs may decrease. Focusing on the quality of all players, typically represented in the collectivistic culture may also reduce the intense competition that seems to trigger drug use in sports. If we emphasize more in the quality of play in sports for intrinsic value and focus on the social contributions that sports provides for us in society, then athletes will feel less compelled to "juice up" and engage in a "win-at-all-cost" attitude.

■ WHAT REALLY HAPPENS WHEN PEOPLE USE STEROIDS?

When we discuss the use of drugs and steroid use in professional sports and athletics, we hear several reasons why athletes tend to use it. Most of these reasons that have been described by athletes address the seemingly endless positive effects: More power, more strength and endurance, and an overall sense of euphoria. Athletes have reported "feeling on top of the world" and "nothing can stop me." But are the effects and consequences of steroid and drug use always positive for each athlete? Absolutely not, and in a recent article published by the U. S. Department of Health and Human Services (2004), men who take large and consistent quantities of anabolic steroids place themselves at risk for a number of health-related problems. Some of these include: changes in sexual performance (because steroids are hormones, there is a negative side-effect that impairs the male reproductive system), shrinking testicles, lowered sperm count, baldness, impotence, enlarged prostate, and painful urination. Additionally, the Department of Health and Human Services noted that "megadoses" of steroids not only results in psychological addiction, but also classic symptoms of physical addiction, as noted by increased cravings, withdrawal symptoms, and difficulty in cessation of use. Men are not the only ones who may suffer from negative side effects of anabolic steroids. Women have been reported to be using steroids with increasing frequency, especially in some of the sports where power and speed are crucial (i.e., track and field and swimming). Similarly, women suffer from the "masculinization" effect of anabolic steroids: Facial hair, deepening of the voice, enlarged clitoris, and reduced breast development. The negative side effects for both men and women include acne, jaundice, physical trembling, swelling of joints, liver damage, high blood pressure, and reduced HDL (the "good" cholesterol) (U. S. Department of Health and Human Services, 2004).

These physical descriptions address negative side effects of the use of anabolic steroids, but there are also negative psychological consequences as well. For example, depression and mood swings are commonly reported among those individuals who have reported consistent use of steroids. A colloquialism that describes mood swings among steroid users is "roid rage." Violence, extreme jealousy and aggression have been associated with the use of steroids. Continued or prolonged use of steroids may even result in paranoia, delusional and psychotic thinking, impaired judgment, delusions of grandeur. Many individuals who were previous users of steroids commented that they felt they could "accomplish anything . . . and that my power was never ending." These feelings of invincibility and superiority have also been reported with the use of anabolic steroids. Perhaps one suggestion in addressing the widespread problem of drug use in competitive sports is through information describing the negative side effects of even short-term use of these drugs.

■ THE 5 MAJOR CLASSIFICATIONS OF DRUGS

The term drug is used in many contexts, therefore we should first describe the term before we identify the classifications of drugs. Drugs are typically described as any substance that influences cognitive functioning or biological processes. Reasons why individuals take drugs vary, but in this text, typically athletes take drugs (steroids) to enhance and improve performance over other competitors. Steroids do not fall into the traditional category of drugs (i.e., stimulants or depressants) but are rather considered to be a growth hormone. As the athlete increases his or her usage of the illicit substance, their reliance on the drug typically increases (a term that we call "tolerance"). In severe cases, the athlete may develop more and more dependence on the drug, both from a psychological and physiological perspective. The body that physically becomes dependent on drugs actually experiences withdrawal symptoms upon sudden termination of the drug, and psychological dependence occurs when the athlete feels that he or she can no longer adequately compete without using the drug. What actually makes an athlete a "drug user"? Most experts agree that an athlete who experiments with illegal substances (such as steroids) even once is considered to be a drug user. However, for other athletes, the criteria vary. For example, many doctors agree that if a person has used the substance within one month, and that the substance is causing some form of difficulty in the athlete's life (i.e., professional or emotional problems), and the athlete uses the drugs while in hazardous situations, these criteria usually indicate that the athlete has a drug problem. An athlete becomes a drug (i.e., steroid) abuser when he or she relies on a specific drug to excel and compete with others in their respective sport. The five specific criteria used to determine the degree of severity of drug use among athletes is listed in terms of duration, history, and consequences of the use of the drug:

> ➤ The athlete must have used the drug or steroid at least once prior to competition;
> ➤ The athlete uses the drug with the intention of improving athletic performance;
> ➤ The athlete who uses the steroid or drug encounters some difficulty with personal, professional, emotional or legal areas;
> ➤ The athlete jeopardizes his or her career when using the drug; and
> ➤ The athlete is aware that the drug they are taking is illegal, but still continue to use it.

Historically, drugs have had five primary classifications:

   a. Stimulants (caffeine, amphetamine);
   b. Depressants (alcohol, barbiturates);
   c. Hallucinogens (LSD, Mescaline);
   d. Inhalants (glues, solvents);
   e. Marijuana (hashish).

Steroids have traditionally been classified into three categories:

a. *Anabolic Steroids.* The anabolic steroid is the most commonly used steroid by athletes. The infamous steroid that previously was proclaimed to be "non detectable" was THG (the "designer" steroid);

b. *Androstenedione (andro).* This form of steroids is most commonly used by athletes who want more physical power and strength and wish to recover from intense training on a faster level;

c. *Creatine.* Creatine monohydrate is a compound produced by the body that helps release energy in the athlete's major muscle group. This substance is a naturally occurring element that helps muscles to relax faster and accelerates fast bursts of strength necessary in such sports as weightlifting and track. Danger areas include damage to the kidney, heart, and liver.

■ SYMPTOMS OF COMMONLY USED DRUGS

The symptoms of stimulants are rather obvious: The symptoms include increases in activity, alertness, and excitability. Many athletes who are in training may actually intentionally ingest a variety of stimulants (i.e., caffeine) to improve the intensity of their workouts. Several weightlifters, for example, may want a "rush" before lifting so they increase their consumption of coffee and amphetamines. Many individuals who consume stimulants use them to facilitate weight loss, as many "over-the-counter" drugs used to lose weight have significantly higher levels of stimulants. Cocaine is used to produce a general sense of well-being and sexual arousal, whereas amphetamines are consumed for specific reasons to decrease appetite and increased alertness. The drugs under the classification of stimulants are most commonly used by athletes, as many athletes feel that their performance is ideal when they are in an elevated mental and physiological state. Depressants are consumed to help people relax and typically are described for purposes of "unwinding." With the frequent use of depressants, people feel more relaxed, reduced tension, induced sleep, and alleviates pain and tension. While not frequently ingested or used by athletes to facilitate athletic performance, the hallucinogens and inhalants are classifications of drugs that produce mood and perception changes. The category of hallucinogens typically produces quality of perception, visual and auditory levels. Inhalants (although typically very dangerous even when used in small amounts) produce hallucinations and delusions due to deprivation of oxygen to the brain. Most common drugs that are used by athletes would fall under the stimulant categories including steroids. We will now describe a true (although the athlete's name has been changed for anonymity) story involving how an elite athlete can become introduced to drug use and ultimately how the illicit drug influenced his life.

■ "COMING CLEAN": REHABILITATING THE ATHLETE

Greg (not his real name) is a 21 year old college (senior) football player who has always dreamed of being recruited by a professional football team. Ever since Greg was a small child, he has been very active in a wide range of sports and has always been praised by his coaches. Greg was the sort of athlete who would come to practice early, train hard, and stay late to help others who needed his help. Greg was team captain of his high school football team and has always trained hard under the supervision of his coach. Greg was an "All American" high school athlete and was awarded a full scholarship to a local university. Greg was a scholar while playing for the university and graduated with a 3.5 GPA. He has always been proud of his ability to balance the demands of his athletic program (which took up at least 3 to 4 hours daily) and the academic rigors of a university program. He weighs 220 lbs. and his position is offensive tackle. While playing at his university Greg excelled and started as first-string offensive tackle, however, more and more linemen starting to play are physically larger and certainly more aggressive while on the playing field. He knows that if he wants to get even a fair chance at being recruited in the NFL he has to put on weight, play harder and more aggressively. He has heard through friends that many of them are taking "Dynaballs"—a relatively inexpensive steroid that is commonly used among athletes who wish to increase muscle strength and weight.

Greg has become concerned about his ability to play in the professional league and is seeing some of his team mates becoming stronger and faster in a very short period of time. His coach has commented that his running speed and reaction times seem to be dropping, and that he is at risk of losing his first string starting position as offensive tackle. It isn't as though the new players coming in are just naturally more talented, but rather there seems to be a difference in how and why they are training. Greg has noticed more and more often younger players are disregarding the concept of "team play" and focusing more on individual success, despite the fact that they are playing on a team with other members. Low hits or "cheap shots" seem to be more common, and simply can no longer be "pumped up." Greg is concerned about his ability to maintain an even playing field, and feels that athletes who take "performance enhancing drugs" have an unnatural advantage when compared with other athletes. He hears and sees other athletes using anabolic steroids and they seem to work for them. He is very tempted to try "just one time" to measure the impact and improvements (if any). He has decided to try using steroids and measure any change (positive or negative) in his performance.

Greg's Training Schedule: Is Steroid Use Ethical?

After asking a few team mates where he could purchase steroids, Greg discovered a retired athletic trainer who was willing to sell to him the type of steroids he had heard so much about—"dynaball" steroid. He decides to purchase 3 months of steroids, and the retired athletic trainer sells Greg the steroids with the intention to use them for his upcoming training season. Greg knows that this season is very important as he has to perform with other younger athletes who are training for his position as offensive tackle. Additionally, Greg knows that this season is his senior year or last year to play for college football, and that there will be "talent scouts" (trained observers who identify talented athletes for possible recruitment in the professional football league) who will see him play. He wants to play the best that he can for the talent scouts—if recruited by a professional team, Greg knows that his career will advance significantly and his income will also improve.

■■ MEDIA AS INFLUENCERS OF DRUG USE IN SPORTS

Greg knows that the media plays a tremendous role in identifying and representing himself to the public—there would be autographs, endorsements, salary promotions, and a very luxurious lifestyle. Greg remembers as a young boy watching some of his favorite football players being interviewed after winning games, and all of the attention and rewards they would have: New cars, great clothes, and lots of attention. He wanted that—he still loved the game of football but now these other things began meaning much more to him. Because of the increases of value and money that has become associated with successful sports, now Greg's desire to play has become influenced by extrinsic motivational factors as opposed to his previous love for the game (intrinsic factors). Greg has noticed that his style of play is now more focused towards simply winning as opposed to the overall quality of play. Greg remembers watching television and how popular and attractive everyone looked after winning the "big game." Winning, it seemed, is now more important than ever. If someone wins in their competition, then they can have just about anything they want: A great lifestyle, fast cars, and attractive women. Greg saw how the media portrayed "the winners" as very ideal and positive role models. Greg wanted this quality of living for his own lifestyle, and now began to view football as an end to the means of achieving his goal. He would read popular sports magazines, read newspapers, watch television and they all seemed to suggest one thing: In a society such as ours, we value winners—not losers. When you win in our country, you begin to enjoy many privileges, and these were the things that motivated Greg to experiment with steroid use. The individualistic and highly competitive culture in which we live in has created a highly intense nature of training that may influence young athletes to resort to using illicit substances. As many young athletes become aware of the rewards of success in sports (such as full scholarships to colleges, drafted into professional leagues), coaches and educators need to focus on the intrinsic nature of the sport and encourage more team work, not individual work, as the key to a healthy and balanced athletic career.

a. *The Experimentation Phase (drug use occurs once or twice only):* Spring training has started and Greg has now been using his steroids for about three weeks while in training. He is amazed at how quickly the drugs have enhanced his performance—his running times have already dropped by over 2 seconds, and he feels much stronger when running (quarterback) sweeps to the right or left—last year he had difficulty in blocking the opposing defensive tackle and defensive end, but now he was completing removing them out of the play situation with much less effort. He has performed significantly better just in the spring since last year. The coaches have commented to him to "keep up the good work . . . you're looking great!" "Remarkable changes in one year" replied the defensive coordinator with raised eyebrows. Greg's team mates also noticed the differences in his style of play—faster and more aggressive in the blocks and tackles. Now Greg's team mates were asking him questions how to block or improve reaction times off the line. They were congratulating him now and giving him "high fives" after significant plays. He was now very popular, and he enjoyed this increased popularity very much. Additionally, the popularity transferred from the field to the campus. Students noticed him now and asked for his autograph—people knew who he was and he was very popular among his instructors as well. Life was great and he was enjoying the increased attention. Regarding his drug use, he felt that this was something that he "could take or leave anytime . . . I'm the one doing the work, the drug is only a little 'push' that I need every now and then. What's the difference between someone drinking a few cups of coffee before practice and what I take? Not much of a difference." Greg was enjoying the fact that his athletic performance was improving and he was convinced that his improvement was primarily due to his training, *with or without steroid use.* What Greg did not realize was that his "experimental" phase was growing into a form of dependency that was both physiological and psychological. Perhaps most importantly, Greg was now in the process of becoming psychologically dependent on the drugs because of all of the attention and praise he was receiving. He was actually misleading himself to believe that his performance improvement was entirely on his own rather than admitting that the changes in performance were really due to the steroids he was taking. Of course, Greg was rationalizing and trivializing his use of steroids. The truth of the matter was that he was growing in dependency on the drug and he was enjoying the side benefits very much—This experimentation phase soon grew into occasional use.

b. *The Occasional Use Phase (drug use four times or less per month):* During Greg's first few weeks of steroid use, his body responded very positively, and this very positive initial response gave Greg the misperception that his drug use was innocuous and harmless. During the second phase of illicit drug use, Greg was becoming more dependent on using the drug to perform well on the field. Furthermore, he was noticing that his temperament and disposition was changing. For example, the things that used to comfort him and help him to relax were no longer relaxing. He used to go for walks on Sunday afternoons with his dog, but now he viewed this activity simply as a chore. He lacked the patience and insight that he once enjoyed while working in his garden, and viewed this as "impractical with his time." In short, Greg's demeanor and temperament had changed from a calm and relaxed individual to a very short-tempered, irritable and demanding person who had difficulty in relaxing and slowing down.

Where Greg only used the steroid on an "experimental phase" to see how it worked on his individual performance, in the second stage of drug use Greg has now become dependent on its effect to help him through practice. Now Greg was using the steroid occasionally for practice and scrimmages, but perhaps more importantly he was beginning to feel that the only way he could be successful in sports was through steroid use. He still enjoyed the physical changes in his body through steroid use, the added muscle strength and increased running speed, but he began to notice changes in his personality. Greg found that he was becoming aggressive in practice and more irritable with his social acquaintances. Greg was not preparing for the first game of the season, and his use now increased from occasional use to moderate use.

c. *The Moderate Use Phase (drug use four to eight times per month):* During the moderate use phase, the athlete now consumes the drug on a regular basis and feels that his or her performance in sports is dependent on continued use. Greg knows that the first game of the season is three weeks away, so he has increased his steroid use from one or two injections per month to once or twice weekly. His power has seemed to level off, and now when he is not training he fingers tremble and he feels nervous most of the time. Greg has noticed that his quality of sleep has suffered, and he feels like he simply doesn't need sleep anymore. Greg has been placed as first-string offensive tackle and feels very proud to have made the first string offensive line. Greg has also experienced some swelling in his joints, his ankles are swollen in the morning and it takes him significantly longer to stretch and feel limber prior to training. He has also noticed that the amount of money that he is spending on the steroids has dramatically increased—he is paying out anywhere from two hundred to three hundred dollars a week for his drugs, but he still feels that they are worth the investment. His temperament has become significantly worse, and twice last week Greg became involved in pushing matches with other team mates. He now has lost the support from the other team mates as they feel Greg does not play as a team member, but simply an individual out for his own benefit. The coaches have noticed his tremendous physical improvements and congratulate him, but do not seem to be very concerned with his minor injuries that now have developed. His use of steroids is now consistent, and more importantly he is relying on the drug use to compensate his performance on the field. This is gradually increasing his fears and insecurity of being drafted in to the professional league, and thus he feels more compelled to increase his drug use. Thus, a cycle has developed where his insecurity and need for top performance dictates his need for steroid use. As Greg's insecurity regarding his performance and fears gradually increases (see figure 10a), he feels compelled to increase his steroid use to somehow improve performance. His ability to accurately gauge and measure his physical performance is now compromised, and he is experiencing difficulty concentrating in general due to his insecurity of performance. The effects and the impact of the steroid use are now running their course, and Greg is now suffering from steroid use dependency. Greg will go through one more stage, the heavy use stage, before he realizes he needs help and seeks rehabilitation.

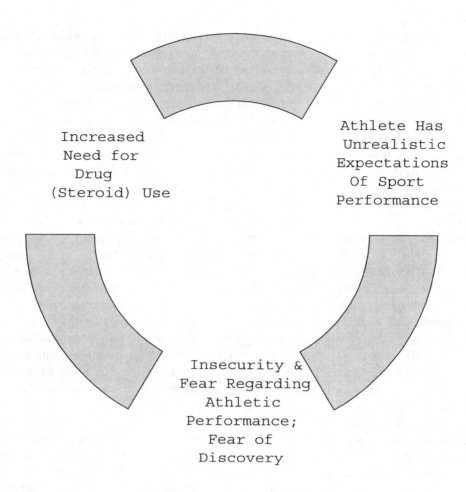

Increased
Need for
Drug
(Steroid) Use

Athlete Has
Unrealistic
Expectations
Of Sport
Performance

Insecurity &
Fear Regarding
Athletic
Performance;
Fear of
Discovery

Figure 10a   The Evolution of Steroid Use in Sports

d. *The Heavy Use Phase (drug use exceeds three times weekly).* Greg now has been using his steroids for several months and is beginning to rely entirely on them for his physical performance. His behavior is characterized by mood swings, irritability and he even shows some signs of paranoia, as he suspects that people are aware of his mood swings. Greg has become psychologically dependent on the steroid use and has gone into debt trying to maintain his dependency on the drug. He rationalizes his illicit drug use by thinking that this is a temporary "investment" that he is making to ensure that he will be playing first string offensive tackle his senior year. Additionally, Greg knows that the talent scouts will be out looking for recruits and that it is essential that he is playing to the best of his ability. Greg was not aware of the fact that he has been steadily progressing in a downward spiral since he began his drug use, and the signs and symptoms indicate now that he needs drug rehabilitation. The coaching staff at the university seems to "look the other way" when Greg's visible signs of steroid use become apparent, and seem to be concerned only about his ability to "do the job." Greg has become so concerned about making the cut in professional football that he knowingly has jeopardized his health by taking the heavy dosages of steroids. His fingers seem to be shaking all of the time now, he has difficulty in concentrating on plays and academic work, and feels now everyone on the team is "out to get me." He decides to consult the team physician and seek rehabilitation to help his deal with his dependency on the steroid use.

e.   *Rehabilitation.* Greg has been through an experience of steroid use that began simply with a desire to enhance and improve physical and athletic performance. He rationalized to himself that "it would only be temporary . . . and that I can use it and stop it anytime." Greg soon discovered that he had created a level of performance with the aid of steroids that was impossible to sustain; his performance during spring training was extremely intense, and he was unable to monitor and control this level of intensity. This inability to maintain unrealistic levels of performance gave way to his insecurity and even paranoia, which ultimately influenced his perception of needing more steroids. He had fallen into a trap, but now he was ready to rehabilitate himself.

The first key to steroid abuse (as with any type of drug abuse) is to admit that the drug has taken over your life, and that the use has evolved into abuse. For many individuals, this is very difficult to detect—we think that we have everything under control, and we cannot see out of our own biased world. Actually what was happening to Greg was that he was alienating himself from his support system, his family and friends because he did not want exposure to his use of drugs. People had noticed the difference, but when they tried to intervene, he disregarded their efforts to help because he did not feel as though he had a problem. After several weeks with a counselor, Greg realized that he was placing way too much emphasis on his football career and not enough on his academic work. He was creating a very difficult world where if he did not become drafted, he felt that his career (indeed his life) would have been a failure. This is an example of what Aaron Beck (1967) refers to as "negative cognition": Placing an unrealistic view of one self in relation to others. For example, Greg felt that in order for him to be successfully drafted into the professional league, he would have to outperform everyone on the team in physical ability. He told himself that he would have to run faster, train harder, and be stronger. More importantly, part of his negative cognition was that if he wasn't able to achieve all of these things, then he was a failure. The combination of the unrealistic standards of performance connected with his fear of failure produced the motivation for his drug dependency and use of steroids.

Greg is now focusing more energy on his academic work and has become "drug free" for three months. He is still playing as offensive tackle for the university football team, but his life is now in more balance and reasonable. Greg is learning to place more realistic goals in his life, and he realizes that even if he isn't drafted into the professional league, he has several options. The first and most important goal he has already achieved—he is living an active and drug-free life again.

■■■ CREATING A "DRUG FREE" CULTURE IN SPORTS

As this article was being written, news and television broadcasts are describing the effects of drugs on sports and athletic competition. Major League Baseball, for example, is considering banning all drugs together and using a random drug testing policy with their athletes. If we want to eliminate illicit drug use in sports, we must first ask the question what has contributed to the proliferation of illicit drugs (such as steroids) in society? This question is best addressed by exploring our cultural values and the media. In our culture, we typically do not consider teachers, doctors or day care personnel as "heroes." No, our heroes are the ones scoring all of the touchdowns, making the last second "3 point" shot as the buzzer sounds, or the athlete who runs the fastest mile. The point is—as a society, our values have become clouded with the glory of winning as opposed to the tributes of training as a group. Team sports in the United States have become a casualty to the individualistic culture that permeates our society. We want to beat everyone, win at any cost, and then brag about the spoils of our victory. We as a society need to re-evaluate our priorities, emphasizing the virtue in hard work for the experience of work itself; in other words, the athlete needs to remind himself or herself that the glory and rewards of training and success come at a price—and that price is never

131

compromised. Training and athletic improvement comes slowly and consistently if done correctly—and we simply cannot increase the pace through drug use. The motivation of training and competition should come from within (intrinsic motivation) rather than the outside (extrinsic). Athletes should be competing and participating in the sport because the sheer activity itself is rewarding—not negotiating contracts and endorsements.

The media too, share part of the blame in drug use in sports. The media, known for its inability to accept responsibility in previewing gratuitous violence, repeatedly shows violence in sport as a vehicle or mechanism for success—that the most aggressive athlete wins. The media perhaps should be focusing more on the style and quality of play, such as good sportsmanship, following rules and regulations, and athletes congratulating each other on different teams. The media should be emphasizing the sport itself and competition—not the materialistic possessions that have become associated with superhero athletes. Finally, the media can play a role in reducing substance abuse in sports by realistic portrayals of athletes and their world. Showing the public the hard work and dedication that is required in successful athletic performance, and that these goals are capable of being achieved in a drug-free environment is critical if we wish to reduce steroid use in sports.

How the Problems Develops:
The Five Stages of Steroid Use Among Elite Athletes

- *Experimentation.* In the first stage of illicit drug use, the athlete typically comes from an environment of athletic training and has a successful history of participating in sports and exercising throughout most of the athlete's career. Athletes in this first stage of drug use and dependency typically have had a rich history of success, winning most tournaments and championships, and feel very confident of their ability and skills. However, competition has been increasing, and the athlete "hears stories" rampant drug use among his or her competitors. The athlete now feels that in order to compete, he or she must "at least try the drug" so they are on even grounds. In this first stage of drug use, the athlete begins to feel the pressure of others, and may experiment with steroid use just to see if they can have an extra advantage in competition. At this first stage regarding the evolution of the use of steroids, the athlete has "done his homework" in the sense that they now know what the specific steroid in question does, how often to use it for maximum benefit, and most importantly where to access the drug. The athlete begins using the steroid on an experimental basis, meaning that he or she uses it very infrequently and rarely.

  In our example with the athlete Greg, the football player, he had heard about the steroid uses and the many positive factors that were associated with its use. He was also beginning to feel somewhat insecure about his own position as offensive tackle during his senior year, and was made even more insecure when the younger (and stronger) lineman reported for spring training. He felt compelled to just "experiment" once or twice to see the effects (if any) the steroids would have on his own physical performance. He wasn't planning on "becoming a user" and just wanted to see if this drug could give him "a little push" to outperform the other players. Greg was not aware of the fact that the process of experimentation is the leading cause of beginning drug abuse among athletes in college and the professional world of sports. Greg now begins to use steroids ("Dynaball") just once or twice before practice to see how it makes him feel during training and exercise. He likes it (a positive experience) and decides to continue.

- *Occasional Use.* In this second stage of illicit drug use, the athlete has made contacts with others regarding accessing the drug, how to use it, and how to obtain the best benefits from the drug specifically for athletic performance. Here the athlete has moved beyond the "experimentation" phase now to occasional use—now, before important matches, such as preliminary heats or qualifying games the athlete uses steroids. The important qualification to note here is that the athlete still feels that they are in control of the use of the drug, and that the rationalization and justification of the drug use is that they could still do "just as good a job" without the drug, but the drug is used only as a form of a "guarantee" to perform at their best. However, the reality is that the athlete is experiencing a greater dependency on the drug and is now using the drug as a distinct advantage over other athletes during competition. More importantly, there also is developing a psychological dependency on the steroid, where here the athlete feels that they would be at a distinct disadvantage among other competitors without the drug;

- *Moderate Use.* In this third stage of steroid use, the athlete now is using the drug or steroid on a regular basis, still believing that "they are in control" of using the drug. Furthermore, at this third stage of drug use, the athlete still feels confident that their quality and style of play is superior with or without the use of the steroid. The athlete at this level of drug use is not aware of the dependency that he or she has developed in using the drug, and is beginning to see some of the negative side effects that are associated with steroid use. Typically, athletes at this level of drug use experience a positive or euphoric level of a sense of accomplishment, an unrealistic sense of power and "being able to do anything I want." However, the individual who is using steroids at a moderate level is experiencing a high degree of mood swings that are associated with their performance. They tend to over-exaggerate their accomplishments and are excessively self-critical of their own performance during training, and are especially prone to criticism of their style of play while under the (moderate use) influence of steroids;

- *Heavy Use.* During this "heavy use" phase, the athlete has now become both psychologically and physically dependent on the drug or steroid use. This is typified as the athlete literally risks his or her career on the clandestine use and maintenance of the drug. Heavy use of the drug includes frequent injections before most practice sessions and before all games. The athlete now has the tendency to engage in delusions regarding his or her accomplishments, and is highly emotional due to the heavy use of drugs. The athlete typically has distorted perception and judgment in their training and practice, are subject to extreme depression and manic phases of athletic skills and performance. The heavily dependent steroid user typically mimics many of the same behaviors that we see with true manic-depression clients: Extreme mood swings, bouts of depression characterized by delusions of grandeur. The athlete at this fourth stage of drug use is especially prone to self-critical analysis of the style of play (which ultimately leads to chronic depression) or highly elevated (albeit unrealistic) perceptions of superior athletic performance. In other words, the athlete is becoming increasingly more unable to adequately judge the quality of his or her performance. Finally, people familiar with the athlete typically begin to notice problems and are become suspicious that some form of drug use is probable for this unexplained behavior.

- *Termination: The End of a Career.* The erratic and inconsistent behaviors are inevitable with illicit drug use. In most cases, athletes who rely heavily on the drug use have sacrificed their careers and are at risk for exposure. As more and more sports (amateur and professional) are requiring random drug testing as part of their protocol, athletes who use steroids are more at risk. At this fifth and final stage of the evolutionary history of drug use, typically three scenarios may develop that will influence the remainder of his or her career:

    a. *Rehabilitation.* A fortunate and very positive consequence of the termination phase is that the athlete now comes to terms with his or her continued drug use. They must admit the negative impact that the drug has had on their performance and must acknowledge a desire to "stay sober" free from steroid use. The fortunate athletes are the one's that have supportive families, coaches and team mates who offer support throughout the rehabilitation process. The greater the ability of the athlete to admit drug dependency and a commitment to abstain from future use, the greater the likelihood that they will remain off the steroid drug and even possibly re-enter the world of sports. Much depends on the philosophy and support of the coaching staff and policy of the team that the athlete happens to be representing;

b. *Athlete Caught Using Drugs—Doesn't Admit Any Wrongdoing.* In this second phase of the termination stage, the athlete is unfortunately still in denial in the dangers of the use of the steroid, and even in some cases denial of using any drug at all. Many athletes are convinced (or at least have been influenced to think) that certain types of steroids are "not detectable" and if they take the right drug, at the right time, then they can use their drug without detection. Unfortunately, this is not true. Typically, the athlete here remains in an unhealthy form of denial, where they argue that a "false positive" developed and they were unfairly singled out. Here, the athlete may suffer consequences ranging from a simple fine, suspension, or even disqualification for the sport altogether.

c. *Athlete Caught Using Steroids—Suspension & Disqualification.* In this third and final phase of the fifth stage of the evolution of drug use, the athlete is caught using steroids as a means to enhance performance and continues to deny use of any illegal drug. Furthermore, this is typically the second or third infraction involving drug use. Typically the athlete who is caught violating the team drug policy for the second or third time may suffer from long term suspension (without pay) through expulsion from the team or league, without an opportunity to play again in the future.

As we can see, the use of steroids in sports can lead to a very unhealthy and unfortunate experience. It is very rare for the athlete to "occasionally" use steroids, experience fame and world class ranking, and never use the drug again. The athlete typically builds the dependency on the drug until exposure becomes inevitable. The athlete's judgment and overall perception becomes distorted through frequent use of steroids, in addition to their growing reliance on steroid use make them especially vulnerable to detection and exposure.

In terms of treatment, the athlete needs to physically withdraw from continued drug use and participate in a drug rehabilitation program. As our society places more and more emphasis in winning, and as we invest more money in to athletic programs, there will be a greater and greater temptation by athletes to use performance enhancement drugs. If we de-emphasize the importance of winning and begin to focus more on the style of play and good sportsmanship, the perceived need for drug use will also decline. Furthermore, if we educate athletes of the inherent dangers of the use of steroids, we may be better able to prevent the continued use of these dangerous drugs.

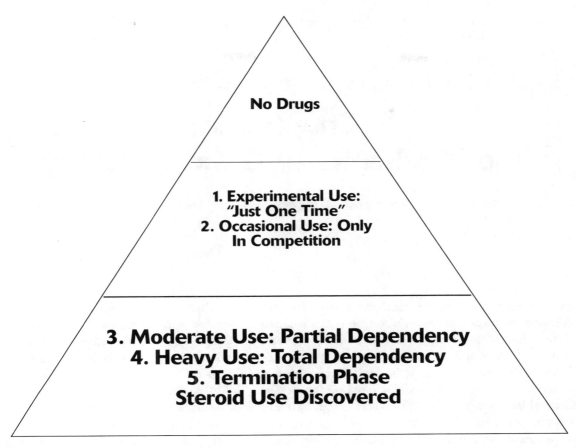

Figure 10a   The Evolution of Drug Dependency in Sports

■ CHAPTER 10 QUESTION & REVIEW

1. In your own opinion, describe whether or not you feel that drugs are a problem in modern sport. For example, is it fair to compare records established in modern sports where drugs have been a known contributing factor to older records where steroids were <u>not</u> available (e.g., Barry Bonds's home run record in National League Baseball with Hank Aaron's record of ?);

2. In your view, can the use of steroids in professional sports ever be justified?

3. Identify the five major classifications of drugs;

4. Identify and describe the five stages of steroid use among elite athletes;

5. Identify a rehabilitation program for athletes using illicit drugs and comment on what you feel are appropriate sanctions.

Chapter 11:
The Mechanics of Good Coaching

What are the characteristics that create effective coaching skills in team or individual sports? This is perhaps the most important question that we can ask when trying to understand the dynamics of human behavior that is involved in competitive sport situations. The dynamic relationship between coach and athlete is a complex one; often, the strategies and communication styles that are highly effective with one athlete may be ineffective with other athletes. Good coaches are compassionate and understanding; great coaches, however, possess the skills that make athletes want to rise above and excel like never before. The great coach earns the respect of his or her athletes, and they are always in total control of what happens before, during, and after the game. The greatest coaches are part psychologists, part drill instructors, and in many cases, the athlete's best friend and confidant. Being a great coach means understanding the psyche and mentality of the athlete—knowing how hard to push, if at all, and when to be demanding as well as yielding. The greatest coaches have the capacity to make athletes realize their true positive potential in spite of mental blocks or negative belief systems. This capacity to see a positive force in light of intense competition is critical among effective coaching skills. Many psychologists call this capacity of the athlete "self-efficacy."

The term self-efficacy refers to a positive belief system that enables the athlete to believe that they can accomplish their goals. The term was introduced by Albert Bandura (1977) in his now famous text: "Self-Efficacy: The Exercise of Control." In this chapter, we use the term specifically to describe how athletes perceive problems in sport competition and their approach in addressing these problems. The highly efficacious athlete feels actually positively empowered when faced with a problem, and believes that they have the skills to master most challenges set before them. Note the differences between "self-efficacy"—self-efficacy refers to the internal belief to master a *specific* problem in sports (i.e., "How can I make this 3-point shot" or "How can we make the first down on 4th and 5 yards?") whereas self-esteem refers more generally how we feel about ourselves. Self-efficacy is very situation and problem-specific. Effective coaches have the rare ability to create and stimulate positive self-efficacy among athletes. More importantly, effective coaches know that descriptive terms such as self-efficacy and self-esteem are learned components that occur in the relationships with parents, teachers, and within the family dynamic. Just as a child may develop a negative sense of self from overly critical (but well-intentioned) parents, an effective coach can tap into the positive belief system that we all have (what Adler called the "creative self") and develop self-efficacy within the athlete.

Successful coaches use many different strategies to help their athletes reach their goals, however, most of the greatest coaches have used a combination of three strategies ("The Three Great Virtues of Coaching"—Figure 11a):

Figure 11a   The Three Great Virtues of Coaching

In figure 11a, we see a combination of several characteristics that have been used to produce some of the most successful athletes in sport competition. In first determining realistic goals, the coach must have an accurate assessment of the athlete's prior training history, their own opinion of their competence, and finally an accurate perspective of future competition and opponents. For example, if a track runner wants to reduce his 800 meter running time by 2 seconds in the next 6 months, the coach would need to first review his training history and determine a pattern of reduced running times combined with specific training regimens. If the coach has determined that interval and sprint training are most effective every two to three months, then the athlete would be expected to be successful in reducing his or her times. Additionally, most athletes excel with a realistic goal in mind—it provides for them something to work towards. An effective coach knows exactly what his or her athlete is *currently* doing in terms of athletic performance as well as what they are *capable* of doing. The most effective coaches utilize in their training programs the three great virtues (realistic goals, positive belief system and a commitment to training) and the effects are very positive. A positive correlation exists among those coaches who have incorporated these three training characteristics and a winning philosophy. Furthermore, the most positive and dynamic coaches are those coaches that have a strong and clear understanding of each athlete's capability (athletic aptitude) and their current levels of performance. Their typically is very little discrepancy among their athletes in terms of what athletes are *capable* of doing and what they are actually doing (figure 11b):

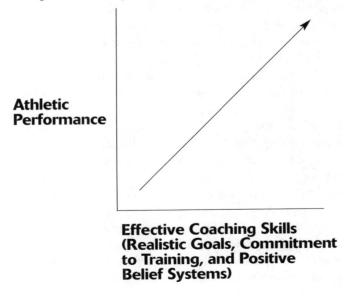

Figure 11b

Now that we know the characteristics of effective coaches, a more important question may be *how* do coaches develop these skills? There seems to be two very different attitudes regarding how good coaches learn their coaching skills. The first camp argues that good coaches are born—not made. This argument would tend to support the trait model. The trait model under personality characteristics argues that individuals are inherently born with predispositions or tendencies to behave or interact with others. Just as great athletes like Michael Jordan or Tiger Woods have outstanding eye-hand coordination and athletic skills, outstanding coaches have inherited certain traits that allow them to motivate and teach athletes to perform up to their maximum standard. Things such as temperament, attitude, leadership skills and dispositions are inherited, and environmental factors can only enhance them. Discipline and styles of communication with team members are also examples of how coaching styles may be inherited.

The other camp argues that all traits and characteristics are learned, just as all forms of behaviors are learned. We learn positive role model characteristics, good leadership skills, and ways to effectively motivate and interact with other people. The group of psychologists that would most likely agree with this view would be the social learning theorists and the behaviorists. They would argue that certain environmental characteristics may influence coaching behaviors to respond in specific ways. For example, coaches with positive and strong leadership and assertive skills have been rewarded by displaying those characteristics in situations that required quick thinking and direct action. Usually these decisions were correct (they "paid off") and the success from this decision provided the reinforcement and impetus to make similar decisions in similar situations.

In truth, most coaching behaviors and human behavior in general is a result of a complex interaction between these two paradigms of behavior. For example, most effective coaches are born with the inherent capabilities or predispositions to be effective leaders and communication skills, but also have been fortunate to have been taught how to improve those skills through a variety of environmental situations and circumstances. The result is a highly effective leader who is capable of motivating individuals in competitive situations. In a recent study that evaluated the time line and progression of experiences that are necessary in effective coaching skills, Schinke and colleagues (1995) discovered seven ideal experiences that are necessary in the development of good coaching skills:

a. *Early Sport Participation.* In order to be the most effective coach, the coach must have some experiences in the sport that he or she is actually coaching in. This is a very controversial point, as several athletes (and coaches) have maintained that personal experience in the sport that you happen to be working in is not that important. It can be argued that coaches may understand the technical points and components of their sport, but the psychological and physical experiences that are associated with each sport can only be understood if that individual has participated in the sport he or she is coaching. Imagine, for example, you are a long-distance track coach working with 10 kilometer athletes and marathon athletes. Clearly, understanding the stamina and pain that one must endure to be an athlete in these categories can only be accomplished by doing it yourself, considered to be a "rite of passage" among many athletes;

b. *National Elite Sport.* At this level, many athletes-turned-coaches have actually participated in national competition representing their schools or universities. The have participated in national level competition and have achieved recognition in participating in a prestigious tournament (i.e., a bowl game for a football player or the NCAA basketball championship series);

c. *International Elite Sport.* At this third level of career stage for coaches, experience in international competition, such as the Olympic games, where you are honored to represent your country, is considered to be the pinnacle of an (amateur) athlete's career;

d. *Novice Coaching.* At this beginning point of a coaching career, the neonate coach has retired his or her athletic experiences and participation and are now using these skills to begin a new career as a coach. While all athletes respect a competent coach, those coaches with a reputation as an elite athlete will clearly have an advantage when beginning work with other younger athletes. However, if the beginning coach is incompetent, even the most illustrious previous athletic career cannot prevent criticism from the public;

e. *Developmental Coaching Skills.* In this second phase of coaching skills, the new coach now is gaining experience as an effective coach and learning the skills necessary to teach and model appropriate athletic skills. The coach at the developmental level now is attempting to create a reputation and begin working in the university environment or college sports;

f. *National Elite Coaching.* At this level of coaching, the coach has established himself or herself as a very experienced and knowledgeable individual about the history of sport and more importantly understands the psychology of the athlete. Successful coaches who reach the level of national elite competition now are considered to be the top 10% of coaches and have brought their teams to national competitive title competition. For many coaches, this level is the crowning achievement of a life's career in coaching. Examples of coaches who have reached this prestigious level would include John Wooden (UCLA 1970–1980) and Pete Carroll (USC 2003–2005). These two prototype examples of coaches have brought their teams to national championship levels, and created a superior team by combining skills, psychological characteristics and self-confidence as deciding factors that influenced opposing teams;

g. *International Elite Athlete.* In this final stage of coaching, the international elite coach has the very rare opportunity to work with a group of highly talented individuals who are representing their country in international competition. This rare honor, however, comes with a caveat: Elite athletes have reputations for being difficult to manage and typically do not respond well to new coaches. Elite athletes typically have been coached by their personal trainers and are resistant to information and instruction given to them by "strange" or different coaches. The U.S.A.'s men's basketball team of 2004 is a very good example, where many of these athletes had experienced difficulty in working with new team members and even problems with new coaches.

■■ WHAT DO ATHLETES WANT IN A COACH?

If you ever happen to interview athletes from a variety of different sports, the majority of their responses indicate someone who is knowledgeable in their sport, supportive, firm and compassionate, but most of all athletes have commented that they want a coach that helps them achieve their maximum ability through positive motivational strategies (see figure 11c). Athletes generally work best with coaches who are effective listeners and know how to motivate individual athletes under a variety of situations. Furthermore, athletes report that their best experiences with coaches are those coaches who remain positive and very clear in expectations of them during the season (see figure 11d). The ingredients that are necessary to make the proper "fit" between coach and athlete are very complicated. Human personalities, communication styles and personal belief system and philosophy all combine to form a very important style for each athlete. As we discussed in figure 11a, the "Three Great Virtues" in coaching appear universal in sport and athletic training: Coaches that appear to be intrinsically motivated to work with their athletes (i.e., "not just here for the salary"), coaches that have the information and experience to set challenging and realistic standards of performance for their athletes, and finally those coaches that enable athletes to make their commitment to the game, to themselves, and finally to their team mates.

Other coaches follow a more basic approach to training: They are highly intrinsically motivated to work with their athletes, and often make personal sacrifices to meet those responsibilities. They also have the positive belief system in themselves and in their team. They tend to disregard what the statistics seem to suggest and focus more on the human element—what people are capable of achieving. Coaches that are highly successful also know the realistic limits of their athletes and work well within these boundaries. Effective coaches are constantly educating themselves with new information, new subjects of interest that will impact performance levels of their athletes. Finally, successful coaches are satisfied with improvements of each athlete and are quick to note and reward those improvements, however small. Effective coaches know that development and growth depend on small but consistent approaches to success. In review, we have identified five methods in achieving success in athletics that are used by dynamic coaches today—known as the **IMPRES** technique (see figure 11c):

1. **Intrinsic Motivation.** Effective coaches themselves are highly intrinsically motivated, and more importantly they know how to motivate their athletes. The most successful and dynamic coaches are those coaches who appear to receive joy and happiness in what they are doing, and often make many personal and professional sacrifices in their attempts to achieve their goals. Clearly . . . coaching is not a job where you "just show up" for a few hours—the best coaches are those that love what they do, and it shows in their behavior. Many athletes are very much aware of those coaches who have a passion for what they do (on and off the court or field) and those who do not. Clearly, the most effective and dynamic coaches are the ones that love the game;

2. **Positive Belief Systems.** Effective coaches often defy the odds and statistics—they know that the "human element" is often much more powerful than any mathematical formula that has been designed to interpret human factors (n. b., The "BCS formula" used to determine college football rankings has been criticized often because even thought mathematical formula suggests that a specific team ranks #1, most often the coaches and sports writers disagree, citing other teams). A positive belief system is contagious—when athletes and players see that the coach believes in something—then they begin to believe in something; conversely, if the coach appears cynical, then athletes wonder to themselves 'why bother?';

3. **Realistic Goals.** The effective coach is aware of what his athletes are capable of producing (a term called *athletic aptitude*) and what levels they happen to be currently performing at. As we discussed in figure 11b, very little discrepancy exists between the highly effective coach and his awareness of athletic ability. The effective coach knows that all athletes build on gradual steps of success, and these goals are only realized through goals that are manageable. As the athlete is becoming more and more successful in achieving these goals, their self-efficacy and self-confidence improves—critical factors in successful competition;

4. **Education.** The highly effective coach is constantly educating himself or herself to improve their overall quality of coaching. The sport world is constantly changing in terms of rules, qualifications, and regulations, and the effective coach keeps himself or herself apprised of these changes. Similarly, education is absolutely critical and important for the athletes of the team regarding academics. Effective coaches are aware of his or her athlete's academic rank and standing. Most coaches are aware that NCAA athletes actually have higher GPA rankings than students in general. One final point worth noting here is the link between effective and dynamic coaching and the positive relationship with the athlete's teachers and professors. The effective and dynamic coach never interferes between the academic integrity of the athlete and the educational system. Coaches should know the quality of academic performance of each athlete but never interfere with a professor's grading system with academically challenged athletes;

5. **Small Steps to Success.** The successful and dynamic coach knows that athletes progress best with a consistent and gradual approach to goal achievement. More importantly, effective coaches are quick to note each sign of success and acknowledge it. Effective coaches are very clear in how they use praise and reward systems. While many coaches appear to be very "perfectionistic"—effective coaches are very adept in identifying what is done well as well as

what needs correction. As Skinner notes in behavioral conditioning, often the most rewarding consequence of a given behavior is a simple nod of approval or praise: *Humans repeat those behaviors that produce positive or favorable consequences and avoid those behaviors that produce negative consequences.*

Five Methods of Success Used By Dynamic Coaches "IMPRES"

1. *I*ntrinsic Motivation. Coaches who are intrinsically motivated participate because they love the game and they know how to intrinsically motivate their athletes;

2. *P*ositive Belief System. Coaches who use a "positive belief system"—coaches that can often defy negative predictions based on their own positive belief system and internal locus of control. These coaches feel that they are in control of events that occur in the world of sports;

3. *R*ealistic Goals. Successful coaches know what each athlete is capable of achieving and levels of effort exerted ("athletic aptitude"). The more successful and dynamic the coach, the less discrepancy we see between athletic performance and athletic aptitude;

4. *E*ducation. The successful coach is constantly improving his or her level of knowledge, and is aware of each athlete's academic rank. The dynamic coach *never* interferes with the academic evaluation of an athlete and the grading system/evaluation system;

5. *S*mall Steps to Success. The dynamic coach knows that each successful step needs to be acknowledged and rewarded—gradual performance.

Figure 11c

■ SIX COMMON PROBLEMS IN SPORTS: HOW GOOD COACHES CAN MAKE A POSITIVE DIFFERENCE

We have discussed the characteristics of good coaching in a variety of sports. The effective coach is one who is sensitive to understanding the needs of each player, but most importantly athletes respect those coaches the most that have created an environment that allows them to maximize their skills most effectively as a team. Good coaches know when to intervene and when to allow athletes to learn from experience. We will now discuss six common hypothetical problem-scenarios involving athletic behaviors and how coaches may most effectively address these problems. Note also that the ages of each of the athletes may influence intervention strategies:

    a.   The Underachieving Athlete;
    b.   The Overachieving Athlete: The Problem of Perfectionism in Sports;
    c.   The Injured Athlete;
    d.   The Malcontent: Mutiny on the Team;
    e.   The Failing Athlete; and
    f.   Poor Communication Among Players;
    g.   Goosen's Theory: Play With Passion

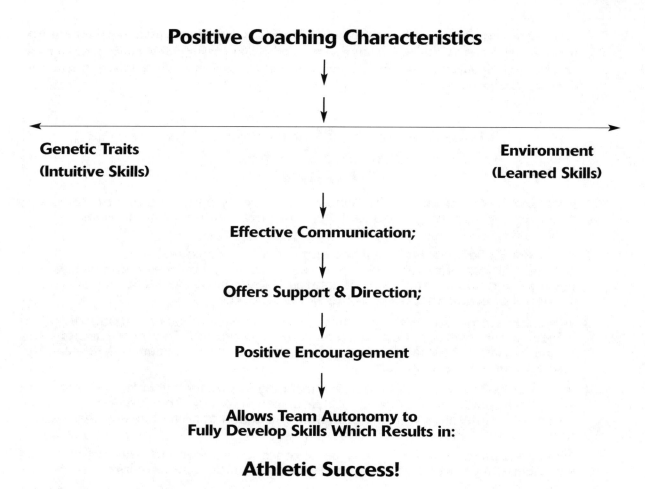

Figure 11d Necessary Characteristics in Successful Coaches

Billy—The Chronic "Underachiever"

Perhaps one of the most common and unfortunate situations that many coaches are faced with is in motivating the underachieving athlete. To compound matters further, the underachiever typically feels that they at best are mediocre athletes and simply lack the self-confidence to keep trying. The underachiever is frustrating for any caring teacher or coach because they can see the ability that lies inside the student athlete, but cannot help them discover the power within themselves. Many parents will comment to coaches that they know that their son or daughter is capable of improved performance, such as hitting or catching a ball, but when their game comes and they are actually playing on a team, the children do not perform up to their levels of performance. In Billy's case, his father was frustrated because at home Billy could catch baseballs and hit balls very well. Billy seemed more relaxed at home and even appeared to be enjoying the activity more at home. Upon closer analysis, when young children (between the ages of 6–12) are not playing up to perceived competency levels, typically self-confidence and experience are two key factors. The underachiever simply has not yet had the opportunity to discover how to apply his or her skills in a wide range of environments. Younger children who are not performing up to the potential may be intimidated by the new area (such as the ball park or the bleacher seats with cheering fans) or other players. Usually, lots of support and encouragement combined with more practice that simulates the game situation are the key factors in addressing the underachiever who is intimidated by external variables. However, a more stubborn psychological problem may be the underachieving child due to limited sport self-efficacy and self-esteem. In this other type of situation, often demanding and critical parenting skills are often the blame for children who doubt their competency and skills in sports. Often well-intentioned parents may criticize their children inappropriately, and if this occurs frequently the child learns to stop applying himself as a means of avoiding criticism. Parents may wish to engage in softer and more supportive styles of interaction with children and incorporate a "shaping program" where children gradually progress from one step to another in a structured and supportive environment.

This positive "sports-shaping" program will not only boost the morale needed by your child, but will also effectively improve your communication skills with him or her as well. Once the underachieving child realizes that they in fact do have the skills necessary to perform the activity in their sport, they become less inhibited and more interactive. This increase in activity with the child's peers will also provide a more positive and supportive environment that improves the self-esteem and self-confidence of the child. Remember—the basic foundation underlying most cases of underachievement is a fear of failure and lack of positive sport self-efficacy. When coaches and parents provide more encouragement and support for the underachieving child, positive results are sure to follow. The coach and parents can believe in the potential of the child, but the child has to realize his potential in order to make effective changes. The coach can provide the environment where these changes are most feasible. As self-esteem and sport self-efficacy increase, underachievement decreases (see figure 11e). As Billy became more relaxed while playing catch, hitting and throwing the baseballs with his friends and coach, his ability began to improve significantly, and he was able to incorporate the information more effectively because he was enjoying the game.

Remember the interesting relationship between Alfred Adler's concept of "feelings of inferiority"—that we all have some feelings of being not good enough" and thus we strive to improve these universal feelings of inferiority by improving and compensating a particular activity and perfecting it. This process, according to Adler, is a naturally occurring psychodynamic process that allows children to strive and excel in areas where they initially had experienced difficulty. At some point the underachieving child will select an activity that he or she is initially inferior at but with the support and encouragement of the parent and coach, will overcome the feeling of inferiority and eventually excel and outperform others. It is precisely the feelings of inadequacy and inferiority that provide the motivation for the child to overcompensate his or her perceived weaknesses. If this occurs with parental support and the guidance of the coach, the underachiever will most likely develop into a highly adaptive and competent athlete.

A second possible explanation of the underachieving child may address the context and quality of the relationship with the parents and coaches. Erikson placed tremendous responsibility on the roles of parents in shaping and developing personality characteristics of the child. For example, if we associate Erikson's psychosocial theory (stage #4: Industry versus inferiority) we can see the profound role that parents have in the development of physical and psychosocial activities. Parents who may be overprotective (i.e., don't let the ball hurt you!) overbearing and controlling ("How many times do I have to tell you . . . keep your eye on the ball!") may inhibit the creative "style of life" that Adler describes. Erikson's theory of psychosocial development emphasizes the importance of collaboration with children and allowing them to learn independently and autonomously. More importantly, according to Erikson children need to learn from their experiences and have fun in the process of learning. Thus, with the underachieving child, parents need to work cooperatively with children when learning sports-related activities and provide an environment where they can learn and benefit from their experiences.

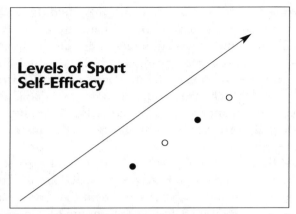

**Levels of Sport
Self-Efficacy**

Quality of Sport Performance

● = Number of Balls Caught by Billy

o + Number of Hits in Baseball

Figure 11e Positive Correlation between Sport Self-Efficacy and Sport Performance

The Overachieving Athlete: The Problem of Perfectionism in Sports

We have been discussing the importance of the role of parenting in sports, and how often our expectations as parents influences the performance of children's behavior in sports. For example, in the earlier example describing the "underachieving" child in sports we identified several factors that may influence the child's potential to play up to his or her ability. The critical parent or coach was one example, identifying the need for children to be encouraged positively to participate in their exercise program. The parent that continually criticizes the child during the formative years may result in the child not willing (or able) to perform to unrealistic expectations of their performance. The (well-intentioned) hyper-critical parent or coach may influence the child to believe that their skills are inadequate for the technique that they are learning in their sport. This is especially important during the formative years of learning, such as ages five through eight or nine years. Just as parenting skills influence children's underachievement, more and more often we are beginning to see how critical coaching and parenting skills may influence the child to have a highly unrealistic perception of their own athletic performance, often resulting in a compulsive individual where individual satisfaction is never achieved. Support for the young athlete during this period of time is absolutely critical—helping the child to understand the mechanics of the sport and how to enjoy the sport at the same time. Good coaches know how to implement new skills gradually, and parents should show support during this critical period.

As competition increases among the academic and sports worlds, we are beginning to see parents getting their children involved in special training camps for baseball, football and soccer, placing more emphasis on winning rather than enjoying the particular sport that they are trying to learn. In the academic world, we are seeing more and more often parents enrolling their children in special tutorial schools, and even kindergartens are now all day (6 hours). When describing the overachieving athlete we should perhaps mention Freud's superego and unrealistic expectations of performance. If you will recall the previously discussed Freudian theory of psychoanalysis, the ego of the personality was considered to be the executive or the "adult" of the personality that met the needs of the id (child—impulsive) and superego (parent—moral objective and ego ideal). Somehow, according to Freud, the ego has to meet the demands of these two counter-opposing forces. When individuals have an overwhelming superego, the moral conscience is constantly telling the athlete to train harder, run faster, and continuously work. Many successful athletes have incredible work ethics, and it could be argued that their personality is dominated by the superego that Freud discusses.

A second (and more plausible) theory addressing perfectionism in sports is presented in an interesting paper by Gordon Flett and Paul Hewitt (2005). In their paper, the authors argue that the existence of perfectionism (defined here as unrealistic expectations of sport performance characterized by an inability to feel or recognize satisfaction in exemplary sport performance) is actually a maladaptive trait that can deter ideal athletic performance. Further, these researchers argue that perfectionism is a negative factor that contributes to maladaptive outcomes. They also show an interesting correlation between (not surprisingly) high levels of perfectionism with low levels of self-esteem. However, while we certainly agree that perfectionism can interfere with exceptional athletic performance and can contribute to a negative or skeptical level of self-esteem, we take issue with Flett and Hewitt in summarizing that all forms of perfectionism are counterproductive. Whether or not perfectionism is productive or counter-productive depends on how it is used in the coaching philosophy. We feel that while perfectionism is *potentially* destructive in athletic sport and competition by providing unrealistic expectations of performance, coaches can encourage athletes to try their best and strive for their own personal (relative) levels of perfection. Athletes who are competitive need to be reminded that the term "perfectionism" is quite relative, and that when athletes are encouraged to strive for "relative perfection" (perfection relative to their own levels of performance) ideal performance typically results. However, when athletes (and coaches and parents) perceive perfectionism in "absolute standards" (i.e., only one level of perfect performance) then pressure builds and performance typically deteriorates. Successful and highly competitive athletes typically perceive perfection as being more relative to the "ideally perfect" concept but also realized that "perfectionism" is itself a hypothetical nonentity.

In other words, the concept of perfectionism is only maladaptive if the athlete truly believes that he or she can become "perfect" in their sport. However, if the athlete (more realistically) understands that his or her behavior has the capacity always for improvement, and that perfection is a *relative* (rather than absolute) standard, performance can then actually improve. The healthy perception of perfectionism in the world of sports exists when the athlete realizes that this concept is a goal that we are always striving for, but philosophically never is truly attainable. We further maintain that critical evaluations of performance are different than expectations of positive performance. Perfectionism in sports becomes highly adaptive when the athlete sees their performance as improving toward an ideal standard. Perfectionism in sports becomes destructive when the athlete obsesses over past mistakes and becomes highly critical of their performance. Perfectionism, then, is a learned trait that is influenced by parents (and coaches) who have high expectations of performance from their children and athletes.

Positive Perfectionism: An Injury Actually Improves Billy's Performance; Negative Perfectionism: Billy Can't Let Go Of His Mistakes

We have described the concepts of perfectionism as being potentially either a positive or negative personality characteristic that influences athletic performance as well self-efficacy. The term "positive perfectionism" refers to a style of athletic performance where the athlete attempts to compete and perform flawlessly according to his or her standards, but also realizes that performance can always be improved. Conversely, the concept of "negative perfectionism" refers to an unrealistic expectation of athletic performance based on one absolute (impossible) standard of sport performance. Furthermore, distinctions between positive and negative perfectionism should address the personality *consequences* of sub-standard levels of performance during competition. Positive perfectionism athletes who do not perform to their perceived levels of ability of course are disappointed,

145

but the disappointment serves to motivate them to try harder. They are more motivated to correct their mistakes in future competition, and view the failure as a challenge that they are capable of mastering. Conversely, the negative perfectionism athletes who do not perform to their absolute standards of performance dwell on their perceived failures and have difficulty becoming motivated in future training—they begin to question their own competency and often become angry or depressed with themselves. We will now discuss again a hypothetical scenario of "Billy" and describe Billy's athletic performance from two very different perspectives: Positive perfectionism and negative perfectionism.

Positive Perfectionism: A Healthy Response to Injury

As a 22 year old track and field athlete, Billy has accomplished many goals during his athletic career. At age 18 he was given a full scholarship to UCLA for holding one of the fastest 800 meters hurdles times in the United States. He was also a champion triple-jump athlete and held the school record for three years. Billy was strong, young, and the future appeared to be very bright until two months ago when he pulled his hamstring while training. At first he didn't think much of the injury, but now for the last several weeks he hasn't been able to train at the levels he had wanted, and now he was becoming very frustrated with himself, with his trainer, and with his coach. Billy realized that his performance was based on his ability to maintain a healthy and sensible level of training and recuperation, and that most injured people he knew in track tried to come back off the injury much too rapidly, only making it worse. He vowed not to make this mistake. Billy's life time goal was to run the 800 meters under a 1:30 pace (a 45 second split on the 400). This clearly was a world class time, but before the injury Billy was on pace to break this record. Just two weeks before his injury he had run the 800 in 1:35 and this was a relaxed pace. His athletic intuition somehow told him that if he maintained a positive frame of mind and recuperated slowly, that the record would be his.

For the next six months, Billy's coach and trainer placed him in a vigorous and intense rehabilitation program—the hamstring felt fine (great in fact) and Billy was tempted to begin training early, but he decided against it. It was frustrating knowing that he could break the record, and the timing of the injury could not have been worse. However, his levels of performance and expectations of performance were right on target, and his positive frame of mind and support from his family helped him through his rehabilitation process. One year after his hamstring injury, Billy began training again for the record in the 800 meters. He trained harder than ever before. People told him all of the time that no athlete in track ever comes back after a hamstring injury such as his, that he should try a different event. Billy ignored the negative and critical information and focused more on his own levels of positive perfectionism: High levels of expectation tempered by months of diligent training. Billy had seen his times drop due to consistent and very disciplined training. His coach was very supportive and positive of his efforts. He remembered what his coach had told him of the three virtues of training: A positive sense of self, consistent training and most importantly realistic goals. He had questioned whether or not breaking the world 800 meters was really "realistic." His coach felt that he had a chance, due to his very consistent times dropping during training, but more importantly, he believed in himself. His levels of positive perfectionism allowed him to break through the negative stereotypes of injured athletes and excel as he had never done before. Then it happened—at the NCAA finals later that spring he broke the 800 meters. He had wanted this goal because he felt it was possible for him to achieve, but more importantly he wanted to attain this goal because he had felt it was his destiny to do so. The only way Billy was able to achieve his goal of winning the 800 meters was through the development of a philosophy to achieve what no one had ever achieved— especially after becoming injured. In his case, expectations of perfection was especially meaningful after Billy had injured his hamstring. Billy continued training after wining the 800 meters because the training itself was rewarding for him. He now volunteers coaching at the local high school and teaches young athletes track techniques.

Negative Perfectionism: An Unhealthy Response to Injury

After his injury, Billy became reclusive and withdrawn. He had heard from many "authorities" that hamstring injuries can end careers in track, and something deep inside him told him that his career was over. He was very angry—he had invested years of training and work, only to be injured in a senseless training mishap. He was warming up two months earlier and tripped over his shoelaces. This was a stupid and careless mistake that could now cost him his athletic career. He consulted with his coaches and trainers—and they all recommended taking off six to twelve months for rehabilitation. He reluctantly agreed, however, complained throughout the entire process. He insisted to himself and to others that he would be back—better and faster than ever before, and that nothing would ever stop him. His expectations of performance were higher than ever before—he wanted to run faster than he had before the hamstring injury. He told himself that he had to do this, and that if he failed, his career simply would be ended—there simply would be no excuse for failure. His rehabilitation went well, however, Billy began training too soon, and re-injured the hamstring. He was depressed and angry at himself. Most importantly, his negative perfectionism contributed to his premature training that ultimately caused the re-injury (see figures 11f and 11g).

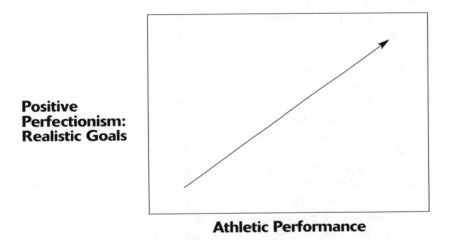

Figure 11f

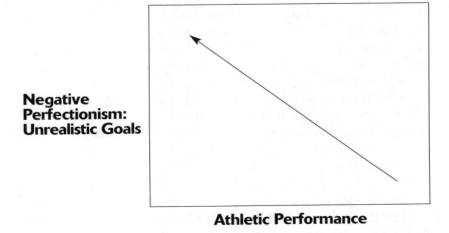

Figure 11g

The Injured Athlete

When working with the injured athlete, coaches must be aware of the fact that athletes are typically depressed and frustrated, and this frustration may influence their willingness and ability to maintain a healthy rehabilitation schedule. Many factors go into the nature of the injury of the athlete, such as the personality characteristics and attitude of the athlete. This chapter will focus on five sections that are relative to sports-related injuries:

   a. Who gets injured? Specific personality types of the athlete do appear to influence the rate and progression of therapy;
   b. Healthy and unhealthy psychological attitudes and traits of the injured athlete;
   c. Specific training procedures and programs for the injured athlete (muscle strains and pulls and ligament injuries);
   d. Psychological Rehabilitation Goals for the injured athlete; and
   e. Five Stages of the Athlete's Injury Recovery (AIR) Program.

Recent research suggests that specific types personality characteristics of the athlete may play a significant role in the successful recovery program for injuries the athlete may have encountered during training and competition (Silva and Hardy, 1991). Silva and Hardy discovered that some of the personality traits and characteristics that contributed to the sports-prone athlete included introversion and "tender-minded" (sensitivity) characteristics were positively correlated with sports-related injuries. Conversely, those athletes who ranked or scored high as "Tough minded" on the "16 PF" personality test were significantly less likely to become injured, and responded faster in rehabilitation than the "tender-minded" injured athletes. Additionally, those athletes who scored higher in "reserved" were more likely to become injured during competition that those athletes who scored "outgoing." Of course, there are potentially methodological flaws in any psychological construct study. For example, those athletes scoring higher as "Tough minded" on the personality test may simply have responded in a socially desirable way, not indicating the true and full extent of their injury.

It seems that the constructs "tough minded" and "tender minded" refer to general attitudes and responses that generalize beyond sports competition. For example, the tough-minded athlete may be thinking: "This injury won't prevent me from competing in next week's game" or "I'm just going to block out the pain." The tender-minded personality responds more directly to injury and is more likely to focus on the injury: "I better stop . . . I don't want to make this injury worse than it already is." Furthermore, the characteristics of the "tough-minded" or "tender-minded" athletes may be generalized to other personality traits that that influence a variety of behaviors. For example, the characteristics that were positively correlated with "tough-minded" personality types included extroversion, outgoing characteristics, self-reliant and realistic in the approach to life problems. This self-reliant and autonomous attitude that is reflected among the "tough-minded" athletes probably influences their attitudes towards injury, minimizing the severity of the most common types of injury. Conversely, the characteristics that were most commonly associated with the "tender-minded" personality types included dependency, sensitivity to other people and coach's comments, and introversion. The research is continuing in addressing personality types of athletes and injury, but we may conclude that the attitude and belief system of the athlete does have an important role in the rehabilitation of most injuries. The athlete that maintains a realistic but optimistic perspective regarding the nature of his or her injury is most likely to recover from their injury.

In summary, it should be emphasized that the single most important factor in recovery from an injury may not necessarily be the type of physical injury that has afflicted the athlete, but the athlete's mental outlook and attitude regarding the nature of the injury. The psychological predisposition of the injury is very important in determining the severity and duration of the injury. Those athletes who ranked "tough-minded" in the personality scale had significantly faster recovery rates than the "tender-minded" athletes, regardless of the injury. Thus, our personality and predisposition is critical in determining the severity of the injury and how soon the athlete will be playing again in their sport activity. This point is critical and cannot be underestimated when an athlete first encounters a serious injury. A positive and realistic outlook, those typically found in the "tough-minded" athletic personality, is critical in a speedy recovery of the injured athlete.

Healthy & Unhealthy Attitudes Regarding Athletic Injuries

Given the fact that over one-third of all injuries in the world are considered to be sports-related (Uitenbroeck, 1996), it is very important that we fully understand the impact and ramifications of sports-related injuries on the individual athlete. The individual who is not familiar with intense athletic training and exercise should be aware of the subjective elements of the word "injury." The successful athlete has historically tolerated numerous minor injuries and aches and pains, and perhaps for over 95% of these injuries, a positive mental attitude is all that is needed in the recovery process. Minor sprains may require some ice for a few hours before practice resumes, so it is understandable how the serious athlete develops a philosophy about injuries that influences his or her overall training program. However there are some consistent and general patterns of attitudes that have been developed by athletes in responses to their injuries, and we will identify some of the more common ones used by athletes:

The Injured Athlete (Positive Responses): Things I Will Be Doing!

✓ "I can get over this injury, and I *will* recover from this injury . . . it won't stop me from achieving my goals";

✓ "I *will* be playing soon after this heals . . . I will come back after I follow the trainer's recommendations";

✓ "There are many things that I can be doing while in rehabilitation . . . I can stretch, watch the game videos, and go to meetings with the other players and coaches";

✓ "My team needs me to come back and play—there are many reasons why I need to get healthy again";

✓ "I am going to be as resourceful and helpful as possible while I am in the rehabilitation process—I can help the other players study their diagrams and go over play strategies with the coach. I am going to take advantage of this time to study and improve myself";

✓ "I have control over the process and quality of the rehabilitation program—I can control how it unfolds over time by being patient, diligent and positive in the overall rehabilitation process";

The Injured Athlete (Negative Responses): Things I Won't Ever Be Doing!

✓ "Why did this have to happen to me? When will I ever be able to play again? Why are these bad things always happening to me?"

✓ "I don't care what the trainer or team physician say to me—I know that I can come back much faster than they think"

✓ "Why bother even trying anymore? I'll never get back to where I once was before";

✓ "No matter what I can do—bad things will always happen to me—there's just no controlling things in my life!"

✓ "I let the team down—they were all relying on me—I guess that I'm just a failure after all."

Specific Training & Rehabilitation Procedures for the Injured Athlete

(note: this information is not intended to serve as a replacement for a medical doctor or team physician—If you are injured, seek medical assistance first)

a. *Sprains and muscle pulls:* Ice and gradual training and flexibility exercises. The most common problem with sprains and muscle pulls is that the athlete tries to begin training too soon, and subsequently re-injures the muscle or tendon. The best recommendation for these "nagging" types of injuries is taking some time off to allow the injury to adequately heal.

b. *Tears and strains.* Tears and strains, typically found in the ligament areas, are significantly more serious injuries. With all tears of ligaments (most commonly knee ligaments), the athlete must stay off the afflicted area and immediately apply ice to the injured area.

c. *Fractures.* Injuries such as fractures and breaks usually result in hospitalization and the season is over for the athlete. At this point, the injured athlete who has experienced a fracture should focus all of his or her attention on recovery and look forward to next season.

The Five Stages of Athletic Injury Recovery (AIR)

1) *Injury Discovery.* In this first stage of injury recovery, the athlete first discovers or becomes aware of the injury. The injury discovery itself usually has two different types of development that influences how the athlete responds to it:

   a) *Sudden and dramatic injury.* In these types of injuries, the athlete may have been training and twisted his or her ankle while running on the soccer field, or the track sprinter comes out of the blocks and suddenly a groin muscle is pulled. There is no mistaking the sudden and dramatic injury—it occurs quickly and painfully and interrupts the athlete's training. This form of injury typically requires immediate intervention;

   b) *Slow and nagging injury.* In the second type of injury, the injury has been slow in developing and seems to be "always present." In the slow and nagging injury, there is a usual reminder of pain somewhere in the body, such as in the left knee or right shoulder. The injury does not disrupt performance to the athlete, but nonetheless is present and lingers throughout practice and competitive situations. The athlete typically procrastinates in receiving attention to the afflicted area. In both cases, the athlete has now discovered the injury during practice or competitive situations;

2) *Injury Rejection.* In the second phase of the Athlete's Injury Recovery theory, most of the competitive athletes tend to outright disregard the serious nature of the injury and continue with their training program. Depending on how serious the nature of the injury is, this may or may not be a successful approach. For some injuries (and serious athletes typically have had numerous, a positive outlook and perseverance was all that was necessary, maybe "going easy" a few days), injury rejection is the most adaptive approach as the athlete simply focuses on his future goals and disregards the minor aches and pains that are associated with minor injuries. With the "tough-minded" athlete, most nagging or minor injuries are entirely disregarded. However, with more serious injuries, even the most seasoned and veteran athlete must make some type or form of acknowledgment of the injury;

3) *Injury Trivialization.* In the third stage of the athlete's injury recovery theory, the athlete has discovered the injury and cannot outright reject it. He or she has made some admission that there is a problem that needs to be addressed. This, in itself, is very remarkable for the serious athlete, as those close to him or her readily admit that they are not even likely to admit

to anyone that they are not feeling well, let alone discuss an injury. To the competitive athlete, acknowledging an injury is akin to admitting a flaw or weakness in one's character. In the third stage of the athlete's injury recovery theory, the athlete no longer rejects the idea of injury, but now most commonly "trivializes" the injury. The phenomenon of trivialization is very common among athletes in general, as they tend to try to focus on the positive components of the injury while disregarding the negative elements (i.e., "It could have been worse . . . I could have torn the tendon"). Such tendencies among athletes are referred to as "counterfactual thinking" where the athlete focuses on the (hypothetical) worse scenario as a means of making their true or actual injury less catastrophic. This phenomenon is very common in general and in social psychology we see people focusing on much worse occurrences as a means of making their current situation less negative (i.e., "This sprain could have been worse . . . it could have been a ligament tear"). In sports trivialization, the athlete downplays the serious nature of the injury, and in most cases (depending on the injury) this can be a very positive response;

4) *Injury Rehabilitation.* In the fourth stage of the athletic injury recovery theory, the athlete has identified the problem and no longer rejects or trivializes it. Now the athlete accepts the realistic fact that he or she has a serious injury that needs attention. In this stage, the athlete consults with his trainer or physician and a treatment or rehabilitation plan is underway. Depending on the nature of the injury, the athlete will need to take some time off training and focus entirely on recovery. In this fourth stage, a monumental step has been taken as the athlete has made the admission of the physical injury and has allowed for the rehabilitation program to begin. The importance and significance of this fourth stage cannot be understated—with many intense and competitive athletes, admitting that an injury exists is of itself highly significant. The important point to focus on now is that the competitive athlete listen and conform to the physician's recommendations and most importantly that he or she *not* come out of rehabilitation too early;

5) *Full Recovery.* In this fifth and final stage of the athlete's injury recovery theory, the athlete now is in the recovery stage. The recovery stage is post-rehabilitation and focuses on the psychological and physical behaviors that allow the athlete to either come back fully rehabilitated from the injury, or to remain in a sub-standard state. During the injury recovery stage, the athlete has completed the rehabilitation program and now is attempting to get back to the point of athletic development he or she once was at prior to the injury. This fifth and final stage is most critical and fundamental in terms of psychological support systems, as the athlete is attempting to re-establish his or her status in sports. They are also trying to re-establish previous levels of training and are fighting off their "ghosts" and insecurities of never being able to achieve previous athletic skill. Healthy support from family members and teammates and encouragement is vital for a full recovery.

The Malcontent: Mutiny on the Team

A major purpose of this chapter has been to describe the importance of coaching skills and how an effective coach may bring out the best skills in his or her athletes. An effective coach has an understanding of the needs of each of the players on his or her team—they know when players are both physically and psychologically sound and content that ensures a healthy playing environment. Morale and a collective attitude on and off the field or court is absolutely essential for a team to remain productive. Some of the most talented teams in both amateur and professional sports have been defeated not necessarily because they lacked the talent, but due to internal problems that impacted the quality of play on the court. Perhaps the most recent example of how one or two influential players can negatively impact an entire season and create team chaos is the Los Angeles Lakers NBA team of 2004. The two influential players who were in conflict with one another were Kobe Bryant and

Shaquille O'Neill. When one very influential player expresses dissatisfaction and discontent over the team (such as Kobe Bryant), player communication ceases and the overall quality of play is dramatically impacted. Players often "take sides" among each other and a "team mutiny" often is the result. In the case of Kobe Bryant and Shaquille O'Neill, coach Phil Jackson left the team at the end of the season and Shaquille O'Neill was traded to the Miami Heat. Now the Los Angeles Lakers are often referred to as "Kobe's team" where Kobe typically is averaging 25 to 30 points per game. However, in the most recent rematch between Kobe Bryant and Shaquille O'Neill (Saturday, 12/25/04), Kobe Bryant scored an impressive 42 points against the Miami Heat, but still lost in overtime 102 to 103. An unfortunate end to a team that had three previous national championship titles.

How teams interact during sport competition often is a matter of how they understand, communicate and respect each other during practice times. If an influential player (i.e., "the malcontent") becomes unhappy about a coaching decision and does not take the proper channels to express and communicate his or her frustration, disaster and chaos can result. Furthermore, when the media senses discontent on the team, problems can become exaggerated and overall team frustration and dissension often result. This next section on coaching skills will address problems that are very common in team sports, when individual players on a team may "split" due to a variety of differences in philosophy. This philosophy may address the decisions that you make as a coach, so it is very important that coaches always understand the level of morale and keep communication channels open during the season. Research suggests that the single most important factor in preventing team conflict is communication among players and the coaching staff. Three effective tools that coaches can use in avoiding conflict include the "3 C's: Communication, Concern and Compromise."

Conflict Resolution in Preventing Team Mutiny: Communication, Concern & Compromise (CCC)

a. *Communication.* Perhaps the single most important tool that a coach can implement in preventing team conflict is communication. The effective coach understands what his players are thinking and feeling by frequently communicating with each member of the team. Many times athletes and players report feeling better when they feel that the coach has at least taken the time to listen and consider the problems of individual players. Players also report feeling more content when coaches have shared time with them in listening to the problems. Communication implies that the coach and athlete respect one another to listen to each other and take measures in good faith to prevent problems in the future. There may be things that coaches do that may annoy players, just as certain players may engage in behaviors that annoy coaches. The first step in conflict resolution is communicating what the problem is and then trying to make adaptive and positive changes. One problem area in particular for coaches is not necessarily the information given to teammates, but *how* the information is given. For example, critical information that is offered by the coach can be either very constructive and positive or that same information can be very destructive. It really depends how the information is disseminated to the individual athlete or team. When providing information and communicating with players, coaches need to be sensitive and understanding to all players;

b. *Concern.* Concern means not only taking the time to listen and communicate with each other, but also valuing each other's contributions and making good faith efforts to improve the relationship with each other. Concern implies that each member of the team as well as the coach has fundamental and mutual goals. For example, players and coaches may agree that they both have in common a strong drive and interest to reach national championship status, but the disagreement may be in how to arrive at that point. Furthermore, the concept "concern" means that both player and coach respect each other enough to try and improve the overall psychological climate and competitive environment of the team. Finally, the concept of concern means that both coach and players share common goals and respect one another in achieving these goals;

c. *Compromise.* Perhaps the most important category of the conflict resolution, compromise means understanding that sometimes coaches and players may have mutual goals, but the strategies on arriving to the goal may differ. In these cases, compromise may be the most effective measure on overcoming the obstacle. When players and coaches compromise, it represents that each group is trying to achieve some form of common ground. When coaches see that players are compromising with each other, then they too will be more sensitive to the needs of the team. A good example of compromise among coaches and players may be the frequency of practice times during the season. Some coaches may require athletes to be available for practice seven days a week. If athletes feel that this is unfair, they may request practice doubling on one day to allow for a six day a week practice session.

d. *The Failing Athlete:* **Good Coaches <u>Do</u> Get Involved!** Given the fact that most college athletes must maintain a minimum academic grade point average while participating in NCAA sports, academic work and rigorous standards of study skills are absolutely vital in any athletic program. While this text is designed to help improve the student understand the psychology of sport and athletic performance, it should also be noted that student athletes who achieve a "balance" between academic work and physical performance usually excel in both area. Humans function best when goals are clearly defined and each person knows what their capacity is in achieving those goals. Coaches should have clear guidelines for student athletes in terms of standards of performance while competing, and any athlete that appears to be struggling should proactively be approached by the coach to communicate problem areas. There are several are several possible reasons why the individual athlete may be suffering academically, and here are a sample of the most common reasons:

- Student athlete is new to the school and program and is adjusting to life changes;
- Student athlete is devoting too much time to practice and not enough time to academic work—student needs to develop a structured program to devote more time to studying;
- Student athlete is under-prepared for current course work;
- Student athlete is devoting too much time to social activities / lacks emotional maturity.

There are many possible solutions to the problem of the academically failing athlete. Coaches and trainers of athletic programs in schools need to be realistic in terms of the ramifications of their responsibilities and duties as a coach. The first and foremost responsibility of the coach is the welfare and future of his or her student athlete, and therefore each coach should have a sound and working relationship with the faculty of each athlete. If student athletes are experiencing difficulty with their academic program, the proactive coach consults with teachers or teaching assistants to determine what needs to be done in order to improve the situation. All too often, the student athlete does not take advantage of the school or university's numerous tutorial programs and training programs for all students who need remedial assistance. The following list is just a sample of some of the more effective methods coaches can help improve the quality of academic work by his or her student athletes—what we call the "PROACTIVE" Methods:

PROACTIVE Coaches Do the Following:

a. **P**articipation. Coaches should participate in academic programs with their student athletes to better understand the requirements of courses and expectations of professors; Coaches communicate with the professors to better understand what is needed by each student athlete—the relationship between the coach and professor regarding the student-athlete should be collaborative and a partnership—certainly not adversarial

b. **R**esponsiveness. Responsive to the student- athlete's needs. If the student-athlete needs tutors or remedial resources that will help improve the quality of education and academic performance of the student-athlete, coaches should be doing everything possible to enhance this process. For example, the coach should communicate with the professor of his or her student-athlete if (as is often the case) they will be missing a specific number of days due to tournaments and practice schedules—Coaches should be accommodating (as student-athletes) to the requirements of the course work and hopefully professors will also be understanding of the schedule of the student-athlete;

c. **O**pen Dialogue. Open dialogue between the student-athlete, the coach and professor are absolutely vital for successful academic and athletic performance. The life of the student-athlete is a very complex one, where responsibilities to the classroom and studying, as well as to the coach and team, often depend on one another. Coaches and student-athletes are well advised to communicate with each other and understand schedules to prevent conflicts;

d. **A**ctivate Resources. The student-athlete should take advantage of as many resources as possible, such as tutoring programs, remedial programs, teaching assistants and so on. The student-athlete and coach both need to be fully informed of the college or university's academic resource center to help students with educational and academic challenges. Coaches and student-athletes should also be aware that the first-year student athlete is typically the most at-risk for academic failure, due to the numerous changes and adjustments that are typical with any athletic and academic program;

e. **C**oncentrate. The student athlete should concentrate and simply prioritize the importance of academic work (what needs to be done first) and athletic work. Coaches should help his or her athletes prioritize their time most accurately and understand the full responsibility of academic and athletic work. Understanding how to prioritize and list the importance of work topics is absolutely critical to success in these areas. For example, if a student has an exam in one course, the material for that course should first be addressed, and then other course work should be addressed afterwards. Student-athletes also need to know their practice scheduling times so they may be able to balance and concentrate on what is most important first. Coaches can assist with this process by communicating clearly what is necessary to the program to allow student-athletes to better concentrate on important material first;

f. **T**eaching Skills: After the student-athlete has learned their program and they understand the requirements of the academic program, teaching these skills as a way of review often has tremendous success. For example, if the student-athlete has experienced problems with understanding plays in during football practice, have the student-athlete review and teach these same skills to other team mates as a means of preparation. If the student-athlete has experienced problems in academic curricula, they can teach the problem areas to other students or team mates as an adequate process of review. When team players work together, both academically and in athletics, communication improves and team work improves;

g. **I**nterest. Good coaches show interest in the academic program of each of his or her student-athletes. Good coaches are involved and are interested in what each athlete is doing in all of the classes and shows interest in the academic progress of each athlete as well as the athletic progress. Furthermore, student-athletes know when coaches show an interest in their overall performance as a student—this conveys to the athlete that their overall welfare is a priority to the coach and clearly will help improve performance in the classroom and on the playing field;

h. **V**alues. Great coaches show their values to each of the student-athletes by becoming involved in every important component of his or her life. Values refer to a system of measuring and knowing the differences between what is ethically right and wrong, and demonstrating to the student athlete that the most successful athletes have achieved a balance or have actualized their physical development with moral and intellectual development. Great coaches now how to instill values in each of his or her athletes by being a role model and demonstrating what they want by being a model themselves.

i. **E**xcellence. Great coaches expect nothing less than excellence from their athletes—excellence in the academic world and excellence in the world of sports. Some of the greatest college athletes were also the brightest students and were academic scholars. Great coaches know how to stimulate and motivate all student-athletes so they may achieve their highest goals. Additionally, coaches know that for most of their student-athletes, the education they receive is their most important method of achieving success after they graduate. Coaches value the importance of a balance educational experience, which includes academic skills combined with athletic skills as a means of excellence in both areas.

Poor Communication Among Players

Perhaps one of the most important sections in addressing how players relate to one another is the communication process. If poor communication exists among players on a team, information is not being utilized appropriately that will ultimately negatively impact overall performance. Players within the team must feel comfortable in expressing their views without fear of reprisals from the coach or other players, and a specific strategy or plan should be made available to players. When team mates feel that they cannot communicate with each other, or if they feel that their views are not valued, team performance ultimately will be affected. Good coaches allow for weekly player-meetings which in many cases serves as a "release" for players to get things off their chest. Some sample ideas include:

- Weekly team meetings with and without the coach. During the more traditional meetings with the coach, players are afforded time to express their views with each other;
- Weekly meetings without the coach. Meetings among players-only is an excellent methods to facilitate communication in a more relaxed manner. Sometimes players may feel intimidated or threatened during meetings with coaches, and team meetings provide an open and safe venue for players to discuss their own personal views among each other. If the information needs to be discussed with the coach, then a team player or representative can communicate the information back to the coach during the coach-players meeting.

Goosen's Theory: Play With Passion

Many coaches may describe different elements to effective coaching, however, one element that most coaches agree on is the necessity of passion in play and competition, regardless of the particular sport. Coach Greg Goosen, former Notre Dame High School football coach, comments that the most effective coach is one that knows when to push the athlete and when to hold back: "One of the rewarding elements for a coach is to live vicariously through his athletes." Coach Goosen was known to be one of the effective and demanding of coaches in high school sports, but he possessed the rare ability of knowing how to instill passion and drive in his athletes. Without the drive and passion, competition becomes meaningless. An effective coach helps athletes realize their goals by pushing them farther than they would have gone by themselves. Coach Goosen also indicates that in today's world of coaching, there are significantly more distractions to the young athlete than say 10, 15 or 20 years earlier. Technology, such as cell phones and video games and other technologically-related devices in society simply create more distractions in the world of coaching. In the real world of coaching, you simply have your athletes, the field, and practice—that's all there is and that's all that there should be. Another perspective from a coach's view is from Mr. Aaron Youngblood, who is athletic director of Compton Community College: "One of the most important psychological characteristics for athletes today is perseverance and drive in achieving their goals . . . athletes also need to remain flexible and tolerate constructive criticism from the coaching staff."

The problem with our culture today is that we tend to avoid taking personal responsibility for our actions and blame others for our own shortcomings. In the individualistic culture (as we see in our culture today), individuals become self-oriented and egoistic in their style of play and interaction. The culture that teaches young athletes to focus on how their contributions can improve the group (i.e., the football team) will produce outstanding athletes that accept responsibility for their own behavior—they ask the question how their (individual) behavior may help the group's behavior or team performance rather than how the team may help them. Coach Goosen concludes his interview by commenting on the importance of everyone becoming (and *feeling*) as part of the team and playing a vital role in competition. When people feel as thought they are contributing to the team, first-string or second-string becomes irrelevant to the athlete.

■ AVOID COACHING BURNOUT: LEARN TO RELAX

A final note to end this chapter is in the coach realizing the distinction between being capable of making good decisions with a balanced work schedule and when you simply have too much and become overwhelmed. The effective coach is most likely to make the right decisions when you are not exceeding your limit. Know when to limit your work schedule and plan events in a structured and organized manner. Trying to do too much in too short of time to appease administrators is a sure fire way to make the wrong decisions. Be aware of your limits and make your decisions in a clear frame of mind.

■ CHAPTER 11 QUESTION & REVIEW

1. Identify and describe the "three great virtues" of coaching: How can these three characteristics influence good coaching skills?
2. Identify and describe the five methods of the IMPRESS technique.
3. Briefly summarize and review how good coaches can overcome problems with the following types of athletes:
   a) The Underachieving Athlete
   b) The Overachieving Athlete
   c) The Injured Athlete
   d) The Malcontent Athlete
   e) The (academically) Failing Athlete
   f) Poor communication on the team
4. Identify the distinctions between "positive" and "negative" perfectionism.
5. Identify and describe the five stages of athletic injury recovery (AIR).
6. What does the PROACTIVE coach do?

Chapter 12:
Different Body Types as Indicators of Different Training Strategies: The Endomorph, Ectomorph and Mesomorph: Personalized Training in a Non-Personalized World

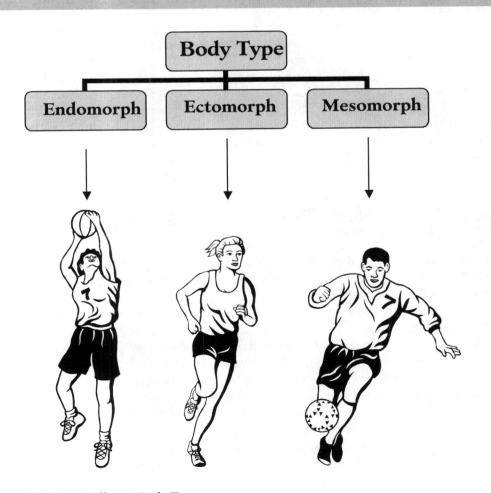

Figure 12a   The Three Different Body Types

Often in health and exercise we describe the importance of adapting to the "right" type of training program that suits the individual needs of each person. Some individuals feel that they are "better suited" for cardiovascular training, whereas others feel that weights and low-impact training are best suited for them. Given that our world has become more and more depersonalized, with a "one training program fits all mentality" it has become increasingly clear that different individuals with different body types require different types of training. The same individual utilizing the same exercise program and diet may respond very differently than another person with a different body type, therefore, individualized training programs are required to ensure maximum success in health training. Short, stocky and muscular body types (such as body builders) often prefer weightlifting exercises as opposed to aerobic or cardiovascular training) and research dating from the 1940's era (Sheldon, 1940) and more recently (Gardner & Tockerman, 1994; Ryckman and colleagues, 1989) suggest that whether or not there is truth to the concept, people associate personality type with body type. The strong and athletic body type (mesomorph) has historically experienced the stereotypes of being strong and less than intelligent (i.e., "the dumb jock") whereas the thin and angular body types (ectomorphs) have historically been exposed to the stereotypes of being bookish, overeducated and highly intelligent. Finally, the endomorph has had to tolerate the stereotypes of being slovenly, depressed (or jolly) and lazy (see Chapter 5: Modern Society and Obesity for more information on this topic).

While there is virtually no evidence in justifying these stereotypes that have been associated with body types, we must agree that simply the *expectations* of behaviors may influence some people to behave in specific ways, a term commonly referred to as "self-fulfilling prophecy" (i.e., "If everyone believes it to be true, then I may as well as behave that way."). Just as no two personalities are ever identical among individuals, the most effective types of training programs are those programs that "match" or suit both the physical body type of each individual as well as the personality type that is often associated with the body type. We will first describe the classic three body types (ectomorphic, endomorphic and mesomorphic) and will offer specific training recommendations for each of the three body types. We will also offer different types of exercise programs that may be better suited for specific personality types: Introverted and extraverted personality types and personality types A and B (topics that will be further discussed in chapter 13). Finally, we will briefly revisit the literature that describes the body types with personality types and offer specific training information and exercise tips that are associated with each personality type.

■■■ THE 3 CLASSIC BODY TYPES: ENDOMORPHIC, ECTOMORPHIC AND MESOMORPHIC

The first researcher to suggest that perhaps specific body types may be correlated with personality types was William Sheldon (1940). In this groundbreaking research article, Sheldon associated over 4000 pictures of college students with specific body types. Sheldon argued that there are three primary forms of body types that gain weight and muscle mass differently, and perhaps more importantly, that each of the body types correlates with specific personality types. While the research supporting body types and personality types is still controversial and ongoing, researchers clearly agree that there exists three different body types that influence how weight is gained (or lost) and how muscle mass is produced. We will now discuss the best forms of training for each of the body types and compare the body types with personality types: Endomorphs, ectomorphs and mesomorphs. In terms of personality characteristics of the endomorph, Sheldon's (1940) classic research identified endomorphs as being predominantly socially gregarious, food-oriented, and having an overall pleasant disposition. While recent research has conflicting results regarding personality characteristics and body types, we can see how the media and advertisements clearly perpetuate body types with personality types. The media often portrays endomorphs as being haphazard in appearance (i.e., John Candy or Christopher Farley), outspoken, food-loving and gregarious in nature. Whether or not there is truth to the correlation of body types and personality types is still questionable, however, perhaps a more accurate assessment of body types and personality would be in exploring how our portrayal of endomorphs in the media may influence their actual behaviors.

Sheldon (1940) spent most of his professional and academic career in studying physical body types and correlating them with personality characteristics. Often in sports and exercise programs we see how important individual personality types and temperament are in influencing the quality of the activity that is being performed. We will now offer a brief description of the three major body types and the personality characteristics that have been associated with those body types: Endomorphic, ectomorphic and mesomorphic. Sheldon described the personality type of the endomorph (a term that he referred to as "endotonia") as being very friendly and open with other people. The endomorphic personality type craves relaxation, comfort, food and social activities with other people. Historically, the endomorph has had difficulty with maintaining the exercise program due to their love of social activities with food. Sheldon even created a numerical scoring system for rating the endomorph, ectomorph and mesomorph, describing them in terms such as "extreme endomorph" or 7-1-1. The "extreme mesomorph" was described as 1-7-1 and the "extreme ectomorph" was described as "1-1-7." Furthermore, Sheldon described each of the body types as having corresponding personalities that matched their physical body type. However, in most cases, their typically was a "blend" or combination of body types, where a mesomorphic body type may also have characteristics similar to the endomorph, such as a very muscular individual who enjoys food and social activities. Another example of a "blend" of body types with personality characteristics would include the ectomorph (thin and angular) who enjoys outdoor activities with other people.

Sheldon described the "extreme endomorph" as an individual who enjoys relaxation, social activities with other people, and as being very deep and relaxed sleepers. They are typically slow-moving and they often assimilate food, social activities within their daily routines. In the mesomorphic personality type, personality types have been described as being very active, muscular, intense in completing a variety of activities and highly adventurous. Sheldon describes the mesomorph as being very competitive and sports-oriented, often to the point of being aggressive. Typically the mesomorph has been described as being highly "extraverted"—they prefer engaging in a variety of activities and are accustomed to being the center of attention. The ectomorphic personality is described by Sheldon as being very intelligent to the point of "bookish", aware of his or her surroundings, and highly "self-aware" of their environments and relationships with other people. Finally, the ectomorphic personality is described by Sheldon as very idealistic, seeks privacy and prefers intellectual stimulation. We will now describe the physical training and exercise programs for each of the body types based on their unique personality characteristics. As a final note, it is very common for people to categorize and classify individuals as being "either ectomorphic or endomorphic" without considering that often individuals may embrace two or more of the characteristics simultaneously. Thus, an individual who appears to be endomorphic and enjoys social activities may also be muscular and posses mesomorphic traits and qualities as well.

■ TRAINING PROGRAM FOR THE ENDOMORPH: CARDIOVASCULAR AND MORE

Given the fact that the vast majority of individuals in our society today our overweight (over two-thirds for adults and the vast majority of children) we will address the most common body type training exercises for the endomorph. We will first discuss some of the most common problems for endomorphs and provide sample exercises that have had the most success for people who are struggling with obesity. The endomorph body type is the overweight body type that currently affects over two-thirds of American adults in today's society—and the trend keeps increasing as our society becomes more automated and individualized. Furthermore, doctors and sport psychologists are arguing that exercise by itself today simply is not enough anymore to combat the overweight or endomorphic syndrome. In a recent study by the *New England Journal of Medicine* (December 23, 2004), Dr. Frank Hu discovered that obese women who exercised only (without dieting) and lean women who did not exercise both were at risk for premature death. For example, among the lean women that averaged less than 3.5 hours of weekly exercise had an increased risk of premature death by 55% when compared with lean women who did exercise on a regular basis. Among the obese women who worked out at least 3.5 hours weekly, they had an increased death rate of 91% when compared to lean women who were exercising on a regular basis. Finally, and perhaps most dramatically, the obese women who did not exercise at all had a premature death rate that was 142% higher when compared to the lean women. These results are clear evidence that the endomorph needs to adapt not only a regular exercise program into their daily life pattern, but also make conscious efforts to reduce saturated fats and high caloric foods. An overall health plan is vital to improving the quality of life among the endomorph. The health plan should not only include a regular and challenging exercise program, but also information on limiting the caloric intake and reducing size portions in the typical diet of the individual. It is very important to note, however, that the health and exercise program for the endomorphic individual who is obese should include a very gradual and progressive form of cardiovascular exercise. A recent study by the Journal of American Medical Association (1999) determined that overweight, sedentary people are more than 30 times likely to suffer from a heart attack during vigorous exertion than at any other time. The journal explains the importance in the endomorphic individual in finding an appropriate and gradual form of exercise that is cardiovascular and that may be incorporated in a daily ritual. It is not impossible, and is in fact very appealing when we read about endomorphic individuals who have been training and exercising for some time and is a success story. In a recent article by the *Daily News* (January 17, 2005) newspaper (Health and Fitness section), a column focused on an individual (Tom Burns) who was a classic endomorph (5'8" and 220 pounds) who had all but given up on exercise. He started running only two blocks before he became fatigued, but continued and gradually improved his stamina. Now he has lost 40 lbs. and is much healthier, but he commented that it is still difficult to exercise and run: "the one mental block that I face and still face to this day . . . is getting off the couch and going to run."

Our society today is constantly being inundated with catchy devices that sound very appealing but do not truly address the source of the problem of health management: sedentary behaviors and foods that are high in saturated fat. Recently an article (cover story) in the *U.S.A. Today* newspaper (January 4, 2005) addressed French-born Mireille Guiliano commenting how Americans "gulp down their food, hamburgers and French fries while working on their laptops [Chicago's O'Hare International Airport] . . . talking on their cell-phones, or reading the newspaper. I couldn't see anyone eating with pleasure. Food is one of the best pleasures in life, and we should not eat like we are robots or on autopilot, it's like stuffing yourself." Guiliano recently authored the book: "French Women Don't Get Fat: The Secret of Eating For Pleasure" where she describes eating as more of a cultural experience in France. She refers to her book as "the ultimate non-diet book" that has no pills, powders, no counting calories. Just eat food "sensibly" and "savor every bite." Guiliano further argues that eating in France is more like an experience: "We [the French] sit down, take our time, look at the sandwich, admire the bread or the butter on it. We eat slowly. We chew well [and] we stop between bites."

Let's see if we get this straight—just enjoy eating more, "savoring" the experience and somehow you lose weight? It seems ironic that where in a culture the foods are typically more fattening (such as creamy sauces, red meat, butter and cheese) the people actually are healthier. As ironic as this may sound, the data suggests this is true: 11% of the French in general are considered obese, whereas in the United States 30% of the people are considered overweight (*U.S.A. Today,* January 4, 2005). Thus, the cultural experience of eating as well as the types of food we eat all play a role in overall health. In addition to the foods mentioned earlier, Europeans in general eat healthier, combining fresh fruits and vegetables with fish. They also eat less food more often (sometimes referred to as "grazing"), where Americans tend to eat larger meals once or twice daily.

The two factors that have been identified as the key to increases in obesity in American society are sedentary activities and high caloric foods. To some degree what Guiliano says is true, as most Americans prefer to eat fast foods that are significantly higher in saturated fats and because they can "save time" (i.e., eat while driving) rather than enjoy meals as an experience with their families. There are many incentives for the endomorphic individual to lose weight—being obese *triples* the likelihood of diabetes and more recently radiologists have detected obesity as a problem in identifying a variety of health-related problems during routine medical imaging tests (*Los Angeles Times,* December 27, 2004). Furthermore, the problems of obesity and the endomorph body type have become so pronounced that some doctors are actually recommending having adults (and children) to insert a dental appliance when they eat to limit portions of eating and to reduce the rate of eating ("Want to eat less . . . Shrink your mouth" *Los Angeles Times,* December 27, 2004). The point of using the dental appliance is to encourage individuals to take smaller bites, chew more slowly. Thereby allowing the brain to register that the body has eaten enough food. Given the fact that the body requires approximately 20 minutes for the hypothalamus to signal satiety, the device has proven quite successful for people with BMI's ranging from 27 to 40 (overweight to obese). Although there are critics of the device, results were very successful, with over 50% of the obese subjects in the study eating 25% less and reduced caloric intake by an average of 659 calories. While these results are very encouraging, we need to ask ourselves if this technique is addressing the real problem of overeating, or merely serving to address the symptoms of obesity. Think about this for a moment: If you are overweight, do you really want to insert a dental piece in your mouth every time you sit down to eat a meal? This answer is, probably not.

Some recommended exercises for the endomorphic body type include the following exercises (see below—"Fatbuster" Spin):

- High-intensity/Low weight circuit training;
- Track—Outdoor jogging (4 miles) easy pace;
- Flexibility & Stretching (30 minutes) {arrow} See Cardio-Deck Training Cards;
- Dance Aerobics (30 minutes) Moderate Pace;
- Consecutive Rowing (30–45 minutes) Moderate Pace;
- Swimming (2000 meters); 6 sets of 500 meter sprints (Moderate Pace);
- Cycling (45 minutes) Easy Pace;
- Free Day! Your Choice Workout (Moderate).

a. *Endomorph.* The endomorphic body type typically gains weight very easily and quickly, however, they also gain muscle mass very quickly as well. The weight for women is gained particularly around the hips and for men in the middle stomach region. The personality type that historically associated with the endomorph is primarily negative: Endomorphs typically are sloppy, jolly, and depressed (Sheldon, 1940), where as the mesomorphs are classified as strong but lacking in intelligence (Gardner & Tockerman, 1994). Historically, the endomorphs have had the most difficulty in losing weight and keeping the weight off. The endomorphs typically gains weight around the hips, stomach and thigh region. *The key to fitness for the endomorph is consistent, regular high intensity cardiovascular training with a high number of repetitions in a weight training circuit and to change the types of foods consumed, from a high calorie diet to low fat, low calorie diet.* The endomorph must reduce caloric intake as well as increase intensity of training. It is much more productive for the endomorph to choose a low-weight training circuit and execute a high number of repetitions (say about 20) rather than high weight and low repetition strategy. The general rule of thumb in exercise training is high weight/low "rep" circuits is to put on muscle mass, whereas high rep and low weight circuits burn more calories and help the endomorph to lose weight more rapidly. *Key to Success:* Incorporating the training program as a "way of life"—the most common problem area with the endomorph is that the training becomes temporary, and the bad eating and training habits resurface. The endomorph has to convince himself or herself that they are on the right track and select some program that they enjoy enough—at least 30–45 minutes daily of cardiovascular training. Repeat: 30–45 minutes of cardiovascular training is essential for success—this is a significant change of activity and the importance cannot be overstated. The endomorph must discover some form of cardiovascular training that they enjoy and can participate in five to six days weekly. Some recommended cardiovascular training exercises include (see figure 12b—"The Fatbuster Spin"):

Training Strategies for the Endomorph: Utilizing "The FatBuster© Spin"

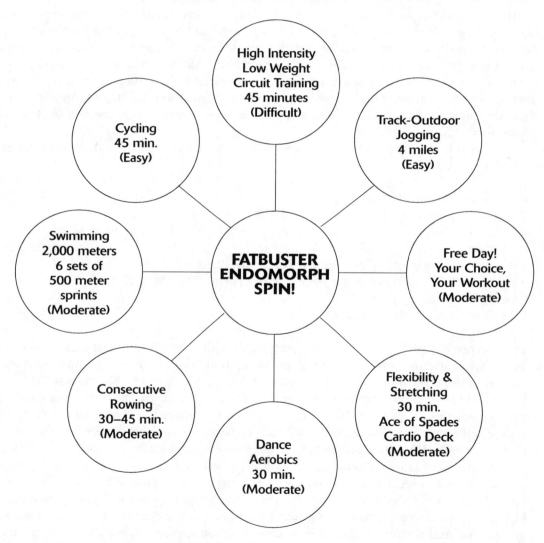

Figure 12b   "The FatBuster© Spin"

- **Rowing.** Perhaps the single most effective cardiovascular training for endomorphs is the rowing (ergonomic) machine. The ergonomic rower is ideal for the endomorph because it can record improvements based on time elapsed and adapts to the rower—in other words, the ease or difficulty in actual rowing is based on the intensity of the rower. When the rower slows down intensity, the ergonomic rowing intensity decreases as well. As the rower increases rowing intensity, the resistance increases from the machine as well. Rowing for 30 to 45 minutes daily, with the heart rate elevated to 60% is ideal for weight loss. For example, the endomorph should row 30 to 45 minutes daily, followed by stretching and flexibility exercises. Most importantly, however, the endomorph rower must learn to appreciate the exercise and actually feel the benefits afforded by the ergonomic rower in order for it to become most effective.

- **Swimming.** Another ideal training exercise for endomorphs is swimming. The advantages are that swimming allows for cardiovascular exercise without force or impact on joints and is excellent aerobic activity. Suggested distance includes 2000 meters of warm-up swimming followed by interval training of five 100 meter sprints followed by five 100 meter "warm down" laps. Total swimming distance: 3000 meters. If swimming distances appears to be too ambitious for the beginning endomorphic athlete, there are a series of effective exercises that can be executed while simply standing in waist-deep (shallow end) water. As an effective beginning exercise in the water, individuals should engage in a series of leg raises in the water, forward, backward and sideways, where the water offers resistance to the lower back and quadriceps muscles. A third effective exercise in the water is simply having individuals walk or jog from one end to another. Note the resistance from the water increases as the intensity in jogging increases;

- **Cycling.** A great exercise for lower body, either stationary or outdoor cycling is ideal for exercise and fitness for the endomorph. An excellent beginning exercise program for the endomorph is continuous cycling for 30 to 45 minutes. Most stationary cycles (i.e., the Lifecycle™) have a variety of alternative programs, and the beginning endomorph should select a program that offers gradual resistance for a minimum of 30 minutes, perhaps followed by 15 minutes warm-down (easy) cycling.

- **High Intensity Weight Circuit Training.** The High Intensity Weight Circuit Training program is one of the most effective and time effective training programs for all body types, but especially the endomorph body type. Circuit training involves the use of a variety of free weights involving upper and lower body muscles executed in a consistent manner. For example, the first exercise may include an upper body training program, such as: Upright rowing, bent-over rows, lateral pull-downs; forearm curls, followed by a set of chin ups. Note that each set of exercises should be completed in three sets of decreasing repetitions, typically beginning with 15, 10 and 8. After the upper body workout, the endomorph should immediately begin lower body training, including full squats, forward leg extensions, reverse (hamstring) leg extensions, followed by 15 minutes of moderate running on a treadmill or 15 minutes of stationary cycling. The High Intensity Circuit Training program should conclude with 15 to 20 minutes of flexibility and stretching exercises.

- **Track Jogging.** One of the most versatile and all around beneficial training exercises includes that of jogging or running. The endomorph athlete should remember that a standard track "lap" is 400 meters (one-quarter mile) and four laps is equal to one mile. The primary benefit of jogging and running is to improve overall cardiovascular and aerobic capacity. Athletes should start relatively slowly and for short distances, such as 10 to 15 minutes of a light pace. An area of concern in any running program, but especially with endomorph body types, is joint and tendon damage. It is very important to spend at least 15 minutes each morning in flexibility and stretching exercises to properly prepare the muscle groups prior to running. Running and jogging are excellent training exercises as the athlete can clearly monitor any improvement based on time (distance to run a specific distance) and distance. As the mileage begins to increase, the overall benefits and rewards (and self-confidence) also improves. Many times we read about an individual who has an endomorph body type and begins to incorporate running in their training program—they begin to shed pounds and feel much healthier, gradually training for the marathon (26.2 miles)! A sample jogging training program for the endomorph athlete might include:

Week 1: Stretching and flexibility 15 minutes. Begin *walking* the first half-mile to adjust the lower body and then slowly incorporate the walk into a slow jog, allowing the muscles of the lower body to adapt. The first week of the jogging program should include 3 days alternating 1 to 2 miles, such as Monday–Wednesday–Friday (1–2 miles); the beginning athlete should learn to recognize cues and signals from his or her body in terms of intensity—how much to either increase or decrease in terms of mileage;

Week 2: Stretching and flexibility 15 minutes; Slow 2 miles, gradually increasing tempo and pace (total mileage: 2 miles) ;

Week 3: Stretching and flexibility 15 minutes; Slow 2 miles; One extra mile moderate pace (total mileage: 3 miles);

Week 4: Stretching and flexibility 15 minutes; Slow 2.5 miles; increasing extra mile to moderate to higher intensity pace; Warm-down 1 mile (total mileage: 3.5–4 miles). Gradually increasing mileage in weeks 2–4 to a total of 5–10 miles up to 8 weeks of training.

- **Dance Aerobics.** 15 minutes of stretching and flexibility exercises. Note that in particular the dance aerobics exercises are particularly cardiovascular intense and rigorous; particular care should be emphasized in proper preparation and training; 30 minutes of continuous aerobic movement. Types of music vary based on intensity of program; Rhythmic and slow classical music for beginning stretching and warm-up routines; high intensity/high tempo for cardiovascular elevation.

- ♥ **Cardio-Deck for Endomorphs: A high-intensity cardio card game found in aerobic training cards. Each card offers a descriptive training program each day of the month for endomorphs who need their "cardio-fix." Sample exercises include:**

Legend:

♥ = **Easy/Beginner's Choice (First 4 weeks of training);**

♥♥ = **Moderate/Not For Wimps (Four to 8 weeks of training);**

♥♥♥ = **Difficult/Top 15% (Eight to 12 weeks of training);**

♥♥♥♥ = **Intense/Top 5% (Twelve to 20 weeks of training)**

2 ♥ Subject draws "2 of hearts": 15 minutes of preliminary stretching and flexibility work. Two minutes of push-ups; two minutes of sit-ups; two minutes of jump-rope, rest two minutes. Fifteen minutes of your choice light cardiovascular training (cycling–rowing–swimming); Enjoy the experience—feel your body respond to the activity;

3 ♥♥ Subject draws "3 of hearts": 15 minutes of preliminary stretching and flexibility work. Three minutes of sit-ups, three minutes of push-ups, three minutes of jump-rope, rest three minutes. Fifteen minutes of moderate aerobic activity (rowing–cycling–swimming); Enjoy the experience—feel your body respond to the activity;

4 ♥♥♥ Subject draws "4 of hearts": 15 minutes of preliminary stretching and flexibility work. Four minutes of sit-ups; four minutes of push-ups, four minutes of jump-rope, rest four minutes. Thirty minutes of moderate aerobic activity (rowing–cycling–swimming); Enjoy the experience— Your body now understands and experiences the differences between a "light" to "moderate" exercise activity;

5 ♥♥♥ Subject draws "5 of hearts": 20 minutes of preliminary stretching and flexibility work. Five minutes of abdominal work (sit-ups, crunches and knee raises), five minutes of push-ups (minimum 50–10 sets of 5), five minutes of jump-rope, rest five minutes. Thirty minutes of moderate aerobic activity (rowing–cycling–swimming–bicycling); Enjoy the experience—Your body now understands and experiences the "moderate" exercise activity;

6 ♥♥♥♥ Subject draws "6 of hearts": 20 minutes of preliminary stretching and flexibility work. Six minutes of sit-ups and abdominal work (crunches and knee raises), Six minutes of push-ups (minimum of 60–10 sets of 6), six minutes of jump-rope (minimum 2000 skips without a break in stride) rest six minutes. Forty minutes of high intensity (60–80% aerobic capacity) (rowing–cycling–swimming–bicycling); Enjoy the experience—Your body now understands and experiences the differences between a "moderate" to "intense" exercise activity;

7 ♥♥♥♥ Subject draws "7 of hearts": 20 minutes of preliminary stretching and flexibility work; 100 sit-ups; 3 x 25 pushups; 3 sets of 3 minutes of jump-rope; Forty-five minutes of high intensity aerobic work (swimming–cycling–rowing).

◼ A FEW WORDS ABOUT DIET, HEALTH & NUTRITION

Given the fact that so many individuals are concerned about training, exercise and overall health, diet and nutrition should be mentioned briefly in this section. There are several myths when discussing health and nutrition, and perhaps the most prolific myth is that when you are exercising you can eat anything you want. This is absolutely untrue. Similar to the performance of a car and the fuel that you use, our body primarily functions based on the types of foods we consume. If we wish to maximize health and nutrition, a healthy and well-balanced diet is critical, especially during physical training. A healthy and balanced diet is essential in normal and every day functioning, but critical during exercising and training. While this text is primarily designed to improve our understanding of the psychology of exercise and health, we would be remiss if we ignored or neglected at least some information pertaining to diet that should be used as a model when training for weight loss.

Often we hear individuals describe with great enthusiasm the benefits of a new diet or a discovery of some unusual combination of foods for a specific period of time as the "key" or the "magical solution" or formula for losing weight easily. Remember earlier in this chapter we discussed Mireille Guiliano who described losing weight was as simple as "savoring each bite and taking our time and looking at the sandwich" (*French Women Don't Get Fat: The Secret of Eating For Pleasure*). Unfortunately, for most people it takes more than just looking at food and savoring it to lose weight—it takes a personal commitment, reduced caloric intake and increased aerobic activity (indeed, many overweight individuals savor their food too much). Furthermore, those same people who have "discovered" their magical solution to easy weight loss through some bizarre combination of foods typically resume their unhealthy weight levels within a matter of a few short weeks or months. Even "pure vegetarians" or "vegans" often elaborate about the virtues of limiting their diet to vegetables or limiting protein to soymilk and soybeans. The medical fact of the matter is that the healthiest diets are those diets that are nutritionally balanced and varied. Evolutionary theory posits that those humans had the greatest ability to survive by consuming the most wide ranging diets—everything from nuts, to beef, to all forms of vegetables and legumes. Humans were practically omnivorous, and based on the theory of natural selection, human evolution required that our diets be very different, ranging from green leafy vegetables to some protein and some fruits. Human evolutionary theory also explains our tendency to prefer the unhealthy foods (fats and sweets) because these foods were the most difficult to obtain, but nutritionally afforded us the necessary fat and energy that helped us through the inevitable lean periods. If someone has the time to obtain all of their protein through soybeans and legumes, they can do this. However, the vast majority of us do not have the luxury of time in obtaining a specific and limited food source that is usually impractical and expensive. Ironically, the healthiest foods are usually the least expensive—rice, fresh vegetables (such as broccoli, cauliflower, and carrots) and chicken. However, because we are living in a technologically advanced era where few people seem to have the time to prepare healthy meals (i.e., cutting them up and steaming them), we resort to purchasing pre-cut, pre-cooked, and fast foods, all of which tend to be more expensive and have higher levels of saturated fats. The key to a healthy and balanced diet is to eat in moderation, watch portion sizes, and if you have a "sweet tooth" or crave something sweet, have fresh fruit handy or around the house. When you get a craving for a cookie or piece of cake, just try eating a ripe orange or slices of apples and see if this won't satisfy your cravings (it probably will).

Here is a sample diet especially designed for the endomorph, or those individuals who are at risk for weight gain. Remember, there are no special pills or powders, or magic devices that you strap to your stomach to give you the equivalent of 10,000 sit-ups. There is only your body, what you put into your body, and what you do with your body: More calories consume than burned at the end of the day means eventually weight gain; more calories burned than consumed at the end of the day means eventual weight loss—period (see figure 12c):

Sample Diet for the Endomorph

Breakfast	Lunch	Dinner
Fruit (citrus)	3–4 oz. Tuna or chicken	3–4 oz. of Fish
Oatmeal	Salad	Steamed vegetables
Skim Milk	Water with lemon	Rice and fruit
Wheat toast/juice		

Total calories: Approximately 2000

Helpful Tips While Training: Remember snacks are okay, just keep the snacks healthy (fruit that you have prepared ahead of time, or vegetables such as carrot and celery sticks or almonds) and remember to bring your healthy snacks with you throughout the day. If you suddenly get a craving, you can reach into your purse or pocket and eat a healthy snack. Always drink fresh water throughout the day—you will feel better, foods will taste better, and your skin will be clearer.

Figure 12c   Sample Diet For The Endomorph

■ TRAINING PROGRAM FOR THE ECTOMORPH: MORE CALORIES & BALANCED EXERCISE

Training and exercise that incorporates daily activity that is challenging and stimulating is the key to maintaining a successful training program for the ectomorph. Remember, the ectomorph is a general term that describes individuals as being lean or thin. Ectomorphs typically have the opposite problem of the endomorph—instead of trying to lose weight, they are trying to put on weight. However, we should remember that physical appearance can be misleading. Someone can actually *appear* to be lean or thin and be actually unhealthy or physically unfit, whereas an individual can *appear* to be heavy and actually remain physically healthy and fit. Remember—a key component of this chapter is that each individual body type needs to train according to their preferences and identify what types of exercises work best for them. For the ectomorph, the key to successful training is balance—balance between the aerobic and cardiovascular health needs to weight training and placing demands on the muscle groups of the body. According to the *Daily News* (Health Section), over 60% of individuals who begin a health and exercise program discontinue after only a few months (January 3, 2005). The key to success in any training program, regardless of the body type, is identifying one that works for you and is satisfying and challenging.

The reason why many individuals discontinue training is due to what I feel is a "mismatch" between the proper exercise and needs of the individual. The ectomorphic body type is one that needs more weight training combined with moderate aerobic activity. Unlike the endomorph (who needs at least 30–45 minutes of cardiovascular training), the ectomorph requires more balance in physical training, such as three days of weight training (i.e., Monday, Wednesday and Friday) with two or three days of moderate cardio-training (i.e., walking, cycling or rowing). For most individuals, people who discontinue their training program do so not because of a lack of motivation, but what I regard as a lack of a fit between the body type and the exercise. The key question, then, is how to find a program that affords a suitable "fit" and one that is challenging and exciting? Perhaps the solution is looking at the "Four P's of Exercise": Passion, Planning, Partnership, and Proximity (see figure 12d).

a. **Passion.** The most important training requisite for successful exercise is passion—do you love what you do in terms of exercise? Do you look forward to engaging in exercise on a daily basis? Do you often think about your training, how to improve it, how to modify it? If not, then you are not passionate about your training. Passion in exercising is the single most important element in training—without it, your program will eventually fade. Loving what you do, and feeling excited about your progress is inherent in passionate training. Something else you will notice is that passion is contagious—other people will see you training and loving what you do and they will want to become involved as well.

b. **Planning.** Developing a plan is also critical to successful training for the ectomorph. In other words, does your program have a sequential plan that addresses each of the muscle groups that you are trying to develop? A suggested plan for the ectomorph who wants to add weight might be something like: Weights three days a week (Monday–Wednesday–Friday) and cardiovascular training two or three days a week. The program might be intense (3 days of intense training), moderate (5 days of moderate training), or easy (6 to 7 days of light training);

c. **Partnership.** Selecting a partner is also vital to the exercise program. No matter how vigilant you may think you are, no matter how stoic or independent, all of us at one time or another need a "push" from a training pal or partner. Ideally, your partner or training pal should know you and your goals, and more importantly know your current levels. Your training pal should also be a little more advanced (physically) than you so you are working towards your goal, whether is lifting more or running faster. Your training partner should push you and know your limits, and you

The 4 P's of Exercising for the Ectomorph

Passion

Planning   **Partnershiip**   **Proximity**

Figure 12d   The 4 P's of Exercising for the Ectomorph

should be able to motivate and push your partner as well. In many cases, a physical trainer is someone who is a training partner and someone who is knowledgeable about physical training. If you have a friend who is both, then you do not need to pay him or her to train with you;

d. **Proximity.** A practical concern is the location of the gym or training spa—obviously, the closer the gym and the easier access you have to training, the more likely you are to adhere to your training program. In some cases, you may wish to purchase some simple equipment, such as a jump rope, some light weights, and a rower or a bicycle. The simple fact of the matter is that the more access and easier access to training, the more likely we are to maintain our exercise program.

The diet of the ectomorph should maintain a high-protein and low carbohydrate balance, averaging between 3000 to 4000 calories, depending on the individual and level of activity. Many individuals with the ectomorphic frame have expressed a desire to add muscle and weight to their frame to appear healthier and stronger. The idea behind putting on muscle mass and increasing weight is in working with moderate weights and executing several repetitions to the point of fatigue and exhaustion. Maximizing repetitions (sometimes called "supersets") builds muscle mass and endurance. The individual then gradually decreases the amount of weight and continues with a high number of repetitions, or until the point of exhaustion. Three to five sets of training is ideal for the beginning ectomorph see figures 12e and 12f):

Sample Ectomorph Exercise

Set #1 (Monday)

40 lb. Curls	30 lb. Curls	20 lb. Curls
▼	▼	▼
12 reps	10 reps	8 reps
Push-ups (25)	Pull-ups (10)	Bar-dips (10)

Jump rope (3–5 minutes)

Repeat sets 2 and 3, resting 10 minutes within sets

Set #1 (Wednesday)

Bench-press (80% maximum)

▼	▼	▼
Bench 12 reps	Bench 10 reps	Bench 8 reps
Push-ups (25)	Pull-ups (10)	Bar-dips (10)

Walking (brisk pace—15 minutes)

Set #1 (Friday)

Lateral Pull-Downs (80% maximum)

▼	▼	▼
Lats 12	Lats 10	Lats 8
Push-ups (25)	Pull-ups (10)	Bar-dips (10)

Figure 12e

Sample Diet for the Ectomorph

Breakfast	Lunch	Dinner
Fruit (citrus)	4 oz. Poultry	5 oz. of Fish or Red Meat
Oatmeal (6 oz)	Salad/fruit	Steamed vegetables
Skim Milk	Water with lemon	Rice and fruit
Wheat toast/juice		
Protein (3 egg whites)		

Total calories: Approximately 3500–4000

Helpful Tips While Training: Eat often and healthy eating is vital. Remember snacks are okay, just keep the snacks healthy (fruit that you have prepared ahead of time, or vegetables such as carrot and celery sticks or almonds) and remember to bring your healthy snacks with you throughout the day. If you suddenly get a craving, you can reach into your purse or pocket and eat a healthy snack. Always drink fresh water throughout the day—you will feel better, foods will taste better, and your skin will be clearer.

Figure 12f

■ TRAINING PROGRAM FOR THE MESOMORPH: TIPS ON KEEPING A HEALTHY BODY

The mesomorphic body type has traditionally been the envy of most individuals who are trying to either keep weight on and develop a more muscular build, or the individual who is concerned about dropping a few pounds and looking leaner. The mesomorph has traditionally had the most attractive appearance of both worlds: Looking stronger and muscular with a lean "cut" look (high degree of muscle mass with relatively low percentages of body fat). The mesomorphic body physique has traditionally been very athletic and coordinated in a variety of sports and athletic activities. The appearance of the mesomorphic resembles something of the "inverted triangle" with the broader shoulders tapering to a narrow waist. For some genetically fortunate individuals, this body type comes naturally. However, for the remainder of us, we need to devote time and energy to develop this appearance. We will now offer a short review of a training procedure to maintain the mesomorphic physique combined with a sample nutritional diet. The mesomorphic individual understands the benefits of exercise and the numerous psychological and physiological advantages that have become associated with a regular exercise program:

> ➤ Decreased feelings of depression (from *Sport Psychology,* Cox text. North, McCullagh, & Tran, 1990);
> ➤ Reduced states of anxiety that is associated with depression;
> ➤ Improved cardiovascular fitness;
> ➤ Improved overall emotional states (i.e., happiness and well-being);
> ➤ Higher degree of personal self-efficacy (from *Sport Psychology,* Cox text. DuCharme & Brawley, 1995);
> ➤ Transitional state from external to internal locus of control—Feeling more in control of life events and greater resiliency to life stressors;
> ➤ Improved stamina and endurance;
> ➤ Greater resistance to injury and illness;
> ➤ Reports of positive emotional states and euphoric training periods.

The mesomorphic individual combines a healthy balance between daily activities and work and incorporates a healthy diet with exercising. The mesomorphic individual trains or exercises almost daily, and the exercise program fluctuates between aerobic activity and exercising. For many mesomorphic individuals, training and activity is often a blend of several different types of exercises. If we were to review some of the most common practices and exercises of the mesomorphic individual, we would find that several combine aerobic activities (jogging, swimming and rowing) with a series of weight training exercises, ranging from moderate to heavy weight lifting. The mesomorph eats often and healthy, and is very consistent and regimented in his or her training program. Another common practice among the mesomorphs is that they often "cross-train"—a term that is used to describe combining different sports training exercises together. For example, a swimmer may incorporate weight lifting in his or her program in addition to swimming several thousand meters, or a rower may incorporate lower body workouts and exercises (such as cross-country running or bleacher work) to strengthen lower body muscles. The key advantage to the mesomorphic body type is power combined with stamina and endurance—two key components to successful athletic participation and overall health.

A sample of an exercise routine for the mesomorphic individual looks similar to this figure 12g):

Sample Mesomorphic Exercise

Set #1 (Monday)

50 lb. Curls	40 lb. Curls	30 lb. Curls
▼	▼	▼
12 reps	10 reps	8 reps

Push-ups (25)

| Sit-ups (100) | Pull-ups (15) | Bar-dips (15) |

Jump rope (5–7 minutes)

Repeat sets 2 and 3, resting 10 minutes within sets

Set #1 (Wednesday)

Bench-press (80% maximum)

▼	▼	▼
Bench 12 reps	Bench 10 reps	Bench 8 reps
Push-ups (25)	Pull-ups (15)	Bar-dips (15)

Jogging (brisk pace—15 minutes)

Set #1 (Friday)

Lateral Pull-Downs (80% maximum)

▼	▼	▼
Lats 15	Lats 12	Lats 10
Push-ups (25)	Pull-ups (15)	Bar-dips (15)

Figure 12g

Sample Diet for the Mesomorph

Breakfast	Lunch	Dinner
Fruit (citrus)	8 oz. Poultry	8 oz. of Fish or Red Meat
Oatmeal (8 oz) or Cereal	Salad/fruit	Steamed vegetables
Low-fat Milk	Water/Beverage (protein)	Rice and fruit
Wheat toast/juice	Rice	Bread (wheat)
Protein (3 egg whites)	Granola Chews	

Total calories: Approximately 4000–5000

Helpful Tips While Training: Eat often and healthy eating is vital. Remember snacks are okay, just keep the snacks healthy (fruit that you have prepared ahead of time, or vegetables such as carrot and celery sticks or almonds) and remember to bring your healthy snacks with you throughout the day. Occasionally the mesomorph may supplement his or her diet with protein shakes and protein bars. If you suddenly get a craving, you can reach into your purse or pocket and eat a healthy snack. Always drink fresh water throughout the day—you will feel better, foods will taste better, and your skin will be clearer.

Figure 12h

■ CHAPTER 12 QUESTION & REVIEW

1. Briefly describe the classic body types and how personality may influence styles of exercise.
2. Describe the exercise components of the "Fatbuster Spin."
3. Identify and describe the "Four P's" of exercising for the ectomorph.
4. Describe sample exercises for the endomorph and mesomorph.
5. Identify and describe advantages of training each training technique for each of the three body types: Ectomorph, endomorph and mesomorph;
6. Identify healthy diets and caloric intakes for each of the three body types.

Chapter 13:
Different Personality Types as Indicators of Different Training Strategies: The Extravert and Introvert/Types A & B Personality

The last several paragraphs of chapter 12 have focused on different physical body types as indicators of specialized types of exercise. The physical components of the body seem to respond best to different types of exercises, where the endomorph is designed best for longer duration of aerobic exercises, the ectomorph designed for weight training, and the mesomorph body type balancing the aerobic activities with weight training. Just as there are different body types that serve as indicators of specialized exercise training, we would like to identify specific personality types as indicators of exercise training. While there are several different types of personalities, the four different (yet interrelated) personality types that we will be addressing here in relation to athletic training are the classic "Types A and B" personality types and the extravert/introvert personality types. We will first define and describe these personality types and then more importantly describe how personality types may influence the development and progress of exercise training.

■ THE PERSONALITY TYPES A AND B: IS IT POSSIBLE TO HAVE THE BEST OF BOTH WORLDS?

The personality Type A is often described as competitive, always in a rush or hurry, has a sense of time urgency, and responds typically in a hostile or aggressive manner if his or her goals are not met. Conversely, the personality Type B is described as more relaxed, pleasant and humorous with others, not in a constant hurry, seldom hostile to others, and usually only *moderately* competitive. Many theorists have described the personality Type A as a common characteristic found among successful athletes. While it is true that most of the successful athletes in amateur and professional sports are highly competitive, and it is also true that many of these athletes play aggressively in order to achieve their goals, we would argue that successful athletes have characteristics of *both* personality Types A and B. But we would also argue that competitors who have personality Type A with *extreme levels of hostility* may be at a significant disadvantage when competing. Conversely, the personality Type B that also remains competitive may be a significant advantage from a health perspective. Why is this? Because the classic personality Type A with extreme hostility has difficulty in controlling and maintaining his or her composure during competitive games or matches, and often the Type A athlete loses their emotional composure that typically results in penalties and ejections. The Type B personality is capable of a more balanced and relaxed interaction with others that may also prove beneficial during competition with others. Furthermore, recent research (Barefoot and colleagues, 1989) suggests that the descriptions of the traditional Type A personality are too vague and general—many, many people may be described as competitive, work in a hurried manner, and are time efficient. Many people also become frustrated (although not necessarily hostile) when they cannot reach their goals. Barefoot and colleagues determined that the key factor in promoting heart disease and problems with the coronary arteries was *hostility* characterized by a high degree of suspicion, anger and resentment. These characteristics are seen frequently with a higher percentage of Type A athletes.

Thus, athletes who remain competitive in wanting to succeed and win games appear to be most successful in competitive situations if they can play without the hostility. When emotional outbursts interfere with the athlete's style of play (such as flagrant fouls), the quality of play and the overall health of the athlete begins to deteriorate. The personality component that is best suited for winning and excelling in sports and competitive matches are those athletes that have strong desires to win but can control their emotional outbursts, and use their anger or energy in a positive way. Remember, personality Types A and B are not absolute, and there may be variations of both types. For example, an individual may be highly competitive without the hostility, and be able to control his or her emotions during matches to play at their best level. Thus, most importantly, the most successful athletes seem to have characteristics of both personality types, including their ability to maintain their composure and relax when necessary, but also remain aggressive in competitive situations.

Recent research documents the numerous health disadvantages of the Type A personality. Rosenman and colleagues (1976) discovered startling evidence that cites personality Type A as a strong indicator for men risking coronary heart disease and heart attacks. In a very compelling and dynamic study that evaluated over 3000 healthy middle-aged men over a period of 8.5 years, Rosenman discovered that the Type A males had significantly higher (over twice as many cases) levels of coronary heart disease than those males who were identified as Type B. What makes this study even more alarming is that the other factors that are normally considered to be contributing factors to heart disease (such as smoking and obesity) were controlled for. Thus, the personality factor of Type A by itself was identified as the single most important precursor to coronary heart disease. Even children can learn behaviors that contribute to either a relaxed and non-competitive personality type such as Type B, or a more hostile and competitive personality type, such as the Type A personality. Weidner and colleagues (1988) discovered that fathers who were classified as being Type A had more sons who also were classified as Type A, thereby indicating that personality characteristics and traits are both learned and genetically inherited. In a related study that seems to corroborate Rosenman's findings, Friedman and colleagues (1968) discovered that individuals who were diagnosed as Type A personality also had a higher incidence of blockage of coronary arteries. Finally, the American Heart Association classifies any individual who has been diagnosed as having a Type A personality characteristic as a risk factor for coronary heart disease. These studies provide convincing evidence that our personality characteristics have a profound influence on our overall health. What we would like to suggest is that while exercise cannot change the personality of the individual, we feel that exercise can reduce the tension and stress that contributes to the negative health factors that have been associated with the Type A personality. Research suggests that those athletes who have been characterized as Type A with hostility frequently experience more emotional outbursts and activation of the sympathetic nervous system. As the sympathetic nervous is frequently activated (commonly referred to as the "fight or flight" syndrome), certain neurotransmitters are released (endorphins) and catecholamines that causes stress and wear and tear on the arteries, thereby contributing to coronary heart disease. Further, the athletes that are classified as Type A may resort to consuming drugs or unhealthy substances as a means of combating stress that is typically associated with the Type A personality. We can see how vulnerable the Type A personality is to a cycle of stress and threats to physical health (see figure 13a):

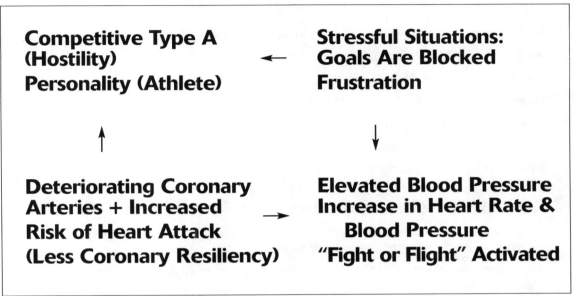

Figure 13a   The Cycle of Stress in the Type A Athlete

■ CARDIOVASCULAR & COGNITIVE RELAXATION EXERCISES FOR THE TYPE A ATHLETE

The previous description of the Type A athlete identifies key factors that may trigger coronary heart disease: Competitive and hostile to reactions over a period of time trigger specific substances and neurotransmitters that wear and tear the coronary arteries. Think of a tire that you have been driving on for several years, and stress is continually placed on the tire combined with other factors, such as heat and pressure. Eventually the tire will be at risk for rupture. This analogy is similar to our arteries—as more and more pressure is placed (and released) on the arteries, they begin to fatigue and weaken. Eventually, competitive environments, anger and hostility may become too great, thereby causing the arteries to "burst" similar to the tire. Indeed, what makes stress, high blood pressure and the Type A athlete especially a dangerous combination is that high blood pressure is often referred to as the "silent killer"—meaning we seldom see signs or signals that the arteries are at risk of rupture.

These personality components place a significantly higher emphasis on cardiovascular training to relieve some of the tension and pressure that is exposed to the Type A personality. Personality characteristics, such as cognitive coping strategies in stressful situations and positive "self-talk" dialogues are learned and very effective in combating the negative side effects of the Type A personality. Furthermore, it can be argued that specific types or forms of exercise are more vital for certain personality types. For example, the Type A personality type is characterized by hostility, a sense of urgency in completing tasks, and a high degree of competitiveness. When cardiovascular and aerobic exercises are incorporated in training and exercise on a regular basis with the Type A personality, the negative side effects may be reduced significantly. We will now describe several successful exercises for the Type A personality (see figure 13b):

Cardiovascular Training for the Type A:

Rowing (45 minutes);

Swimming (5000 meters);

Stretching and Flexibility + High Intensity Weight Training;

Jogging (5 miles) / Running (3 miles);

Handball/Racquetball (30 minutes);

Dance Aerobics (30 minutes—High Intensity);

Basketball (Full court) 45 minutes;

Bicycling (1 hour) High Intensity;

Indoor Cycling (45 minutes) High Intensity.

Cognitive Relaxation Exercises for the Type A:

Positive Self-Talk Dialogues: ("I am going to play my best, no matter what the outcome is"—i.e., focusing on positive outcomes);

Relaxation Techniques: Guided Imagery (visualizing a calm environment during especially intense competition);

Self-Induced Relaxation Techniques (a psychological and muscular relaxation technique that "relearns" the distinctions between physical stress and relaxation from a mental and physiological perspective);

Counterfactual Thinking: De-emphasizing a negative event and placing it in perspective ("Even though I was called for a penalty, I didn't get ejected from the game" or "I was fouled by an opponent, but it could have been worse, I didn't get injured").

Figure 13b　Techniques for Relaxation for "The Type A" Athlete

■ THE "TYPE B" ATHLETE & LAUGHTER: A HEALTHIER RESILIENCE TO STRESS?

We have been discussing the Type A athlete in some detail as being both advantageous and disadvantageous in competitive sport. The Type A athlete is more competitive and is more capable of responding physically and aggressively in a variety of sport and athletic situations. However, when physical behavior evolves into hostility, quality of play and even physical health (coronary heart disease) rapidly deteriorate. Interestingly, while much research has been devoted to the Type A athlete, little research has been devoted to the Type B (relaxed) athlete. We will now review briefly the mechanisms of the Type B personality and offer describe how the Type B personality dynamic may be more successful in certain types of sports and exercise activities, especially when humor is combined within the personality. We will then describe the "Extraverted" and "Intraverted" personality type and review how these personality characteristics influence the quality of individual and team sport interaction. The Type B athlete refers to an individual who is capable of relaxing and works without a sense of time urgency. The Type B athlete is typically non-competitive and not aggressive while competing with other individuals. There is a significantly higher number of Type B personalities who also seem to fit the endomorphic body type, where relaxation, social activities and food comprise important daily activities of the endomorph's life. Conversely, the Type A personality type appears to have a strong correlation with the mesomorphic body type, where stronger and muscular individuals are more competitive and aggressive in a variety of athletic situations. The classic mesomorph is very active, competitive, and dominant that seems to match many of the characteristics of the Type A personality (see figure 13c):

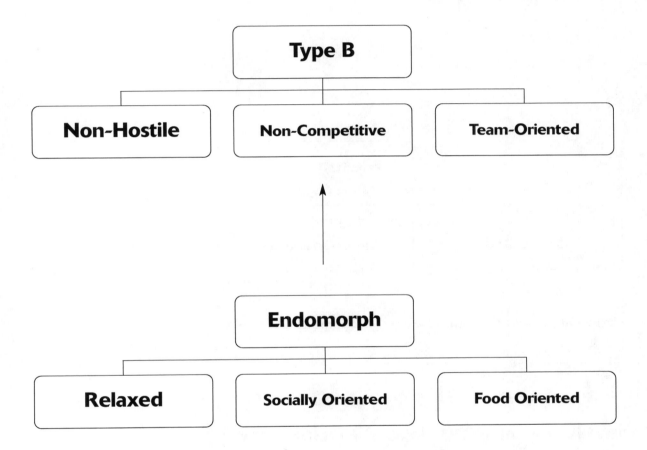

Figure 13c   Positive Correlation Between Endomorph and the Type B Athlete

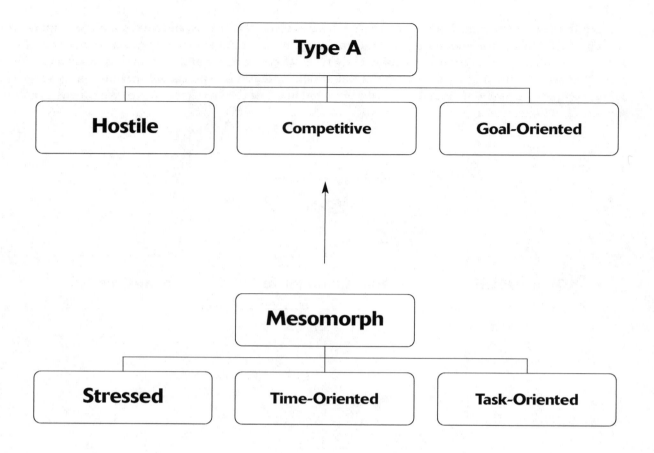

Figure 13d   Positive Correlation Between Mesomorph and the Type A Athlete

■■ HUMOR AND THE TYPE B PERSONALITY

We have been discussing various characteristics of the both personality types A and B. the personality Type A has been described as highly competitive in sport situations and task oriented. The Type A personality can be viewed as a desirable trait if hostility and other negative factors are avoided. However, in many competitive situations Type A athletes may experience problems in controlling emotions and tempers if they perceive that their goals (i.e., winning) may appear to be threatened. Conversely, the Type B athlete seldom has problems similar to the type A—the Type B athlete's behavior is typically viewed as very relaxed, socially-oriented and non-competitive. We have also briefly discussed how cultural values may dramatically influence the development of each of these personality types. In highly competitive and individualistic cultures such as the United States, there is an emphasis on winning and individual achievement. Many sports seem to appeal to the Type A personality because of the emphasis on individual achievement and winning. However, in collectivistic cultures, there is an emphasis on group support, personal sacrifices for the group or team, and a devaluation of winning with more focus on team or group performance. We have speculated that more Type B athletes are more group oriented and have been influenced by the collectivistic culture. We will now emphasize an important topic relative to health and the Type B athlete: Humor.

Given the fact the Type B athlete is less competitive and social that the Type A athlete personality, we should explore key behavioral characteristics of each personality type that influences overall health of each athlete. For example, we have described the damaging effects of hostility on the Type A athlete, and how Type A athletes are significantly more at risk for coronary heart disease due to increases in the sympathetic nervous system and endocrine glands. The Type B personality has been described as being more group and team oriented, less competitive and more relaxed in a variety of social environments. Another key component that has been associated with the Type B individual is laughter. Norman Cousins (1985) has described anecdotal experiences of laughter as being highly effective in not only improving overall levels of psychological well-being, but perhaps more importantly effective in warding off illnesses and disease. In 1964 Norman Cousins was diagnosed with a painful disease called ankylosing spondylitis. Given the fact that Cousins believed in the curing effects of laughter, he watched several episodes of a comedy program for the period of several weeks. Cousins noted that the laughter allowed him to relax more and thus sleep without any form of medication.

More importantly, his disease was in remission and Cousins was able to return to his successful career as a writer for the *Saturday Review*. How do these results of laughter relate to health, exercise, and well-being? Quite simply, if we better understand holistic intervention such as laughter we can apply these therapeutic interventions to groups of individuals who are at risk of heart disease and coronary disease (commonly seen among the Type A athlete). Furthermore, although at this point we are speculating, perhaps part of the reason why Type B personality types have significantly fewer cases of coronary heart disease may be they are exposed to more relaxed, social and humorous environments that enhances the endocrine system and immune systems. Finally, an interesting study for the Type A athlete would be to expose them to various types of environments that promote humor and laughter to determine the overall effects of reduced heart disease, as well as improved athletic performance.

■ THE PERSONALITY TRAITS OF THE EXTRAVERT AND THE INTROVERT

Earlier in this text we described the arbitrary term "personality" as a combination of several traits that make people relatively unique and create. In this text we often describe personality as a result of behavioral consequences and responses to a variety of situations within our environment. For example, if a child associates negative characteristics with healthy foods and activity, they may develop a negative attitude about health and well-being that may prevent them from exercise and athletic activities as they mature. Conversely, children who are taught to incorporate healthy daily activity and to eat nutritionally healthy foods are significantly more likely to live healthier lives and incorporate exercise on a daily basis. We will now discuss two of the most common personality characteristics and identify how personality characteristics such as extraversion and introversion may have profound consequences on the quality and efficacy of their exercise program.

Researchers who have conducted extensive work in the field of personality traits and characteristics include Gordon Allport (cardinal traits, dispositions) and Raymond Cattell (surface traits versus deeper more profound traits such as source traits), and Hans Eysenck (basic traits). One common theme among all of these researchers is that they agreed that each individual has a combination of unique and creative traits that define human behavior within a myriad of different situations and environments. For example, Allport described dispositions as being similar to personality traits, and he identified several: Cardinal traits (dominating traits that basically comprise the individual's personality); central traits (qualities that are important components of the individual's personality); and secondary traits (how we respond only to specific environmental stimuli). An individual such as Babe Ruth in baseball may be described as having a cardinal trait entirely in baseball, or the cardinal trait for an individual such as Mother Theresa may be considered devotion and giving to the needy. More recently, Hans Eysenck described two dominant components of the personality that seem to be important predictors of success in sports and athletics: The extraverted and introverted personality.

The extraverted individual is described as being very gregarious with other people, sociable and impulsive. They enjoy environments where they are the center of attention and generally are very popular. Successful athletes such as Kobe Bryant and Venus Williams may be described as extraverted athletes who crave attention from the public. These athletes also need to be in controlling positions (such as team captain) and have a strong need to be dominating the decisions made by the team. Conversely, the introverted personality type as described by Eysenck includes someone who may be non-sociable (craves privacy), cautious, quiet, and preferring a routine activity. The extraverted athlete excels in sport situations and competitive environments that require dominance and split-second thinking. For example, Michael Jordan of the Chicago Bulls (extravert mesomorph) required competitive and close matches in order for him to play his best. In several of Jordan's highest scoring games (40 points or more), the winning point was made with less than 3 or 4 seconds on the clock. Typically Jordan would shoot outside shots (3 points) or play while being heavily covered by his opponents, and more often than not, would make the game-winning shot. Figure 13e illustrates the relationship between the athlete's personality type and body type:

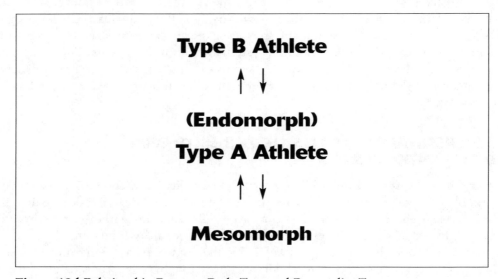

Figure 13d Relationship Between Body Type and Personality Types

■ ATHLETIC PERSONALITY TEST

While much research has established a correlation between specific personality types and preferences to types of exercise, little research has been conducted to determine the effects of preferences to exercise and physical activity while training with a partner. In an interesting study conducted by Molock, Zamora and Hwang (unpublished paper, 2005), athletes were compared with their preferences to exercise training initially by themselves and then with a training partner. Subjects were exposed to a variety of different types of exercise activities, from weightlifting and running to stretching and flexibility exercises. Subjects were administered the Athletic Personality Test (APT; see Appendices A and B) that initially measured their preferences to exercise and priorities in exercise training. After several weeks of training with a partner subjects were then administered a post-test that measured any changes in preferences and positive experiences to exercise training. The results strongly supported the author's hypothesis that when athletes train with a partner, their overall subjective experiences in training improve significantly as well as lifting more weight. Some of the anecdotal comments included: "I learned things about my body and capabilities that I otherwise would not have discovered [with a trainer]" and "They [trainers] gave me the 'extra push' that I needed to complete the work."

■■■ SUMMARY AND CONCLUSIONS: PERSONALITY TYPE AND EXERCISE

Regardless of what your body type (endomorphic, ectomorphic or mesomorphic) and personality type (introverted or extraverted), a healthy, balanced and challenging exercise program is vital for optimum health and well-being. This final note to this chapter offers just some basic guidelines when organizing an exercise program for yourself or for others:

Creating Your Exercise Schedule: Exercise is Priority! *P.U.M.P.E.D. Program*

✓ **P**rioritize Your Exercise. By prioritizing your exercise program, what we are referring to is that once you have identified a period of time that is suitable and ideal for you, protect it and stay with it. Try not to allow any changes in this designated period of time. Think of this time as your time to improve your health and well-being. For example, if your hours for exercise are between 2:00 pm and 4:00 pm, do not allow or tolerate people to change or switch hours. Often you may hear people say something to the effect: "The movie begins at 2:30 pm . . . why don't you just exercise after the movie is over?" It may sound selfish, but your time in exercise and training is vital to your health and well-being; if you are not healthy, your work suffers, your family suffers, and your overall psychological well-being suffers. Protecting and prioritizing your exercise and training time is critical to your success—do not allow other people to interfere and sabotage how you train and exercise. Try to keep this time for yourself and maintain a regular and consistent training time;

✓ **U**nderstand & Develop a Structured Program. Exercise and training are models for people to adhere to—try to exercise by creating a routine and schedule that is rewarding and challenging. Individuals tend to be very goal oriented, and by developing a structured program that is challenging and dynamic you are more likely to stay with it. Throughout this book we have offered numerous types of training programs. Here it is critical that you visualize what you want to do first—picture yourself participating in and completing the series of exercises and feel your muscles responding to the demands made on the muscle. For example, you may wish to elect three days a week for upper body weight training, and the remainder three days a week for cardiovascular training. Upper body training may include bench press (pectoral muscles); lateral pull down press (lateral muscles); and curls (forearms and biceps). Lower body training may include treadmill work, leg curls and leg press, rowing, and squats. As with any exercise or physical training program, flexibility and stretching are vital to improve muscular flexibility. Finally, once your plan has been developed with the aid of health trainer, look forward to participating in it and have fun! a plan, look forward to your training, and enjoy what you do;

✓ **M**onitor Your Progress. How are you able to measure progress? If you are exercising in order to lose weight, have you consulted with a nutritionist or your doctor to determine what diet should be incorporated in your exercise program? In developing an exercise and health program, measure your progress by noting repetition increases and weight increases. For example, if you are exercising in a weight lifting routine, how much weight have you increased in curls and bench press? Have the repetitions increased? If you are swimming, has your distance increased and has your time decreased? Are your strokes becoming more powerful? If you are rowing, are your times becoming increasingly faster? *Monitoring your progress is extremely important because of two vital reasons: a) You are able to determine if you are improving your strength, stamina and power; and b) When you see yourself improving in exercise strength and stamina, this awareness serves to motivate you to keep working because you see the results and the experiences of exercise are becoming more and more rewarding.* Before you know it, you are "hooked" where you are now a devoted fan of exercise and look forward to training on a daily basis;

✓ **P**reparation. In any successful exercise program, preparing for success is vital. Mentally prepare yourself for difficult periods (slumps) where training and exercise are going to be difficult. Have realistic expectations—if you have been living previously a very sedentary lifestyle, understand that the new changes in your activity level will be initially difficult—some soreness is to be expected. Start slowly and realistically—you are not going to begin running a marathon, but maybe start by walking for 15 minutes to adjust to the new demands being made on your lower body;

✓ **E**ducate yourself. Understand what you want your body to do—Understand that your body has taken several, several years to attain the physique that it has now, and it will take some time to change the body composition from fat to muscle. "A watched pot never boils" refers to someone having little patience to see positive or desirable long term changes. Instead, be more realistic and focus more on the experience of exercise itself rather than the end result. Have positive yet realistic expectations, learn to value and appreciate the *experience* of exercise and training and "go with the flow" of training. Positive changes in your physique such as lowered weight, feeling stronger, losing a few inches on your waist, will all come gradually with a consistent and regular training and exercise program. Educating yourself means not only understanding what you actually need to do in terms of exercise, but also in terms of nutrition and health, such as diet.;

✓ **D**rive. The drive is the key to the success of your program. Drive means persistence and determination in achieving your goals—even when you may not be feeling up to the challenge. Some days you may feel tired or lethargic and may not want to train or exercise. On these difficult days, a very good idea is to do something different, such as going outside for a brisk walk or hike, or simply changing routines. Drive means not relenting in achieving your goals, but remaining flexible enough to change routines in order to adapt to those goals. Only you can achieve your goals, and with a positive and optimistic perspective regarding your training and exercise program these goals will be realized!

■ CHAPTER 13 QUESTION & REVIEW

1. Describe the basic differences between the personality types "A" and "B"; how can our personality types influence our styles and approach to exercise?

2. Briefly explain the relationship between the classic "Type A" personality type and aggressive behavior in sports—do aggressive people proactively seek out sports where they can "vent" or release their aggressive instincts?

3. Identify some of the health disadvantages of the "Type A" personality—what are some of the things the "Type A" personality can do to limit these negative consequences?

4. Identify and describe specific techniques that may help the "Type A" personality reduce stress in exercise and training;

5. Explain the relationship between the "Type A" personality and the extroverted personality type—where do you consider yourself?

6. In your opinion, can personality types change? Support your reasoning and explain how this may occur.

Chapter 14:
Gerontology and the Aging Athlete:
Growing Older and Healthier

"When the body is strong, it obeys orders . . . when the body is weak, it gives orders"
—Rousseau

The impact of science and technology has had tremendous ramifications on health and longevity, styles of living and human behavior. More than ever in our society today, individuals are living longer lives and remaining active by participating in a wide range of exercise activities. Improvements in medical technology, nutrition and recreational activities have had a profound influence on the life span of Americans. Consider the following: Currently over 12% of the U.S. population is aged 65 or older—this works out to be roughly over 34 million individuals. Over half of the U.S. population will be over age 50 by the year 2006, and the proportion of the elderly is expected to increase 25% by the year 2030. The *median* age of Americans will increase to 41.6 years by the year 2050. People are living longer than ever before, with an average of 76 years for males and an average of 82 years for women (2002 U.S. Bureau of the Census). Sporting events that have age categories such as running events, rowing events and swimming events are now extending the age categories into the eighth, ninth and even tenth decade to accommodate older athletes who are still competing. Given the fact that more and more Americans are living longer, we need to be especially concerned about problems that are associated with longevity. One significant problem that arises with older adults who are living on fixed incomes is psychological depression. In this chapter we will discuss how exercise and sport activity can help fend off depression and in fact improve the overall quality of life. Additionally, we will review the physiological benefits of exercise for the older adult, such as delaying osteoporosis and improving bone density. Further, those older adults who remain active in a consistent exercise program are more likely to remain cognitively active (thereby delaying dementia and Alzheimer's Disease) with improved memory skills as they participate in a structured and consistent health and activity program.

■ ATHLETIC CENTENARIANS

In an interesting article addressing improved athletic behaviors among seniors (*Los Angeles Times*, November 26, 2004), John Whittemore of Montecito, California still participates in sports such as track and field and javelin throwing. In fact, Whittemore is 105 years old and still competes in A.A.U. official track and field competitions. The oldest category of athletes for A.A.U. competition is 100–104 year olds, and now because Whittemore exceeds that limit, the A.A.U. is now considering expanding the age limit from 105 years to 109 years. According to the U.S. Census Bureau, there are approximately 685 men now living in the United States who are aged 105 to 109 years. Although he is rapidly approaching 106 years, Whittemore still walks with the aid of his walker at the U.C. Santa Barbara track, and took about 45 minutes to walk 100 yards (he was adamant in refusing assistance from anyone). Amateur Athletic Union (A.A.U.) official George Mathews indicated that currently there are about 20 athletes in the A.A.U. who are in their nineties, and 5 athletes who are registered with the A.A.U. who are 100 years old or older. Whittemore is an outstanding example of how sports and athletics can improve the quality of living as we get older, and Whittemore still works out with weights daily, stretches and participates in a flexibility program, and carries around hand weights and uses them throughout the day. He attributes his longevity to "good genes, good diet with fruits and vegetables, no smoking, and only 'a taste' of alcohol on special occasions" (*Los Angeles Times,* November 26, 2004). Clearly, Whittemore does not consider himself to be hampered by his age and attributes his exercise activity as contributing to his positive outlook and overall healthy psychological demeanor (how can you argue with someone who has reached the age of 105?). A second older athlete (golfer) who lived to be 105 years old was John Elliot (*Los Angeles Times,* January 20, 2005). Elliot served in two world wars, played golf with his son at the "Octogenarian Open" and saw three different centuries throughout his lifetime. He witnessed household lamps change from kerosene, to gas and then finally to electricity. Elliot attributed much of his longevity to golf and compared the game of golf to life: "Life is like golf in that it has many ups and downs. One minute you're great. The next minute you can't do anything. What are you going to do? . . . You just move on to then next shot."

Older adults and exercising have not just been limited to men. In a recent article published by the *Daily News* (January 17, 2005, "Call Them Triple Threats: Seniors, Boomers Boosting Triathlons' Popularity"), 71 year-old Jean Runyon began training for the triathlon (a competitive sport consisting of three consecutive endurance activities: running 3, 6 or 10 miles, swimming usually one-half mile, and bicycling usually 25 to 50 miles. The article cites the fact that Runyon actually began exercising as a way to avoid surgery for arthritis. When she entered the first Danskin (all women) triathlon, all that she wanted to do was complete or finish the event. Now, however, she has improved her overall time in the triathlon and feels very positive about exercise not only helping her avoid surgery, but more importantly develop an improved level of self-esteem: "It [triathlon training] made me feel so good . . . it isn't about age, it is about determination. When you hit those magic numbers, when you are in your late 40's, and early 50's, it is a time to recommit, and re-engage [in exercise and physical activity], it's a powerful feeling." The article also accurately notes that certain types of training, such as the triathlon, holds particular appeal for athletes who are approaching the late 30's, 40's and 50's as the triathlon is a relatively short series of three different exercises, as compared to one very long and excruciating event (such as the 26.2 mile marathon). Older female athletes have also been dominating the world of water polo sports. In a very interesting article addressing how older female athletes are beginning to participate in water polo ("Pool Sharks: Moms make big splash with water polo club" *Daily News,* January 25, 2005). Susan McElvaney formed the Conejo Valley Moms Water Polo Club and have been avid water polo players ever since. The idea was so popular among the women that another club was formed in Oxnard, California. What makes the sport so exciting is that the women (all ranging in ages from 40 to 50 years) participate in all kinds of weather: "People think we're crazy, but we love it." Twice a week for the last several years the group of women have been playing water polo and there are no signs of stopping. These women are outstanding examples of how to continue to be active despite age—they are also choosing a unique sport that is very exciting and physically rewarding.

▬ JUST WHAT EXACTLY DOES "OLD" MEAN?

If you were to interview any older adult who is currently maintaining a healthy and active lifestyle, you may hear them respond that they "feel very young and healthy" and that an exercise program is very important to them. In fact, in many of the older adults that we interviewed regarding their subjective reports of health and well-being commented that they "feel much younger . . . like I was forty again." Most of the comments made by the older adults suggest that chronological age and psychological age (i.e., how one actually physically feels) may be very contradictory. For example, most of the 80 year-olds interviewed who were currently participating in an active health and exercise program commented that they "felt great" and "looked forward to the day's activities." Conversely, many chronologically younger individuals (under 40 years) may lack this enthusiasm and zest for life due to sedentary and stressful lifestyles. The crux of these interviews suggests that age and more importantly how we physically and psychologically experience the process of aging is a highly relative concept, and one that is very much influenced by physical activity and exercise. Recently a student of mine entered my office to consult with me regarding her classes when she noticed the pictures of my children in my office. She then asked me "how old are your grandchildren?" (the pictures are of my seven year old son and two year old daughter—I have no grandchildren *yet!*). I was somewhat startled, given the fact that I was 44 at the time and had never actually considered myself as being "old." This comment made me reflect that age and the concepts of maturity are very arbitrary, and one person's idea of being old really depends on their own culture and subjective experiences. We should note, however, that typically the older we get, the more our ideas of being "young" expand from thirty to forty to fifty years and so on! Not so long ago, even reaching the "ripe old age of 40" was considered to be the rite of passage of entering the stage of adult maturity, where both men and women were expected to "slow down" and "take life more easily." What this translated to for many people was to simply stop remaining active, avoid exercise, and stay home and watch more television. These stereotypical views of the elderly and the mature adult are now changing rapidly. As adults are living longer thanks to medical advances and improved diets, we are seeing more and more of an emphasis in encouraging older adults to remain active and participating in a variety of meaningful activities that promotes not only physical health but also psychosocial health and psychological well being.

The good news is that the majority of people are living longer. However, many physical problems associated with old age may develop and negatively influence the overall quality of life of the individual. The purpose of this chapter is very important in the sense that the most older Americans are in need of maintaining and participating in some form of exercise, but may not be aware of what forms or types of exercise are most appropriate. We should first encourage older individuals to embrace and take advantage of their ability to now participate in a variety of activities that will improve their health. Many older Americans were probably unable to participate in some of the physical activities when they were younger due to working demands and employment responsibilities, raising children and supporting their families. Now we should remind and encourage older Americans to value and cherish their free time in life to participate in a variety of fun and challenging physical activities. An important incentive in convincing older Americans of the value of exercise and increased activity is in improving the overall psychological quality of living and simply feeling better about themselves. For example, empirical research supports the fact that older adults who remain active in some form of cardiovascular exercise are less at risk of suffering from depression and report a higher subjective quality of living (Goldberg and colleagues, 1996; Stones & Kozma, 1996; and Kushi and colleagues, 1997). More recent research by Light, Reilly, Behrman and Spirduso (1996) found that activity programs and exercise helped reduce delayed reaction times (RT) that are commonly associated with old age. Furthermore, Spirduso and Clifford (1978) discovered that consistent and long-term exercise provides numerous benefits to the older adult. In comprehensive literature up to the 1980's era, Spirduso concluded that problems that are associated with brain functioning and old age (such as memory loss and cognitive impairment) were able to be significantly delayed when the older adult participated in what she refers to as a "simple, unobtrusive and inexpensive self-imposed" exercise routines. In other words, the researchers discovered that older adults simply needed to be consistent in their daily walks (or some other exercise routine) in order to enjoy both the physical and cognitive benefits afforded to them by exercise.

Numerous research articles have supported the hypothesis that seniors and older adults who have been consistent in their exercise and activity programs have benefited both physically and mentally. Given the fact that approximately 50% of physical disabilities and that are associated with late adulthood are due to sedentary lifestyles as opposed to overactive lifestyles (such as exercise), it makes sense that those individuals who remain active will remain significantly healthier than older adults who remain inactive. Additionally, health benefits including improved strength and cardiovascular systems was reported among older adults in as little as eight weeks (Morey, Cowper, Feussner, DiPasquale, Crowley, and Sullivan (1991).

■ EXERCISING AND SOCIAL ACTIVITY FOR THE OLDER ADULT: DEFEATING DEPRESSION

The primary reason why most people exercise (regardless of age) is improved physical health and psychological wellness. Another important component to consider when exercising is the psychosocial component of exercise. While other people may not have similar problems in establishing relationships and friendships with others, a common problem that has been associated with late adulthood is depression, despair and loneliness. Depression is characterized as a sense of hopelessness and futility, where often we feel very much alone in the world or that no one can understand our feelings. Depression can develop for several reasons, however, among the older adult population a contributing factor that leads to depression is a sense of meaninglessness ("I have lived my life already . . . there is no need to continue on" or "No one in my life cares about me . . . I feel alone with no family or companions." Perhaps most importantly, depression is an important concern during late adulthood because many older adults lack goals or structured activity. Depression has also been linked with physiological deterioration. Depression may also develop when we realize that our body has become weaker with old age and that we are no longer capable of (physically) accomplishing things that we once took for granted. In a recent study (*United Press International,* January 25, 2005) published by the University of Texas' Southwestern Medical Center, researchers found that those subjects (aged between 20 to 45 years) who participated in an aerobic activity for 30 minutes three to five days a week showed a significant (over 50%) decline in depression rates. The key factor, according to the author of the study Madhukar Trivedi, was maintaining active participation in the aerobic program for a minimum of 30 minutes: "The key is to exercise at least 3 to 5 days a week and continuing it for 30 to 35 minutes per day."

Comer (2001) cites depression as being a serious problem, as more than 10% of Americans suffer from depression at some point in their lives, and approximately 80% of suicides committed were associated with psychological depression. We should clearly note here that the older adult who happens to be suffering from depression typically wants to feel better and they want to take away their pain, but often they *simply do not know how to make themselves feel better and they typically feel that no one can understand their pain.* Exercise and physical activities have been shown through empirical research to prevent depression specifically among older populations (Greist and colleagues, 1978). In an interesting study that looked at a running program designed to treat depression among adults, Greist and colleagues compared the effectiveness of a running program (stretching, flexibility and running for 30 minutes) with a psychoanalytic counseling program (limited and unlimited sessions) for a period of 16 weeks. Although the study had some methodological flaws, the results are interesting as Greist and colleagues determined that the adults who participated in the running group reported similar levels of therapeutic success with those adults in the psychoanalytic counseling group.

An important point to note in the research done with depression and the effects of exercise is that the treatment modality (i.e., exercise) is non-specific. In other words, it doesn't matter specifically what type of exercise that is done by the older adult, as long as there is a consistent approach to maintaining exercise most adults report feeling better with less reports of depression. One other benefit to most forms of physical activity and exercise is that they can be performed with others, thereby allowing social activities and friendships to develop while promoting physical health. Physical exercise and health activities can reduce depression by allowing the older adult to communicate and socialize with others. Most of the older adults work out and exercise not only to improve their health, but also to create friendships and provide meaning in their lives. These very important factors that have become associated with exercise should not be underestimated in the life of the older adult, as loneliness and depression are some of the most common problems that have been associated with the older adult.

A recommendation for older adults who wish to participate in exercise programs is to *get involved* with activity with other older adults. Walking is a great beginning point for exercise for the older adult. Seniors who participate in regular walking programs indicate that an important incentive in continuing their exercise program is the friendships that have been created during the process of walking and exercising. Many older adults who walk two, three, four or more miles daily do so in small groups where they can chat and exchange information with one another. Walking may be done in malls or shopping centers, or more traditionally outside in tracks or cross-country courses. In sum, perhaps we can say that exercise is even more important in late adulthood not only for the physical health benefits, but also for the psychological and psychosocial benefits. By communicating and forming friendships with others, older adults may be better prepared to deal with depression.

Furthermore, we should remember to emphasize to older individuals that their quality of living will significantly improve and they will have an improved immune system if they incorporate an activity such as exercise (for as little as 30 minutes a day) in their lifestyle (Baum & Posluszny, 1999). It seems that the key in maintaining a happy and healthy lifestyle that extends into old age is maintaining an activity program such as exercise for at least 30 minutes a day and combining it with social activities, volunteer programs and recreational programs with other people. The key factor for many older Americans is in participating in programs and activities where they are recognized and needed by other people. The *"human element"* is a very important component of exercise where we can exchange our views and experiences with others and be recognized with dignity and respect. Machines and computers are still not capable of providing these necessary characteristics in psychological wellness.

Recent research by Adam deJong and Barry Franklin (2004) have also verified and documented the numerous advantages to a health and exercise program for the older adult. In their research, they focused specifically on low-impact aerobic activity for elderly adults. Rhythmic continuous activity was found to be essential in decreasing age-related deterioration of the muscular system (*sarcopenia*) and improved cardiovascular levels of health. Furthermore, light weight training that was incorporated in the exercise program was also found to be very advantageous for the elderly, as muscle strength was significantly improved for both men and women aged over 60, and in most cases strength increased over 25%. Finally, the authors discovered that those older adults who had exercised at least 30 minutes of moderate aerobic activity resulted in improved overall cardiovascular health and improved mobility and functional independence. What this means is that older Americans who remain active for as little as 30 minutes a day will be able to live longer with less physical complications and remain more autonomous by increased mobility and feel happier about themselves in the process of doing so (see figures 14a and b).

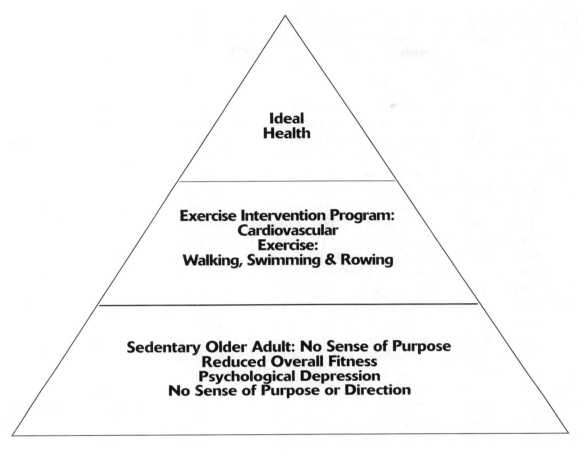

Figure 14a   Stages of Exercise for the Older Adult

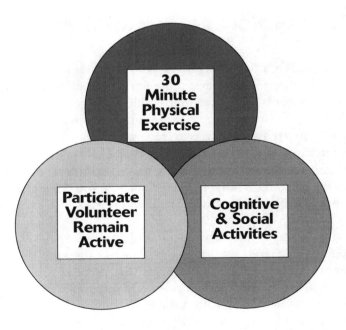

Figure 14b   The Interrelated Cycle of Physical, Cognitive and Psychosocial Health Among Older Adults: Achieving Balance

A final note when considering an activity program for the older adult is in specifically identifying an exercise that is appropriate for each person. Buffone (1984) has identified three important considerations when creating an activity program that is designed to help address the problems that are associated with depression:

a. *Create a specific program that is individually tailored for the older adult.* This is especially true among seniors as they typically have specific health limitations and problems that may limit their physical capacity. Always communicate with the older adult in terms of what activities are most physically rewarding and challenging to properly create and modify each program;

b. *Proficiency of the health trainer.* Buffone identifies this category as essential in the success of an activity program, as the health trainer or specialist must be aware of motivational issues for the older adult and more importantly how to maintain consistent participation. The trainer should allow the activity program to develop meaningful social activities for the older adult and be aware of the limited progress that older adults may typically represent. The health trainer for the older adult should be continually educating himself or herself to maintain a vibrant, exciting and challenging program for the older adult who wants to improve physical health. More importantly, Buffone (1984) argues that the trainer should be a role model for the older adult—perhaps in this case, a healthy role model or peer among older adults who is physically active and in good physical condition would serve as a very inspirational role model. In this way, the older adult who serves as the health trainer can show other older adults that it is indeed possible to stay physically healthy and participate in numerous activities that are physically challenging, healthy, and psychosocially rewarding;

c. *Reinforcing desirable behaviors.* Perhaps most importantly, the individual who is interested in developing an activity program for older adults needs to be aware of the fact that reinforcement, such as praise and encouragement, are absolutely vital in maintaining a successful program. Individual attention, verbal praise and acknowledging improvements are very successful methods in maintaining participation in the exercise program for the older adult.

■ METHODS USED IN HOW THE ELDERLY IS PORTRAYED IN SOCIETY

Ironically the period of time in our lives when we should be content and enjoying ourselves is often marked by depression and unhappiness. Our culture in the United States is very much attracted to or even preoccupied with concepts and perceptions addressing youth, sexuality and individual success. We admire our heroes who are young, versatile, and charismatic. We seem to associate youth with vitality, success and popularity. If we were to review how the media portrays the elderly in our society through television programs and movies, more than likely you would see the elderly as being portrayed in a very negative and less-than-flattering role: Dependent, unattractive, and essentially as being a "nuisance" or getting in the way. I would challenge you the student to test this theory by participating in a few unscientific or qualitative research projects:

a. **Television and Media.** Review a variety of current or past television programs or movies. Record the ages of the characters (approximations are fine) and describe how they are portrayed in the movie or television program: Are they popular, attractive and positive figures that fit within the theme of the movie or television program? Are they antagonistic (i.e., irritable, obnoxious or unpleasant) or are they portrayed in a positive manner? You may wish to incorporate a Lichert rating scale (where scores of "1" are least attractive or desirable, and scores of "5" are most attractive, popular or desirable). Then conduct a quantitative analysis (such as a t-test) and determine if there are any significant differences between age and the context within how age is portrayed in the media. I suspect that you will find significant results indicating that as we get older, the media portrays the elderly in increasing less desirable formats (an interesting caveat to this project would be to also consider gender and ethnicity as variables influencing how the characters are portrayed in the media;

b. **Interviews in Assisted Living Centers.** You may wish to visit any number of "assisted living" centers (previously called "retirement homes") and conduct a qualitative study by watching how the adult seniors interact with staff or with each other. Additionally, you may wish to observe differences in how active seniors (those who are involved in some form of exercise or flexibility programs) interact with each other as compared to adult seniors who are not involved in any form of an exercise program. Things to look for would include overall affect, frequency of communication and interaction, smiling, responding to questions from others, and overall agreeableness in daily activities, such a eating, taking medication, and so forth;

c. **Creating Your Own Exercise Program for Older Adults.** As a final suggestion in conducting research with older adults, conduct your own (informal) study that compares the differences between responses from a questionnaire (see figure 14c) that explores overall quality of life characteristics (such as happiness, depression and mood swings). For example, the questionnaire may address questions regarding the older adult's current typical mood, emotional states (such as happiness and depression), how often they communicate and socialize with others, and the willingness to participate in outdoor social activities. We hypothesize that those older adults who are actively participating in an activity program that involves exercise at least three days a week for at least three months will respond higher in overall positive moods, ability and willingness to interact and socialize with others, and an overall positive psychological experience that we would describe as wellness. Your first step in conducting this informal study is to conduct a pre-test with your "It Gets Better With Age"© questionnaire. In the pre-test, randomly select 20, 30 or 40 mature adults currently living in an assisted-living facility and make sure that they are not already in some form of an exercise or activity program. Administer to them the "It Gets Better With Age" questionnaire and now record the results. Now randomly divide the group into two groups: The experimental group (the group that will participate in the program) and the second group (control group) that will not participate in the program—they will continue living the lifestyle as they have in the past. As the researcher, you will need now to create your exercise program for your senior adults (see figure 14d). The activities that we have been describing may include traditional exercise and flexibility programs, or even volunteer programs. You may even wish to incorporate the positive effects of a gardening program (see Hoffman, 2004) or using pets as therapy in reducing depression for the older adult. *The key factor for many older Americans in maintaining a meaningful and happy life beyond retirement is to maintain a sense of purpose and to remain physically and cognitively active (see "It Gets Better With Age" questionnaire below).* After a period of time that will allow the benefits of the exercise or activity program to fully materialize (six months to one year) re-test your group (called the post-test) and then compare the results of your pre-test and post-test. Hopefully, there will be significant differences in the responses that will support our hypothesis that active mature adults who participate in a consistent and regular exercise program will report anecdotally higher scores of happiness and well-being with fewer adults feeling depressed and withdrawn. The scoring system will calculate all of the responses and the following results will indicate what level of exercise the senior adult is currently at and more importantly how the senior adult values the exercise program. The "It Gets Better With Age" questionnaire will also provide valuable anecdotal information that will determine how the adult senior values the exercise program on a daily basis, and how the program provides meaning to the individual's life and psychological well-being:

191

Scoring and Interpreting the "It Gets Better With Age" Questionnaire

The "It Gets Better With Age" (IGBWA) questionnaire is designed to measure the importance of exercise and physical activity for the older adult and psychological well-being. Add up all of the respondent's scores and compare them with the scale below:

If the Older Adult Scores Between:

a. **0–15 = (Couch Potato):** Very Sedentary and highly inactive lifestyle. The older adult is at risk for depression and frequently isolates self. Scores indicate that the older adult avoids interaction with others and does not exercise or participate in any form of an activity designed to improve overall physical health. Individuals who work with older adults in this category should be aware of the dangers of chronic depression and even possible suicidal thoughts.
   Recommendations: Recommendations include frequent contact with the older adult to explore and investigate causal factors that may be associated with such a high degree of inactivity. Encourage the older adult to simply watch others who are enrolled in the activity program to see how it develops and the types of activities that are performed in the class. Sometimes individuals have misperceptions of the exercise activity that may contribute to their reluctance in exercising. In some cases, individuals who score within this range of the questionnaire may not have ever had any exposure or experiences with an activity or exercise program. You may wish to initially walk and discuss these topics with the older adult. In this way, they have begun their exercise program (by walking) without even realizing it!

b. **16–30 = (Tortoise).** Very low physical activity—but signs of hope; The older adult who scores within this range is prone to isolation and inactivity but may be persuaded to participate in an activity program when he or she sees and is exposed to a popular exercise program that exists nearby. Additionally, the individual who scores within this range may need some minimal encouragement to participate in a variety of programs by the trainer or exercise. Once this encouragement is provided, older adults "rediscover" the value and importance of exercise programs.
   Recommendations: Encourage the older adult to join friends for a walk or some other outdoor activity. Remind him or her of the benefits (both physical and psychological) of outdoor activity and exercise. Tell them that you will help them get started and they may develop the "buddy system" where they will exercise together and encourage each other. Remind the older adult of the numerous social advantages of participating in programs with others.

c. **31–45 = (Mild)** Moderate Activity. In this median stage of exercise development, the individual will participate in an activity or exercise program occasionally (approximately two or three times monthly) and appreciates the activity *once he or she is involved.* The problem with this group of respondents is in *maintaining* an active and consistent program that is rewarding form them. When individuals who score or rank in this category begin to participate in groups (with other older adults), they are significantly more likely to maintain a consistent activity program.
   Recommendations: Try something new! Get of the routine exercise mode and begin to challenge your body with different physical demands. Remind the older adult of the numerous benefits that are associated with exercise—offer new activities or exercise programs that may entice others to join you. Stay focused on goals—re-evaluate and prioritize your own set of goals and strive to reach them by developing a time line or progress chart. Mix things up—try new activities and avoid the "exercise rut."

d. **46–60 = (Healthy!)** Frequent Activity. The older adult who scores or ranks in the fourth stage is considered to be active and consistent in their approach to health, wellness and exercise. The older adult at this stage typically is exercising two or three times a week and values the benefits that are afforded to him or her in the exercise program. More importantly, the older adult at this level is an active and consistent participant in the exercise program and appreciates the benefits from exercise.

Recommendations: Helping others. Now you the older adult have become the role model for other older adults—encourage others to join you—create programs that can be combined with other programs involving older adults. Encourage the older adults to participate and enjoy for the social activities as well (social mixers, picnics, and outings). Remember, when others see you enjoying yourself they will be more likely to participate with you in your activity program.

e. **61–75 (Sexy Senior!)** Outstanding activity in the exercise program. The senior adult who participates in the program is a dynamic contributing individual and actively participates on a very consistent (if not daily) level and actually serves as a positive role model for other adult seniors. Here many older adults appreciate the benefits provided to them by the exercise program and feel that exercising is a very important component to maintaining psychological wellness and happiness. Older adults at this level of participation have incorporated health and physical activity as a very important component of their lifestyle and typically feel that something is missing if they cannot participate. Overall, the experience of a consistent and regular exercise program has contributed significantly to the psychological well-being and happiness of the older adult.

Recommendations: Giving back to others and showing them how to achieve physical and psychological levels of well-being. You are the motivating factor in your older adult group—you are now organizing activity and exercise groups for individuals who have difficulty in remaining motivated in the program. Ideas that may influence others positively and serve as a motivating factor would be in developing the "Senior Games" at the assisted living facility where groups may compete with each other with medals and prizes for the finishers.

"It Gets Better With Age" Questionnaire

Typically I exercise (circle one):
a. 5 times a week or more;
b. 3–5 days a week;
c. 1–3 days a week;
d. I seldom or do not exercise at all.

Please answer the following questions with answers:
"0" (Absolutely not true);
"1" (Seldom or rarely true);
"2" (Somewhat true);
"3" (Unsure);
"4" (Somewhat true); and
"5" (Absolutely true).

      1. I often go outside and take a nice a walk during the day ___
      2. I am happy to be alive ___
      3. When I wake up in the morning, I look forward to all of the activities that I have planned___
      4. I exercise often ___
      5. Exercise makes my body feel good ___
      6. I feel that I have something valuable to contribute to others ___
      7. I participate in many activities with other people ___

8. I enjoy exercising with other people ___
9. After exercising I feel more relaxed and content ___
10. I feel physically stronger when I have exercised ___
11. I feel that I have more energy when I am exercising ___
12. I feel that my life is more balanced when I exercise___
13. Since I have been exercising I feel happier about myself ___
14. My appetite has improved since I have been exercising ___
15. It bothers me when I am not able to exercise ___

■ THE OLDER ATHLETE & EXERCISE: ACTIVITIES THAT PROVIDE MEANING

We have been discussing the tremendous benefits of exercise programs for a wide range of individuals. Young and old people are beginning to discover the inherent advantages both psychological and physical to those who participate in a regular healthy physical activity. Certain cohorts or populations of individuals who are approaching their fourth, fifth and sixth decade (and older) are now discovering the tremendous advantages of exercise that may delay (or remove altogether) the alternative of surgery when addressing physical problems. The two most important factors in delaying common physical ailments that are associated with aging include physical movement (such as walking) and diet. Older adults now more than ever need to "rediscover" the value and benefits afforded to them by exercise. Perhaps the older adult has even more reason to maintain a healthy and active exercise program. Physical benefits, such as delaying osteoporosis, keeping weight at a desirable level, and cardiovascular and heart benefits are just a few of the physical benefits. Even more important benefits for the older athlete include the psychosocial and psychological results of exercise and training. Older adults are particularly at risk for suffering from depression, loneliness and despair. They value and appreciate social interaction (even though sometimes they may not show it) even more because as we mature we become inevitably more dependent on others for daily activities and getting around. In this last section of the older adult and exercise, we will focus on cues to help older adults maintain and continue to grow in their exercise programs. We will offer seven different types of activities (one for each day of the week) that may enhance the quality of living and psychological well being of the older adult.

■ CHOOSING THE RIGHT PHYSICAL ACTIVITY

A major concern in working with older adults is in selecting the appropriate type of exercise. Perhaps the most important factor to consider is safety (i.e., risk factors involved?) and practicality. Important questions that we should be asking older adults include are there any special considerations prior to beginning the exercise activity or injuries that may limit activity. What kinds of activities are appealing to the older adult? Do they specific concerns or issues that should be brought to your attention? Another key factor in determining what sort or type of activity that is most appropriate is in asking how enjoyable is the activity to the older adult? We tend to repeat those behaviors that are particularly enjoyable and rewarding for us, something as simple and practical as walking or gardening. This next section of the chapter will provide several examples (one for each day of the week) that are ideal activities for older populations. For example, walking is a simple and very basic beginning exercise that is very popular. You may wish to begin working with an older adult simply be walking a short distance and asking how they feel. Additionally, remind the older adult that conversation and discussion of topics is recommended during the walks. The next section of this chapter addressing older adults and activity will provide a description of different activities that may be incorporated into the lifestyle of the older adult, combining both psychological and physiological features that will enhance each individual's activity program. Note that each activity is based on a different day of the week, so that individuals may participate in a meaningful and challenging program seven days of the week.

Monday (Health & Nutrition: Identifying Healthy & Palatable Diets For Older Adult Populations)

The diet for the older adult who is involved in a physical activity or exercise program must contain appropriate amounts of protein and carbohydrates for healthy functioning. These dietary requirements are somewhat different for younger adults (see figure 14c) and individuals should always first consult with a nutritionist before modifying their diet.

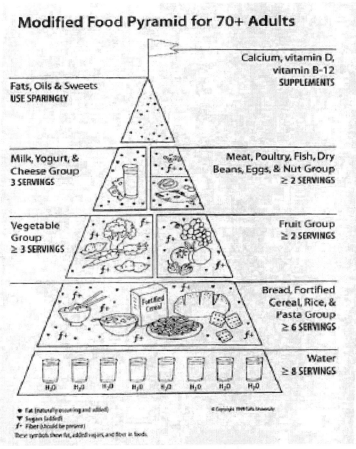

Figure 14c The Modified Food Pyramid for Older Adults

Important factors to consider when selecting foods for the older adult population include nutrition and vitamins, as well as taste and appearance. The healthiest diets are those diets that are varied and offer a balance of nutrients and minerals. An important side effect to exercise for the older adult is the increase in appetite in food consumption. A common problem that is associated among older adults is loss of appetite and withdrawal of social interaction. Eating is an important activity not only in sustaining overall physical health, but also in establishing social relationships with others. By increasing exercise and physical activity, the older adult improves his or her overall eating habits that also influences social interaction with others (see figure 14d):

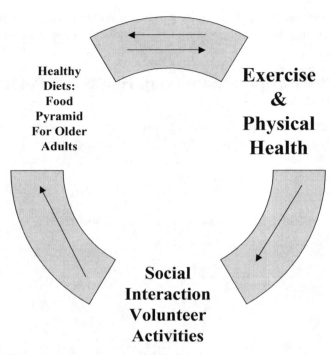

Figure 14d   Psychosocial Factors Associated with Diet & Exercise

Tuesday (Gardening and Landscaping: Planting Seeds of Happiness)

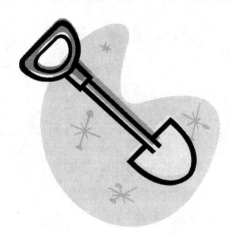

Research has documented the positive effects of gardening and landscaping projects on physical and psychological wellness. Numerous research articles have supported the theory that gardening activity not only addresses self-esteem, but cognition and psychosocial development. Hoffman and Wallach (2005) and Hoffman (2003) have identified a structured gardening program as an effective way to improve psychological levels of self-esteem and self-efficacy among under-represented community college students. Numerous research articles have addressed the advantages of outdoor activity programs such as gardening. McBey (1985) cites gardening as an important influence in improving self-esteem. Self-esteem is described as the subjective attitudes one has regarding their own accomplishments and ego. Thus, self-esteem is especially important in working with the older adult population. Other research supports the theory that gardening improves not only self-esteem, but also a strong sense of accomplishment (Perrins-Margalis, 2000), personal self-worth, pride and responsibility (Relf, 1981). Gardening has also been shown to be effective in improving cognition (Shirtliffe, 1996). Cognition is an important concern with older adults as memory and retention drops significantly in the elderly. Older adults often report anecdotally that the gardening programs they are working in provide them with "a sense of purpose" and an overall sense of well-being. Finally, gardening has also been shown to be a very positive activity with the older adult population as they are capable of establishing new relationships and friendships with others who also happen to be working outdoors.

A major concern among many older adults that contributes to depression is a loss of self-esteem and meaningful activities in their lives. Many older adults feel "left out" of daily activities and feel that they can provide more meaningful activities to society. Unfortunately, due to the many biases and stereotypes of the older adults in the collectivistic society, we overlook the tremendous advantages and resources that older adults may provide. Gardening activity in community parks, community colleges, and public community centers provide wonderful opportunities for the older adult to contribute back to their community and society, and also experience a healthy form of exercise in the process. Perhaps even more importantly, gardening activities provide seniors an opportunity to get outside and share their experiences and knowledge with others, perhaps teaching younger children how to plant seeds, cultivate soil, and grow vegetables that in turn are given back to the community as a viable resource for needy persons, such as the homeless and destitute.

When older adults are provided with the opportunity to contribute to a community gardening program, they are able to see the impact of their efforts in terms of improving the community that they happen to live in. Additionally, older adults who participate in a regular and consistent gardening program are participating in a physically demanding activity. They are working outdoors and often are able to interact with other older adults (or in some cases they may be working with younger people). More importantly, those older adults that have had some experience in working outdoors and gardening may provide this information to other groups of individuals and teach them their skills. This activity is critical, as they are providing an important resource to others and are experiencing the positive effects of being needed within the community. Older adults that participate in the community feel especially "connected" with others when they are able to work with others and provide information relevant to planting and horticultural activities. An overall positive reciprocal relationship develops when older adults can share their experiences relative to gardening with younger individuals who benefit from their knowledge.

Gardening and Alzheimer's Disease

Gardening has proven to be one of America's most favorite activities, as people of all ages seem to enjoy the benefits of outdoor activity and the moderate physical demands that are made upon them in typical gardening. Activities that are typically demonstrated in a normal day of gardening include bending, kneeling, pruning, and cultivating. In a fascinating study published by *Newsweek International* (2004), Joanna Denham is the director of the senior gardening program at the Dedenham Day Centre in London. Here she explains that many of the older adults who are suffering from Alzheimer's Disease have shown progress in their disorder after working in several different gardens. The study provides anecdotal evidence that when older adults are who are enrolled in a structured gardening program and participate on a regular basis, they are less anxious and show improved signs of cognitive activity. The basic premise of the study is that gardening activity not only helps us feel better psychologically, but also reduces anxiety that is often associated with problems that are associated with old age, including dementia and depression. Denham comments: "The [the older adults] used to sit and watch television . . . now everyone prefers to come outside and work in the courtyard and tend to their garden . . . the garden has taken on a life of it's own." The patients at the Edenham Day Centre have planted mint, verbena, and mint. In one particularly striking example of the benefits of gardening and old age, Denham comments: "We had a woman who could barely feed herself, but one day came out to the garden and she began planting plants from pots . . . it was like the soil helped her uncover some of her memory functions."

Given the fact that gardening can be physically challenging, we should be careful when beginning a gardening program of the physical limitations of the older populations. Specific concerns should address lifting heavy objects, such as pots and containers, as well as excessive bending and kneeling. Many older adults may already have difficulty with joints, therefore limiting repetitive movements is recommended.

Gardening Tips for the Older Adult

Other points to consider when older adults are working outdoors in a gardening program include:

a. *Inclement Weather.* Often gardening involves activities that require extensive periods of time outdoors—using appropriate UV protection while working in the sun and drinking plenty of fluids while working for extended periods of time is especially important. Included in this category would be wearing appropriate clothing—wearing light cotton during mild weather or long sleeve shirts and pants with warmer (or cooler weather) to prevent sunburn and exposure. With rain or lightening always stay indoors—no matter how much you want to continue in your program;

b. *Lifting Requirements.* Earlier we described the importance in correct posture in lifting objects. Reminding individuals to lift with legs (not back) to prevent injuries. Many hardware stores also have braces that help relieve stress on the back and are highly recommended in preventing back injury. Back injury is one of the most common injuries among gardeners, and being proactive in preventing it's development is essential for a positive experience in gardening;

c. *Shoveling Requirements.* Often gardening involves repetitive movements, such as digging, pruning (using hand shears) and trimming plants. The repetitive movements may become problematic with older adults who are suffering from physical ailments such as arthritis and bursitis. One suggestion in addressing this problem is in creating several different gardening activities utilizing different muscle groups;

d. *Avoiding Chemicals or Pesticides.* Many older adults suffer from respiration problems, such as asthma or emphysema. While it is always important to remain careful when using pesticides, it is recommended to avoid the use of chemicals altogether with gardening programs designed for the older adult;

e. *Be Prepared!* Because gardening involves outdoor activity, be prepared for minor injuries, such as tripping or falling. Have a plan that helps older adults receive medical attention promptly if needed. Be prepared for common problems when working with plants outside, such as bee stings (is anyone allergic to bee stings?), poison oak or poison ivy;

f. *Always Stretching Before Gardening.* Because of the physical demands of the gardening program, it may be advisable to offer a short "warm-up" session prior to beginning. For example, have the older adults participate in the very short but effective program:

    1. Upper Torso stretch: Stretching the neck from front to back and side to side;

    2. Shoulder Stretch: Grasping elbows with opposite hand and gentle pull to feel stretch of each shoulder;

    3. Lower Back Stretch: Very important stretch, as many older adults have back problems. Have older adults lie prone (on stomach) and gradually lift up upper body with arms and feel the stretch in lower back region.

Wednesday (Writing for Meaning: Older Adults Writing Meaningful Memoirs)

We have been discussing numerous activities that the older adult may engage in that may improve the overall quality of life and happiness. Gardening activity has proven to be highly effective in the maintenance of psychological wellness and happiness. The numerous advantages that are afforded the older adult when gardening include physical activity, social interaction with others, and simply being outside during pleasant weather. The next suggestion that may help improve the quality of living among older adults addresses writing and keeping a journal of activities. Many of these activities are actually interrelated; in other words, after the older adult has been involved in a gardening activity, they may wish to record their activities, thoughts and feelings. Keeping a journal will also help older adults to record their thoughts and feelings after each day and express themselves in a confidential manner while writing. Many people have reported the therapeutic effects of writing about the personal experiences in their relationships with others. Encouraging the older adult to document and write about their positive (and negative) experiences is a very effective method in improving quality of living and cognitive ability. James Pennebaker (1997, 2004) has written much about the numerous psychological benefits of writing. Some of these benefits include:

a. Positive influences on the immune system;
b. Lower reports of pain and lower required use of pain medication;
c. Lower levels of reported depression, and
d. Immediate positive effects on relaxation and muscular activity.

One suggestion that may incorporate the positive effects of gardening with writing would include older adults who are participating in a gardening activity to write about their experiences in a journal. According to Pennebaker, however, there are some suggestions that will allow the positive effects in writing to be most effective:

a. *Structure*. Be consistent in your writing—in other words, always select one common place to write, preferably an area where you will not be disturbed. The time that you write should also remain consistent. Most writers choose a period of time at the end of the day, where they can collect their thoughts and experiences and write about them in the most meaningful way. The purpose of the writing is to provide the older adult with a communication channel, or a release, of their thoughts and feelings that may be too private to communicate to others;
b. *Time period*. Your writing should extend anywhere between 15 minutes to 30 minutes. Remember, 30 minutes of continuous writing can be very mentally and physically challenging—so be sure to enjoy the process;
c. *"Inspirational Writing."* The most rewarding types of writing include creative and inspirational writing that makes the writer somehow feel better. For example, the older adult who has begun walking may want to describe how they feel when exercising with others, or per-

haps they may wish to comment how they feel about themselves, such as self-esteem, since they have begun an exercise program;

d. *Topics For Writing.* Because older adults are often placed in a position where they can reflect upon their lives, one suggestion for them would be to write about their own critical assessment of their personal and professional life. In this way, writing can become highly therapeutic. We cannot change the past in our lives, of course, but we can determine how wrong choices were made and determine what we have learned from them. In this way, writing becomes highly instrumental in serving as a form of "catharsis" or a release, where older adults can describe their thoughts and feelings and reflect with dignity and self-respect. Sometimes, thoughts and feelings may be difficult for the individual to express to family members or close friends. Again, by encouraging the older adult to create a writing journal they may be able to write down what they could not verbally discuss with others. Other very popular topics to encourage older adults to write about include:

1. Life Experiences: What You Feel Most Proud Of;
2. Life Experiences: What You Would Do Differently;
3. Physical Exercise: How Does Physical Activity Make You Feel?;
4. Things That Provide Meaning In Your Life;
5. The Inherent Benefits of Gardening;
6. Your Childhood: What Were The Positive Experiences? Negative Experiences?

Thursday (Swimming for Seniors: Walking in Water)*

In this chapter we have discussed a variety of activity programs for the older adult. This has been very important given the significantly higher increases in the number of people who are remaining physically active as they reach their seventh, eighth and in some cases ninth decade. One common problem for many older individuals is the problem of joints. As we age our joints seem to be the recipient of the most stress, and this is one of the more common complaints among older adults. Swimming and water-related activities offer tremendous advantages to older adults due to the resistance of the water without the pounding and jarring that is typically associated with other sports, such as jogging or jump-rope. This section will include brief information on water-related exercises for the older adult and how to enjoy swimming activities in a physically beneficial manner (**Always Require Supervision By CPR/Water Safety Instruction Trained Lifeguards When Using Swimming Pools With Older Adults!*):

a. *Week 1:* Adjusting to the water. During the first week of water activity, encourage the older adult to gradually progress into the water. Encourage them to familiarize themselves with their surrounding and adjust to the temperature of the water (78–80° Fahrenheit is recommended);

b. *Week 2:* Begin walking in the shallow water. Note that as we walk in water, there is a greater degree of resistance to the legs and hips. Older adults should be encouraged to gradually increasing their walking distance in shallow (waist high) water. The second week should be an assessment of the physical capabilities of the older adult—in other words, ask them to walk at a relatively brisk pace and to communicate to you when they begin to feel fatigued. This point is your base point. For example, if during the second week the older adults are walking back and forth three (3) lengths of the shallow end, use this number as a base and begin increasing the distance on a weekly basis;

c. *Week 3:* Kicking. After the older adult has adjusted to walking in waist-high water, increase the duration of the exercise by proving kickboards to each individual. Have each swimmer extend their arms on to the kickboard and lie prone (on stomach) and begin kicking. The coordination of this movement may take some time, as it is necessary to combine a "flutter kick" (feet moving back and forth) while maintaining balance with the upper torso. Additionally, the older adult swimmers may initially become frustrated, as the kicking requires significant energy expenditure. Design a kicking program that is challenging yet realistic, such as kicking only 10 or 20 yards the first week, or until they have mastered the activity and want to continue. Have the swimmers increase the distance on a weekly basis;

d. *Week 4:* Combine the activity of walking in water (minimum of 5 laps) with kicking (minimum of 2 laps). The combined activity of lower body work while walking in the shallow water with the kicking will increase stamina with minimal stress to joints. An overall ideal exercise program for the older adult, as swimming is highly refreshing and the older adults are afforded social interaction and communication.

Friday (Light Circuit Weight Training for Older Adults)

A very popular exercise for older adults that has very positive and rapid results is exercise and weight training. Light circuit weight training refers to the older adult lifting a variety of light weights that focus on a wide range of muscle groups, ranging from the upper body to lower body. Circuit training with weights is crucial for many older adults to help delay the onset of bone loss and osteoporosis. The amount of weight that is being used depends on the physical levels and capacity of the older adult, however, emphasis should be placed on the continuous cycle of weight lifting, going from one set of weights to another. This continuous process affords the older adult the advantage of both weight training and cardiovascular work as well. It is very popular among all groups but supervision must be provided for the older adults. Emphasis should be placed on light weight and higher number of repetitions (see figure 14e):

Upper Body Training:

Curls (5 repetitions);

Bench press (5 repetitions);

Lateral Pull-downs (5 repetitions);

Lower Body Training:

Reverse Hamstring (5 repetitions);

Leg Press (5 repetitions);

Stationary cycling (5 minutes).

Flexibility and Stretching: 15 minutes.

Total Exercise Time: Approximately One Hour

Total Exercise Time: Approximately One Hour

Figure 14e Light Circuit Training for Older Adults

Saturday (Volunteering for the Community)

Perhaps of all of the activities listed for the older adult, volunteer work within the community and public sector may prove to be the most rewarding for all people. For example, when older adults are given opportunities to share their knowledge and information that they have gained, they receive a sense of fulfillment, meaning and purpose. Older adults may wish to participate and volunteer in hospitals, by working in children's wards or volunteer services with cancer patients. Think of the tremendous impact that an older adult may receive when he or she is provided with the opportunity to communicate and talk to others and provide their own experiences of their lives to others. Children typically want and need to hear what life was like 20 or 30 years ago when the older adult was younger. The older adult receives tremendous psychological benefits and satisfaction by making others happy and helping them to forget their pain. Imagine what the older adult experiences when they no longer feel apathetic and "disconnected" in their life because they can talk to patients in a hospital about their lives growing up during WWII, The Great Depression, or watching the 1962 Baseball World Series. Those children listening to the older adults are being enriched and entertained by a group of caring adults who now have a sense of meaning and purpose in their lives. *Other sample volunteer activities for the older adult include:*

  a. Volunteer work in community centers;
  b. Community improvement activities (picking up trash and litter);
  c. Gardening activities;
  d. Volunteering work in daycare centers for children or other senior centers;
  e. Volunteering as teacher's aides;
  f. Volunteering services in poverty-stricken areas.

Sunday (Holistic & Psychological Well-being: A Time of Reflection)

A final activity for older adults may include holistic and spiritual activities, such as yoga (transcendental meditation) or volunteer work at local churches within the community. Regardless of the denomination, recognizing church activity and spirituality as a key component of achieving purpose, inspiration and meaning in one's life is fundamental in the activity of the older adult. Group sessions in discussing spirituality and mortality actually are often very enlightening and motivating experiences for the older adult. In an interesting article addressing how older adults have achieved meaningful experiences through community work, "Enter Go and Do Likewise" (*Los Angeles Times,* January 23, 2005) is described as a community based organization where individuals (comprised mostly of older adults) seek out community activities and help other people. Created in 1996, founders Bud Potter (62) and Terry Debay (71) decided to go out "actually in the field of the community and work" which is exactly what they have been doing ever since. The two men have over 100 volunteers who make it their mission to improve their community, doing everything from mowing lawns to fixing houses. The organization is based from a passage from the bible where individuals are encouraged to help others who may be less fortunate, beginning with the phrase: "Go and do likewise." The volunteers comment that for them it has been a wonderful way for them to go out and meet people, and they feel much better about themselves in the process. One woman who lived in a Costa Mesa condominium was Justine Sahli and she couldn't afford a new carpet. Her old carpet contained dust and mildew that was preventing her from getting adequate sleep. The older adult volunteers went to her condominium the next day and tore out the old carpet and installed new carpeting. Needless to say, both Justine and the volunteers have a sense of renewed purpose in life. The act of giving and helping people in need is in itself very rewarding—and these individuals are motivated in their lives to continue helping others.

■ MEDITATION

Meditation is another example of an activity that may have positive influences on the physical and psychological well being of the older adult. Many individuals may not be aware of the practice of meditation. Meditation may be described as any form of mental relaxation procedures that involve concentration and focus combining physical and psychological awareness into one entity. These procedures have been used literally for centuries by many groups of people and allow them to focus on one aspect of their consciousness and to block out other aspects of their being.

Meditation perhaps has more benefit for the older athlete as the procedure is very practical (it can be performed just about anywhere) and has been shown to have a positive impact on physical health. Many of the disorders that are associated with late adulthood (i.e., high blood pressure, depression, anxiety) have been treated very favorably with meditation practices.

Other factors that serve to enhance and continue the exercise training program for the older adult include:

> **Creating a Contract with the Older Adult: What Will We Accomplish Today, Tomorrow, or Next Week?** When individuals agree to signing a personal contract (such as committing to participation in a regular exercise program) they may feel more obligated in attending, thereby increasing their participation and success. Older adults are especially at risk for exercise attrition for a variety of reasons: Loss of interest, illness or boredom are typically the common causes. A contract may help to serve as an incentive for the older adult to continue with their exercise activity and also helps them to structure and monitor their progression;

> **"Bingo" Exercise: Types of Exercises for Each Day of the Week.** A novel or different method to motivate older adults in participating in an exercise program is through the devel-

opment of group activities involving a particular exercise. In the "Bingo Exercise" program, the older adults who are participating play a game similar to that of "Bingo" (what older adult doesn't know about Bingo?) where a variety of exercises are matched with key numbers. When the older adult matches all of their numbers they shout: "Exercise Bingo" and they have the privilege to select that day's particular exercise activity;

➤ **Identifying Goals in Exercise: What Do You Want Out of Your Exercise Program?"** Perhaps one of the most important requirements before beginning any exercise program is in first identifying what types of activities are desirable or non-desirable. For example, do the older adults who are exercising prefer to remain indoors in a climate controlled environment or do they prefer the outdoors? Identifying the preferences of an often persnickety population as older adults is vital if you wish to have a successful and positive experience in your exercise program;

➤ **Pet Ownership as an effective physical activity and prevention of depression.** Numerous articles have documented the importance and the benefits of pet therapy on people who may be recovering from depression as well as various forms of surgery (i.e., cancer patients who are receiving chemotherapy). Additionally, pets have been found to be highly effective in helping people feel better about themselves and improve their emotional affect and self-esteem. Older adults who are interested in pet therapy would experience improved physical and psychological health by a variety of mechanisms. For example, older adults who take their dogs on walks are receiving benefits from outdoor walking, and psychological benefits from the companionship offered to them by their dog. Truly, pet therapy for older adults is a "win-win" situation. One area of concern would be the nature and size of the dog, as larger dogs may prove to be overwhelming for some older adults. Furthermore, most pet therapy agencies require pet training programs before their animals engage in the therapeutic process (for more information addressing pet therapy, see Jaqueline Crawford and colleagues: *"Therapy Pets: The Animal-Healing Partnership"* 2004 at Amazon.com or *"Therapy Dogs: Training Your Dog to Help Others"* 2004 by Kathy Diamond Davis). One last note in describing the relationship between pets and the older adult. In a fascinating study that looked at the effects of diet and exercise not on the health of the older adult, but rather focused on the health and well being of the dog was conducted by Molly Wagster, director at the National Institute on Aging. In this report, Wagster discovers that actually dogs and their senior owners actually have much in common in the way of aging, both from the physical and cognitive perspective. For example, dogs also receive plaque deposits in the brain as they age, a phenomenon that has been associated with Alzheimer's Disease. In the current experiment, Wagster and colleagues discovered that older dogs who participated in a play group (playing with toys) combined with increases in physical activity were more likely to show cognitive advances and less decline associated with age. Cognitive advances were measured in terms of the classic "shell game" where dogs had to figure out where treats were hidden under different colored boxes (black or white). The dogs that had improved diets and exercise activities were significantly more likely to discover where the treats were hidden. These findings are especially significant because the dogs used in the experimental group were all middle-aged, indicating that therapeutic benefits are still possible even as dogs get older. The researchers speculate that the findings may be applicable to humans, but more research is necessary before we can arrive at this conclusion. Still, the results are important for older adults, as environments that are rich with cognitive stimulation combined with improved diets may help deter the negative factors commonly associated with Alzheimer's Disease.

➤ **Art Therapy & Painting for Older Adults.** A final area of suggestion to accommodate the physical and psychological needs of the older adult is art therapy. Encourage older adults to draw, paint or sketch what they are feeling has long been a highly effective exercise to improve one's psychological and physical well being. Using a variety of different colors try to encourage the older adult to paint the moods and emotions that they happen to be experiencing. If some of the older adults are a bit more pragmatic and less abstract (i.e., they do not know how to "draw moods") what you may suggest is for them to paint or sketch the beauty of the outdoors that they had experienced during their morning walks. Thus, you as the organizer of the exercise activity are encouraging both physical exercise through walking and psychological awareness and insight by encourage your adults to "paint" what they are feeling after their exercise.

In conclusion, we have discussed several components and characteristics of the older athlete and participation in sport or physical activity. We can summarize by stating that numerous research articles point to the overall therapeutic benefits (both psychological and physical) to the older athlete who participates in these programs regularly. However, as a final note, we should note that older athletes experience a series of psychological transformation as they begin to retire from active sport participation. Similar to Elizabeth Kubler-Ross' (1969) classic work *On Death And Dying,* we can identify distinct stages of growth and development of the older athlete's career:

The Aging Athlete and Retirement: 5 Stages of Transition

1. Denial: My style of play is as good as it ever was; I can still play like I used to;
2. Anger: They don't know my true and real talent—I'm training harder and just as good as the rest of them and I will show them;
3. Bargaining and "Negotiating the Contract"—Can I play just one more season?
4. Depression: Why me?—My life will not be the same without sport;
5. Acceptance of physical limitations and moving on in one's career.

If we review several notable athletes throughout sport history, we may observe that several of them seem to progress through stages that are very similar to Kubler-Ross' stages on death and dying (see figure 14d). While the athlete's life existence may not be a terminal illness such as dying (as Kubler-Ross writes about), his or her sports or athletic career may be ending and these characteristics may match many of the same psychodynamic stages that Kubler-Ross refers to in her work. For example, with many top or elite level athletes, there is strong denial (even perceived betrayal) that some may suggest that his or her career is now waning. This incredulous reaction often turns into anger: "How dare they challenge my talent and skills? What do they know about sport competition?" The anger cannot justify the reality of declining skills and performance, which now results into bargaining and negotiating of contracts ("Can I have just one more season?"). For many athletes, this decline in performance may result in chronic depression, as they perceive their sport performance as a symbiotic function of their persona—once their sport identify dies, then in a very real sense, they also begin to die. Healthy activities may stop, exercise may stop altogether, and in many cases substance abuse (i.e., drugs and alcohol) may begin to avoid the realization that their sport career is now fading. However, with counseling and support from friends and family, the older athlete may accept this transition and move on to other exciting components of his or her life. For example, giving back to others, such as through volunteer coaching and working with younger athletes, is a very real and healthy activity to participate in after retirement.

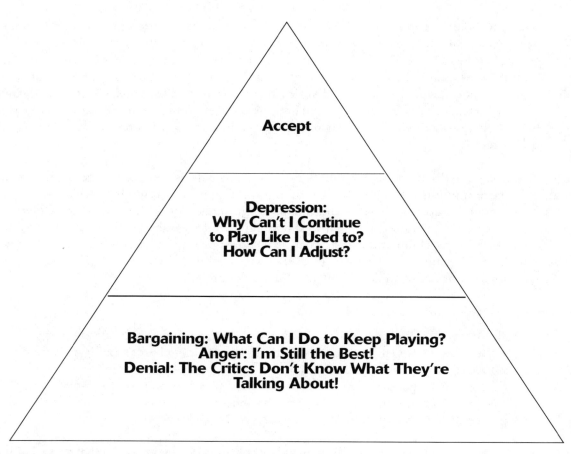

Figure 14d   The Aging Athlete and Retirement: 5 Stages of Transition

■■■ CHAPTER 14 QUESTION & REVIEW

1. Briefly explain why gerontology is an important topic in sports today—Approximately what percentage of Americans living in the United States today is aged 65 or older?

2. Explain the concept how age is relative—Do you consider yourself "old"? Think back ten or fifteen years ago and imagine your age today—would you have considered yourself then "old" today?

3. Explain how exercise may help older adults with depression—in your opinion, why is depression very common among older adults?

4. Describe the three phase pyramid of physical exercise for older adults (see figure 14a);

5. Conduct your own informal survey by administering the "It Gets Better With Age" (IGBWA) survey with yourself and some friends of yours—calculate your results and determine your level of bias (if any) among the older athlete and your responses to older athletes participating in sport;

6. Review the modified food pyramid for older adults—why should the diet of the older adult change?

7. Identify the five stages of the aging athlete and retirement.

Chapter 15:
Interviews with Elite Athletes

We have been discussing a wide range of skills and techniques that have improved athletic performance and training. Within this text we have also reviewed specific populations of individuals that may have special needs or skills that need to be taken into consideration when understanding performance in sport. Chapter 15 will now focus again on a very specific or elite category of athletes who have utilized unique training methods in their preparation to sport. Many of the athletes are Olympians or world record holders in their events. We will focus on the two components of training: The psychological preparation and the physical training involved for each athlete.

Athlete #1: Stan Allotey. 1968 Olympics (Mexico City, Mexico); Gold Medalist in the 200 meters representing Ghana. Mr. Allotey commented that the most important characteristic in training was the mental focus and what he refers to as the "psych out" factor prior to competing. "Many of the sprinters would look at you, gaze and stare at you, to try to confuse you or unnerve you prior to the start. For example, a common trick among many of the track sprinters was to intentionally false start before beginning the race. When an athlete (any athlete) false starts, according to Olympic track and field regulations, the next sprinter (even if he or she was not the original false starter) would be disqualified. By intentionally false starting, it was speculated that the other sprinters would have a significantly slower start off the blocks because no one wanted to be disqualified. "It was a very effective intimidation trick" Allotey commented, "because everyone tried so hard to be there in the first place." Further, Allotey reported that it was very important for the track athletes to avoid direct eye contact with the other athletes. "If you looked at somebody directly in the eye . . . then that was a sign of confrontation and intimidation. All I ever did was look down at the ground before the race."

- **Mechanisms of psychological preparation.** Allotey commented that the most important mechanism in psychological preparation was remaining focused and driven. "Avoid the distractions, temptations and other traps. The best athletes in training are the ones that persist and train without being deterred in reaching their goals. Successful athletes psychologically have the capacity to believe they are achieving their goals and are not intimidated by other "world class" champions. During training Allotey commented that he would visualize running smoothly and flawlessly. Mental rehearsal and visual imagery are key elements in shaping the body to perform physically. Before the body can physically respond, mentally you must create a picture of what you want it to do. When the gun is fired, the successful track athlete literally sees his or her body flowing gracefully over the hurdles, becoming stronger with each stride. The successful elite athlete never looks at others, but only remains focused on his or her performance.

Athlete #2: Olympic Champion Ulis Williams. * Ulis Williams is no stranger to adversity and challenges in his life. Ulis Williams was the son of a sharecropper in Mississippi, and in 1957 his family moved to the city of Compton. It was here where Mr. Williams began running track and field and soon discovered his athletic talents. He comments: "The only sport I knew at the time was baseball and basketball but a local high school coach wanted me to tryout for the track team." His real talent came when he won the 440 in the state championships in 1961 and was named amateur athlete of the year at Arizona State University. Williams then went to the Olympic trials and finished second in 1963. At the Tokyo Olympics in 1964 Williams and his partners in the relay foursome (Henry Carr, Mike Larabee and Ollan Cassell) performed a stunning feat by breaking the world record in the 4 X 400 meter finals with an incredible time of 3:00.7. The win nearly turned into disaster, however, as Williams had to pull up on his finish as Carr started his run late. Williams fell on the ground but safely handed the baton to Carr, who won by over nine yards and almost a full second ahead of the nearest opponent (Great Britain). Williams assumed the position of interim president at Compton College and has overseen the development of the Vocational Technology Building and new math/science center. His dedication and hard work in both community services at Compton College as well as his personal athletic career make him not only an exceptional athlete, but a dedicated individual who is committed to improving his community. Williams notes that his adversity in growing up contributed to his successful philosophy in sport competition. He concludes his interview by noting: "I believe success is where opportunity meets preparation."

■ CHAPTER 15 QUESTION & REVIEW

1. Briefly explain the techniques of psychological preparation of the elite athlete Stan Allote. Why, in your opinion, is it essential that several of the elite athletes prior to competition need time to psychologically prepare?

2. What do you think are the main components of psychological preparation for athletes in general?

3. In your opinion, how do athletes develop the skills in psychological preparation? For example, how do athletes who have broken world records, such as Ulis Williams in 1964, begin to develop the psychological and mental skills necessary to complete their goals?

4. How does social adversity contribute to creating the psychological strength necessary in successful athletic competition?

5. Comment on your own ability to develop psychological momentum to help you achieve your own goals. Do you think that someday you may be able to break a world record?

*Excerpts of this interview taken from the Palisadian-Post, August 19, 2004 issue.

Chapter 16:
Skills Used in Developing Psychological Momentum: Different Sports Require Different Types of Psychological Momentum

Chapter 15 addressed elite athletes and the personal views in improving athletic competition and sports. We will now address several specific techniques and measures used to develop psychological momentum in competitive sport. These measures are often used by athletes in training and competition that help provide them with an advantage when competing with other athletes. The term psychological momentum refers to a positive form of psychological energy that improves sport or athletic performance and mental focus (Hoffman, 1982). As modern sports are becoming increasingly competitive and intense, the differences between first place and second place may be a fraction of a second. Furthermore, in modern competitive sports the physiological training among many athletes is very similar, so that the only distinguishing factor among athletes may be their levels of mental focus and psychological momentum. The concepts of physical and psychological performance should not be viewed as separate components. They should be viewed as reciprocal and dynamic elements that contribute to superior athletic performance. Truly exceptional athletes (such as Stan Allotey in chapter 15: *Elite Athletes*) know how to combine both the physiological and psychological elements to perform at their best possible levels in competition (for other views regarding the ability to develop psychological strategies in competition review Zaichkowsky and Takenaka, 1993). Some athletes may even take advantage of their knowledge of psychological principles to try to intimidate others by staring at them prior to competition, or other athletes simply concentrate and rehearse mentally the things that they need to do. However, certain mental rehearsal skills may be practiced that may give athletes an advantage when competing in sports (see figure 16a):

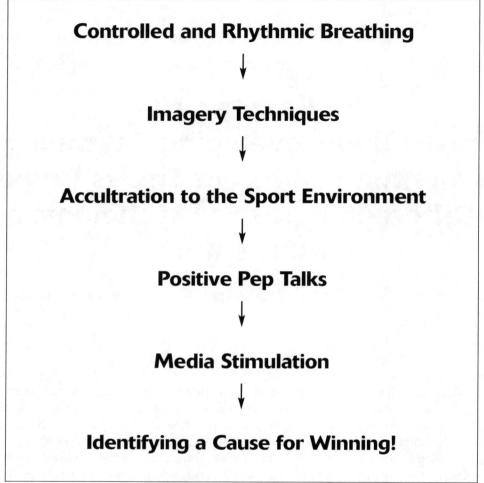

Controlled and Rhythmic Breathing

↓

Imagery Techniques

↓

Accultration to the Sport Environment

↓

Positive Pep Talks

↓

Media Stimulation

↓

Identifying a Cause for Winning!

Figure 16a   Six Components of Psychological Momentum

a.   *Controlled and Rhythmic Breathing.* Perhaps the single most important thing athletes can do in order to remain relaxed and focused prior to competition is through what we refer to as "controlled breathing." When a demand is placed on our system, we typically respond with the activation of the sympathetic nervous system (sometimes referred to as the "fight or flight" response. The pupils become dilated, heart rate and blood pressure significantly increases as the body is physically trying to adjust to the demand or perceived threat. If the autonomic nervous system is activated for long periods of time, we may become physically fatigued and exhausted, therefore it is critical that the athlete knows how to control the responses of the autonomic nervous system. Breathing and respiration also increase as a means to produce more oxygen in the blood stream, however, increased respiration may also result in hyperventilation. The skilled athlete can control the respiration system by focusing on relaxing ideas or through visualizing a calm or serene environment. Additionally, the athlete's respiration and breathing typically increases with anxiety, (i.e., before a competitive match) and thus it is very important to relax and control breathing prior to competition. Remember (and this is very important) when your breathing becomes erratic and out of control when you are competing, your stamina and endurance becomes drained and you lose your pace and rhythm very quickly. Elite runners focus on controlled breathing to the point that even swallowing or coughing during competition may disrupt their breathing which ultimately may cost them time. Endurance training and stamina help control breathing to be more rhythmic and within a consistent pace. Typically when we are becoming physically fatigued and exhausted, the first component that becomes affected is our controlled breathing;

b. *Imagery Techniques:* Imagery techniques are also very effective in developing psychological momentum. Imagery refers to a type of "mental picture" the athlete thinks of before or during competition that can either trigger emotional arousal or calming and relaxing emotions. For example, if the athlete has a history of becoming "over aroused" or even "psyched out" he or she may want to mentally rehearse or visualize a very calm and serene environment. Some athletes think of a "happy place" where they go to help them relax prior to competition. However, some athletes have the opposite problem, where they are not aroused enough prior to competition. In these cases, the athlete may intentionally create a form of psychological momentum through emotional arousal. For example, many power lifters intentionally infuriate themselves just prior to their lift, as power lifting requires a sudden explosion of physical strength. Imagery is a very practical and resourceful skill that can be implemented just about anywhere. It is most effective as imagery helps us control excessive levels of anxiety and stress and can help us achieve the necessary psychological state that enhances physical performance;

c. *Previewing the Sport Environment.* Many times competing in new environments (such as stadiums, gymnasiums, courts, etc.) may be unnerving to the athlete. Many athletes talk about "home court" advantage which refers to feeling more comfortable while playing on their home turf. This typically means more fans coming out to support you and you being aware of the physical location of the athletic environment. This can be a tremendous advantage in competition. When athletes have been afforded the opportunity to preview the actual area where the competition will occur is a significant advantage. Becoming accustomed to new environments and learning the actual physical and geographic region where you will be competing will help reduce anxiety and stress. For example, gymnasts, springboard divers, figure skaters and track and field athletes often need to identify key targets (known as "spotting") that serve as indicators of actual physical body position while performing a specific routine. The springboard diver may need to identify a target on the roof or ceiling to execute the perfect dive, or the gymnast may need to know where and when to end their routine.

d. *Positive Pep Talks.* Often athletes respond very positively to verbal encouragement (often referred to as "pep talks") and motivational talks. Pep talks can be used as important tools in helping each athlete achieve optimum performance—or they can actually have a negative or counter-productive impact on performance. In this section of chapter 14 will offer suggestions on more effective pep talks as well as providing information on what to avoid. The most effective pep talks are those that enhance and boost self-esteem of each athlete in a very realistic manner where team members play as a unit and for a common cause. Effective pep talks remind athletes why they are competing and performing in the first place. Effective coaches who deliver the pep talks emphasize the skills, talent and effort that the athletes have contributed and worked on for so long. Tables 16b and 16c summarizes positive (and negative) characteristics of pep talks used by coaches:

Key Characteristics of the Successful Pep Talk:

✓ Positive pep talks focus on positive topics: Strengths, skills and effort that each athlete has been working on throughout the season;

✓ Effective pep talks focus on specific goals—what does each athlete have to do for the desired outcome?;

✓ Effective pep talks stimulate athletes to want to perform at the best—the coach gives them the motive and the impetus to excel;

✓ Effective pep talks provide athletes with reasons to believe that they can win despite being the underdog; The effective coach delivering the pep talk convinces the athlete that he or she has the ability and experiences to overcome obstacles in achieving their goals. In a word, the athletes believe in themselves and share a committed cause to win;

✓ Effective pep talks focus on the positive components of competition and block out the negative components (i.e., reduced anxiety and fear);

✓ Effective pep talks emphasize the positive belief system in achieving results (i.e., that each athlete can achieve his or her goal);

✓ Coaches that serve as positive role models. When coaches "walk the walk" they are practicing models of what they want their athletes to emulate. This may include personality characteristics, such as coaches having high levels of integrity and showing to practice on time. An excellent coaching role model who incorporated the positive pep talk strategies would include UCLA basketball coach John Wooden;

✓ Most importantly, positive and effective pep talks focus on the athlete's internal locus of control—literally convincing them that *they have the power and potential to make changes in their outcome.* When teams compete and have an external locus of control—they literally feel that the results (i.e., loss) are inevitable and that they have no control in changing the outcome of events. Most of the effective (and popular) coaches can literally change the athlete's perception of causality. Numerous games have been played where the team that was favored to win by over 20 points were actually beaten by teams that had a stronger will to win and belief that they controlled their own destiny.

Figure 16b   Positive (Successful) Pep Talk Strategies

e. *Media Stimulation.* The media does have a profound influence in terms of what we perceive as desirable and what we want to obtain. Not only does the media influence behavior in general, the media and music can specifically influence groups of individuals who face athletic competition. For example, when weightlifters and aerobic instructors exercise to certain types of music, performance improves and tolerance to physical pain that is associated with exercise also increases;

Key Characteristics of the Unsuccessful Pep Talk:

✓ Unsuccessful pep talks are usually unrealistic in the goals that they seek; Coaches need to be aware of what each player or team is capable of achieving;

✓ Unsuccessful pep talks place blame on others and focus on negative factors other than focusing on unity and positive topics;

✓ Any pep talk that involves negative sanctions (i.e., punishment) is the goal of winning is not achieved;

✓ Lengthy and boring pep talks are clearly not effective in the coach's attempt to motivate athletes. Additionally, pep talks that are perceived to be somehow non-authentic by athletes are highly ineffective.

Figure 16c   Negative (Unsuccessful) Pep Talk Strategies

f. *Identifying a Cause For Winning!* Perhaps most importantly, effective coaches incorporate and identify reasons for winning for the athlete. Interviewing some of the most successful athletes indicate that often they compete to win for a variety of reasons, some of them including:

✓ The drive to win because the athlete feels that he or she is the superior athlete;

✓ The drive to win because of the love of the sport;

✓ The drive to win to show support for the coach;

✓ The drive to win to show team sport and unity;

✓ The drive to win to show each other athletic skills and potential.

■ MECHANISMS USED IN THE DEVELOPMENT OF PSYCHOLOGICAL MOMENTUM

Within this chapter we have been describing a variety of different skills used in achieving psychological momentum, such as the development of imagery and controlled rhythmic breathing. In this final section of chapter 16, we will discuss non-traditional methods in the use of psychological momentum. Historically, psychological momentum has been developed and cultivated to help athletes improve their performance in a variety of competitive sport environments. However, many sports require a specialized level of psychological momentum that not only addresses physical and sport performance, but also related factors to sport performance, such as emotional control, emotional arousal, and weight control or weight management (see figures 16d and 16e). The advantages of psychological momentum may best be described in terms of versatility and practical use in training for competition. Hopefully, by now you have a good idea that psychological momentum refers to a combination of psychological strategies used to improve performance in a variety of sport endeavors.

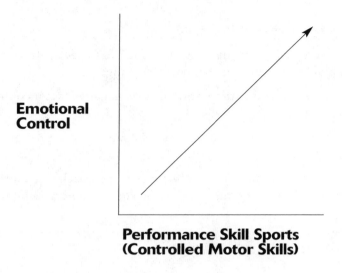

Figure 16d   Emotional Control and Skill Sports

Emotional Arousal in Sport Competition

In some cases, athletes may need to incorporate higher levels of emotional arousal in sports that involve higher levels of concentration and focus. Mental focus, guided imagery and visualization are just a few examples of some of the techniques that are used to increase levels of emotional arousal. In some sports the athlete may actually need to increase his or her emotional arousal to increase power, strength and stamina. Many weight lifters and power lifters, for example, visualize and focus on images that may significantly increase their emotional arousal and autonomic nervous system. Some specific techniques involve power lifters who think of events that may anger or infuriate them where they feel increases in power and strength. They may visualize specific persons or experiences in their personal lives that help them achieve the emotional arousal they need to be successful in their

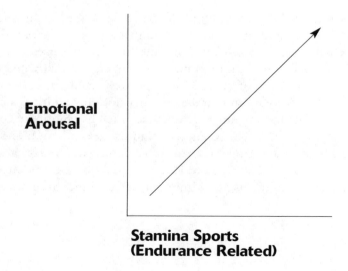

Figure 16e   Stamina Control and Emotional Arousal

sport. In other sports, such as endurance sports (marathon running), athletes may visualize their running performance as smooth, effortless, and gliding across each mile. The elite runners often think or visualize of places that produce the desired physical effect or outcome, such as completing each mile in a relaxed and flowing process without feeling any pain. When athletes feel that they are beginning to fatigue and lose stamina while competing (for example mile 23 of the marathon, commonly referred to as "The Wall"), they focus on the mental skills that may help "push" them through those last few agonizing miles. Common topics or themes of visualization among many successful athletes include creating a mental picture of winning, such as crossing the finish line first or winning the gold medal.

Emotional Control

We have been describing some sports that require higher levels of emotional arousal during competition, especially those sports that require sudden bursts of strength and power (such as boxing, wrestling, and long-distance running). Not all sports require the same type of power or strength. Indeed, in many sports, a sudden burst of strength or stamina may actually produce negative consequences. Think for a moment of the putting situation we described earlier in the beginning of the first chapter. A golfer has made this putt thousands of times. The distance of the golf ball to the cup is no more than two and one-half feet. However, the golfer senses that something is wrong—somehow, things don't "feel" right. He or she is nervous, as many people are watching the putt, or perhaps the entire golfing match rests on making this putt. The golfer is feeling very nervous and aroused (too aroused) and misses the shot. What happened? Many things could have occurred that may have contributed to missing the shot: Excessive anxiety, galvanic skin response (sweaty palms), hyperventilating (breathing out of rhythm), and so on. You can see how many, many sports do not necessarily rely on strength or power, but more skill and eye-hand coordination: A basketball player needs to balance strength with precision eye-hand control and skill to make either a free throw or a three point shot or a field goal kicker needs to make a 40 yard field goal in a football game with three seconds left. In each of these cases, the athlete needs to focus and control his or her emotional arousal, not increase the levels of emotional arousal. In this final section of chapter 16, we will now describe techniques that are used to help control over-arousal or states of anxiety. When athletes try to achieve emotional arousal, they are typically experiencing too much state anxiety and need to incorporate methods or techniques to control their autonomic nervous system. The consequences of an over-activated autonomic nervous system include hyperventilation and an inability to achieve mental focus and neuromuscular control. Athletes can overcome the problem of emotional arousal by practicing the use of mental imagery and visualization. For example, the golfer who in the previous example missed his or her putt due to anxiety and excessive levels of emotional arousal could have implemented specific visualization skills to help regain emotional control. Specifically, the golfer should actually create a mental picture of the calm and relaxing environment and picture themselves. Some examples include calm and quiet physical environments, such as being on the beach by yourself and listening to the waves breaking, smelling the fresh, clean air from the beach, and feeling the sun warming your skin. Note that each of the senses have become utilized and activated for the most successful visualization exercise: *Feeling* the sun, *breathing* clean air, and *listening* to typical sounds at the beach. The more specific the individual is in the location of the calming environment, the more successful the visualization exercise will be in emotional control. The athlete who wants to achieve emotional control through visualization needs to actually picture himself or herself in the environment itself and create a vivid, detailed, and specific picture of the environment: What does the area look like? How does it feel to be there? Many very famous athletes have commented on the effectiveness of visualization. For example, Jack Nicklaus, the famous golfer commented about visualization: "I never hit a shot, not even in practice, without having a very sharp picture in my head" (Nicklaus, 1974, p. 79). Imagine the professional football field goal kicker who has to make a 35 yard field goal in driving wind and rain. The crowd is deafening and roaring and he cannot even hear himself think. How can he overcome this very difficult mental and psychological situation? By simply engaging in visualization and creating a mental picture for himself—he is no longer at the football stadium with over 100,000 screaming fans. Instead, the field goal kicker is now back at home practicing field goals with his friends on a warm and sunny day—no pressure, no problems, just confidence: He sees his leg flowing through the ball making perfect contact—in slow motion he sees the football drive through the uprights, scoring the winning points. *The point is that it **can** happen, it **has** happened, and you **will make it happen**! The more specific the imagery is the more effective it will be in bringing the athlete the desired results.*

▄▄ CHAPTER 16 QUESTION & REVIEW

1. Identify the six components of psychological momentum and how they may be used in sport and physical activity;

2. Explain the relationship between emotional control and skill sports;

3. Explain the relationship between emotional control and stamina sports

4. Describe the importance of psychological momentum in sport activity, and how different sports may require different levels of focus and concentration;

5. Describe how psychological momentum may be achieved and how it may be useful in different sports.

Chapter 17:
Competitive Sports and the Physically Challenged Athlete

When we think of sports and athletic competition, we typically think of a group of talented athletes working together to achieve a common goal. We view and critically judge their athletic performance based on team performance, quality of play and individual characteristics of each athlete. Typically each athlete has been training either individually or in team sports with a relatively similar level of playing ability. More importantly, each athlete has the basic body type and physical skills to compete with each other either in individual or team sports. We simply take for granted that each athlete has two feet, two legs, two arms, visual/hearing accuracy and physical balance and coordination. However, such is not the case with all athletes. In many cases, not only do physically challenged athletes compete with other athletes in a variety of different sports, but in several sport environments these athletes are competing in tournaments either in wheel chairs, prosthetic devices on limbs, or they are visually or hearing impaired.

■ SIMILAR PSYCHOLOGICAL CHARACTERISTICS AMONG PHYSICALLY CHALLENGED & ABLE-BODIED ATHLETES

While some physically challenged athletes may appear *physically* different from other athletes, their psychological and emotional drive and determination are quite similar with able-bodied athletes. Numerous studies have documented through empirical research the similar personality characteristics between the able-bodied athlete and the physically challenged athlete. Furthermore, non-athletes that are physically challenged are very similar in psychological characteristics with non-athletic able-bodied individuals. Athletes with physical challenges or disabilities also have much in common in terms of *competitive* personality characteristics with other able-bodied athletes. For example, athletes with physical challenges want to compete and work to the best of their abilities while in the process of achieving their goals. *More importantly, they want to be provided with the opportunity with other athletes to compete, to work hard, and to learn from their experiences in athletic competition.* They want to work hard and strive for their goals in competition with other athletes and they do not want to be given anything. In this respect, athletes with physical challenges have very similar characteristics with other athletes—being provided with the equal opportunity to compete and interact with other athletes in an athletic and competitive environment. In the past, individuals with a wide range of physical challenges were not only prevented from participating in sport and exercise activity, but their life span was considerably shorter. The shortened lifespan (ironically) was not due to their actual physical challenge or disability, but rather due to related factors, such as limited cardiovascular activities that are associated with exercise. For example, as recently as 1960, individuals who were diagnosed with Down's Syndrome (a chromosomal disorder that causes impairments in learning and mental retardation) had a life expectancy of only 35 years. Today, with advances in medicine, technology *and exercise,* the average life expectancy for those diagnosed with Down's Syndrome has more than doubled (over 70 years). The good news of course is increased life expectancy. However, areas of concern with increased life expectancy are cardiovascular disease and obesity. Recently, the *Daily News* ran an article that emphasized the special needs of physical training, exercise and activity for those with physical challenges (*"Getting The Disabled Fitter",* Friday, February 11, 2005). In this article, Dennis McCarthy writes about an important event to these individuals, the Special Olympics. The Special Olympics is an event that is held especially for those with physical challenges, and health and fitness are two areas that are emphasized in the program. Tri-Valley Special Olympics coach Jeff Morse works with several teams of individuals who show tremendous drive and talent despite their physical challenges. Most of the adults have been living sedentary lifestyles, so it is critical to focus on cardiovascular exercise, such as basketball, golf, and track and field. What a wonderful experience to see those individuals with physical challenges running, playing basketball or even playing golf. Able-bodied athletes should devote more time to volunteer with the physically challenged to help them reach their goals. In this way, everyone lives a happier and healthier lifestyle that builds cooperation among athletes. We will now discuss another area of similarity between the able-bodied athlete and the athlete with physical challenges—the personality. Arguably, the personality composite of both groups of athletes are very similar, as well as the passion and drive exhibited in reaching their goals.

For example, Porretta and Moore (1996) conducted several personality profiles among the physically challenged athlete and the able-bodied athlete and found striking similarities among the two groups. The personality profiles administered to the groups included the Profile of Mood States (POMS) and the Iceberg Profile. The results indicated that both groups had similar responses to anxiety, practiced visualization skills and very similar characteristics in goal setting. The physically challenged groups of athletes in particular have faced remarkable obstacles and are training, competing and enjoying the experience of sport and these factors need to be recognized. Things that we so often take for granted, such as driving to the gym, training and exercising may be incredibly more complicated and time consuming for the physically challenged athlete. The positive energy and psychological confidence that they typically display while competing as well as in their personal lives is truly inspirational for any person who wants to understand human behavior. We should celebrate and acknowledge these athletes as being true role models for all of us in society. Athletes with physical challenges have overcome tremendous barriers and have discovered sport activity as one venue to compete with other athletes and improve their overall quality of living.

Many of the athletes who are physically challenged do not view their condition as a handicap, but rather as a challenge to improve their overall quality of athletic performance—they view their condition as unique circumstances to aspire to higher goals. Furthermore, many indicated that for them they had a choice to either remain bitter and angry over their situation in life, or accept their condition and use sports as one way to interact and compete with others. Few of us ever take the time to realize that a whole new population of athletes exists that may be playing with physical limitations or disabilities, such as wheel chair athletes or athletes who may be competing with a prosthetic device. Current estimates suggest that over 43 million individuals currently living in the United States have some form of a physical disability (Leunes & Nation, 2002). Within this population, there are estimates of 2 to 3 million who participate in sports and athletic competition. Thus, individuals who are physically challenged play a significant role in the world of sports, and we feel that it is important in understand the psychological and physiological ramifications of such athletic endeavors.

▆▆ OVERCOMING BIAS AMONG THE PHYSICALLY CHALLENGED

In some cases, institutions may not be designed or structured for sport participation among physically challenged athletes. Things that appear to be so simple in nature, such as a door entrance to the gym having an automatic opener or a ramp to allow for wheelchair access may make all the difference in the world to the physically challenged athlete. The greater the degree of individuals who are working in the health industry to help and facilitate a "physically challenged friendly" environment, the greater the likelihood of recruiting more successful physically challenged athlete to begin sport and exercise participation. In other cases, some other individuals who are involved in sport activity may actually hold biases and prejudice against those with physical challenges. This is unfortunate because the physically challenged athlete has faced numerous obstacles in their training and practice of their sport, and the last thing they need to be confronted with is another problem with other athletes. How do you rank in terms of bias against athletes with physical challenges? Review the survey: Bias Against Disabled Athletes (see figure 17a) for further clarification regarding the public attitude toward physically challenged athletes and competition.

Bias against Disabled Athletes Survey

Please review each question and answer with the following:
"1" = Absolutely Disagree;
"2" = Disagree;
"3" = Undecided;
"4" = Agree;
"5" = Absolutely Agree

1. I feel that all athletes (regardless of the nature of their physical disability) should be provided with the opportunity to compete with others in a sport environment _____ ;
2. I feel that competition and athletic performance is just as important to the physically challenged athlete as it is to the able-bodied athlete _____;
3. I feel that winning is just as important to the physically challenged athlete as it is to the able-bodied athlete _____;
4. I feel that funding for the development of sports facilities for athletes with physical challenges should be equal to funding for athletes who are able-bodied _____;
5. I feel that athletes with physical challenges work just as hard and are just as committed as those athletes who are able-bodied _____;
6. I feel that athletic activity and competition is important and necessary in achieving a healthy physical and psychological balance in the life of the physically challenged athlete _____;
7. I feel that all sport facilities should be constructed with a "physically challenged friendly" attitude—in other words, in my gym there should be training facilities for the physically challenged as well as the physical structure of my gym should accommodate the needs of the physically challenged _____;
8. I would welcome the opportunity to train, exercise and socialize with an individual who is physical challenged _____;
9. I feel that I have much in common mentally and psychologically with physically challenged athletes when competing in a sport competition _____;
10. If an athlete with a physical limitation wanted to be my partner in sport competition I would welcome him or her _____;
11. I would welcome the opportunity to attend and watch a game or sport competition involving only physically challenged athletes _____;

12. I think that it would be a good idea to combine activities among professional able-bodied athletes and physically challenged athletes during training so we can learn from each other _____;

13. I think that it is especially important for able-bodied young athletes (i.e., high school athletes) to occasionally interact and compete with physically challenged athletes _____;

14. I think that I can learn much from the physically challenged athlete _____;

15. I feel that the physically challenged athlete has much to offer the world of sports _____.

Scoring & Evaluation of the "BADA":

Scores Between: 0–15 = Hostile and Discriminatory Attitude Regarding Athletes with Disabilities (AWD)—Extremely Negative and Close-Minded Regarding Athletes with Physical Challenges
Recommendations: Educate Yourself; Attend a Workshop or Better Still Get Counseling;

Scores Between 16–30 = Negative Skepticism & Close-Minded Views Regarding AWD; Very Limited Views Regarding the Possibility of AWD to Compete in Sport With Others;

Scores Between 31–45 = Pessimistic Views Regarding AWD & Sport Competition However Capable of Being Educated & Open-Minded to AWD;

Scores Between 46–60 = Positive and Accepting Attitudes Regarding AWD; Welcomes Opportunity to Train with AWD; Supports Environments That Promote Training & Exercise with AWD; Optimistic Attitude and Philosophy Regarding AWD;

Scores Between 61–75 = Supportive Attitude and Behaviors With AWD; Proactive in Developing a Positive Relationship with AWD and Encourages AWD to Train and Exercise with Them: Supportive, Positive and Dynamic Attitude Toward AWD.

Sports and physical activities have become important ways for athletes with physical challenges to improve their physical and psychological well-being. For example, consider the numerous agencies that recognize athletes with physical disabilities:

a. Disabled Sports U.S.A.;
b. Special Olympics;
c. The Dwarf Athletic Association of America and
d. Wheelchair Sports U.S.A.

Given the numerous agencies and corporations that exist for athletes with physical challenges, we should be more proactive in encouraging more physically challenged individuals to participate in sport activities.

■ WHAT DOES THE TERM "DISABILITY" ACTUALLY MEAN?

We have been discussing the term "disability" without offering a specific and clear definition of the term. We can define disability as any condition that limits someone from some form of physical or psychological activity in his or her daily living routine. While tremendous amounts of research exists addressing the physical and psychological benefits of exercise with able-bodied populations, relatively little research exists addressing the benefits of physical exercise with the physically challenged and disabled population. In a very interesting and relevant article that addressed the physical benefits of exercise with a disabled population (n = 30), Cooper and colleagues (1999; Journal of Rehabilitation Research & Development) discovered that the benefits of an exercise or physical activity program for individuals with physical limitations is highly relevant to the nature and type of physical limitation itself. For example, if the physical limitation is neurological or musculoskeletal, then there are risks to the tendon, muscle and bone region. The authors also discovered that with many disabled individuals, coronary heart disease poses a special risk factor to persons with disabilities, due to their limited mobility and lack of resources that may be utilized in improving one's physical health.

Additionally, the authors concluded that there are many other health and physical challenges that are disproportionately directed towards those with physically disabilities. These medical problems include osteoporosis, diabetes, and even some types of cancer. The authors in the current study also cited significant factors that should be taken into consideration when reviewing the literature addressing the physically challenged and physical health. For example, physical problems in access to the health facility and maintaining an active program in exercise is especially challenging to those with physical disabilities due to the time constraints involved. The following section of this chapter will now offer some suggestions to improve the exercise environment for the physically challenged athlete and to make facilities more "exercise friendly" to those with physical challenges.

■ IMPROVING CARDIOVASCULAR HEALTH FOR THE PHYSICALLY CHALLENGED ATHLETE

Given the physical limitations and problems associated with physical disabilities (i.e., transportation to health facilities, specialized equipment in physical exercise), Kavanah and Shephard (1973) found that elderly subjects with lower limb amputations had significantly higher rates of cardiovascular diseases (48%) which may be attributed to limited mobility and access to aerobic exercise. In general, athletes who face some form of physical challenge are more at risk in suffering from cardiovascular problems due to the limitations of aerobic activity. The suggested intensity of aerobic capacity depends on age and history of exercise and training. A common formula used with the Body Mass Index is in subtracting your age from the number 220 and then deducting 60%–80% of that number. In other words, assume that you are a 40 year old wheel chair male athlete who enjoys playing basketball, and you want to increase your aerobic capacity. If we subtract your age (40) from the number 220 we end up with the result of 180. Sixty to 80% of this number ranges from 108.0 to 144.0. These numbers refer to your heart rate range in exercise for a minimum of 30 minutes. This may be relatively simple for an able-bodied athlete who can run, swim, or row for 20 to 30 minutes, but for the physically challenged athlete the problem becomes more complicated. How can a physically challenged athlete, such as a wheel chair athlete, increase his or her heart rate between these numbers (108–140) for 30 minutes? Swimming and rowing are considered to be excellent cardiovascular exercises and can be executed in many different ways to accommodate the physically challenged athlete. These exercises are considered to be critical in training for the physically challenged athlete given the sedentary activities that are typically associated with those who are afflicted with physical limitations. Here are some examples that describe how physically challenged athletes may increase their heart rate and improve their overall aerobic and cardiovascular health:

➢ *Swimming.* Perhaps above all other cardiovascular forms of exercise, swimming has numerous benefits for athletes with physical challenges. If the lower extremity of the physically challenged athlete is immobile, devices (such as buoys) can be attached to the ankle or leg where the upper body (stroking) completes the swim. If there is some form of immobility in the upper torso region, then the physically challenged athlete can use the flutter-kick as a means of propelling himself through the water and attach the upper body to the kickboard itself. The physically challenged athlete can either support himself or herself with a kickboard and kick (flutter-kick) for 300 yards as a warm-up to the swimming exercise. Other advantages to swimming include low impact to joints and ideal resistance while paddling that improves the overall aerobic capacity. The physically challenged athlete who is active should strive for a target distance 2000 to 3000 meters using time as a measure of performance. If swimming itself is too difficult for the athlete, then encouraging him or her to hold to the side of the deck and practice kicking. Interval training can also be used with sprints to improve cardiovascular training. Overall, swimming is a very healthy and popular activity that offers tremendous benefits for those athletes with limitations to mobility or those athletes who have joint problems;

➤ *Improvised (land or ergonomic) Rowing:* Rowing is quickly becoming one of America's favorite cardiovascular sports for a variety of reasons. Rowing offers tremendous cardiovascular benefits and is challenging to individuals who want to improve stamina and aerobic capacity. Rowing is quick, simple, and results are very rewarding in a short period of time. Individuals who may have some form of a physical challenge or limitation are also ideal candidates for the rowing machine because of the versatility of its application. Rowing may be completed sitting down with no leg support or may be completed with very marginal force in exerting the catch and release. If the rower exerts minimal effort in rowing, the machine exerts minimal force back on the rower; conversely, if the rower applies tremendous force while rowing, then the machine responds with equal resistance. Furthermore, gains and improvements in rowing distance and speed are very easily recorded and monitored, as rowers may keep journals or logs regarding their distance and time in rowing.

When the rower sees that his or her times are improving (i.e., six months ago one rower required eight minutes to row 2000 meters, and in only three weeks he has improved his time by completing the 2000 meter row in seven minutes and thirty seconds!) his or her self-esteem improves. The physically challenged athlete is now afforded some control and direction over his or her physical training by working harder and the results are empirically validated. When we see physical improvement such as changes in our bodies, we feel tremendous psychological satisfaction and improvements in self-esteem and self-efficacy. The physically challenged athlete can see his or her improvement and this is done without the aid or assistance of anyone—they have done it on their own. This tremendous sense of accomplishment and personal pride is vital in improving not only physical health but also psychological sense of well-being.

▬ HEALTH AND NUTRITION FOR THE PHYSICALLY CHALLENGED ATHLETE

An additional factor to consider with persons with physical disabilities is the difficulty in accessing healthy foods and food preparation. For example, individuals with upper extremity limitations may avoid preparing foods that require cutting, chopping or slicing. Furthermore, those persons with physical challenges may have difficulty in reaching cupboards, stoves or refrigerator shelves. Thus, given the inordinate difficulty in preparing healthy foods many physically challenged persons may resort to eating less healthier foods (commonly referred to as "fast foods") that are significantly higher in saturated fats and cholesterol. Related problems, such as lack of transportation to the supermarket, or just insecurity in going outside and facing the public may cause stress and anxiety in many physically challenged individuals.

■ PHYSICAL ACTIVITIES & CHILDREN WITH DISABILITIES

Earlier in this text we discussed the importance of involving children in a variety of sport activities so that they can learn the many different types of activities that are healthy and fun. Children can either learn very healthy and adaptive behaviors that will remain a part of their daily activity as they grow older, or they can learn unhealthy behaviors that may contribute to illness and premature death. We also discussed the theoretical proposition that children may even have a "critical period" where a limited opportunity of time exists to incorporate and experience exercise and sports-related behaviors that will stay with them as they develop. In other words, children may be most receptive to and enjoy sports related activities during their formative years, typically age six through twelve. This "critical period" or limited period of time regarding the incorporation of sport activity among children may be even more important among children with physical challenges. Note that we are not saying that it is too late to incorporate children in sports activities after the age of twelve, but rather children seem to incorporate these activities most rapidly during this period of time and they seem to maintain interest and higher activity levels when they are exposed to sport during these ages. Parents, teachers and caregivers are usually the best role models to introduce sport to children. Children with physical challenges often have special needs that must be met first in order to incorporate a healthy exercise program, therefore it is critical that we provide opportunities to teach children with physical limitations how to experience and benefit form these activities. Figure 17b offers

I) Physical Fitness Test for the Physically Challenged Youth

Type of Exercise (upper body capacity)		Measures
A. Power	Pull-ups	Upper Body Strength
	Sit-ups	Abdominal Strength/Endurance
	Curl Strength	Bicep Strength
	Upright Row	Upper Body Strength
	Bench Press	Pectoral/Chest Strength/Power
B. Endurance (10 minutes)	Rowing	Stamina
	Swimming	Endurance/Stamina
	Cycling	Endurance/Stamina
C. Flexibility	Hamstring Stretch	Lower Extremity Flexibility
	Quad Stretch	Lower Extremity Flexibility
	Lower Back Stretch	Lower Extremity Flexibility

II) Psychological Fitness Test For The Physically Challenged Youth

Type of Exercise	Measures
A. Self-Esteem	How One Feels About Oneself: Positive or Negative Self-Perception
B. Social Intelligence	How the physically challenged youth interacts in social situations and responds to social interaction with other physically challenged and able bodies athletes;
C. Self-Efficacy	Level of perception regarding how the physically challenged athlete feels about completing specific goals;
D. Psychological Resilience	How the physically challenged athlete responds to failure in reaching goals;

Figure 17b

a wide range of sample exercise activities that are ideal for children who may be physically challenged. What makes the youth fitness test unique is the combination of physical skills (such as stamina) and psychological adaptation (such as resiliency and social intelligence) to challenges that are unique for the population of physically challenged youth population.

Note that earlier in this chapter we discussed the bias and ignorance that typically is associated with individuals with physical challenges and sport activity. This bias and ignorance is even further compounded when the person who has the physical challenge is a child. Children with physical limitations or challenges may be especially prone to discrimination due to perceived physical limitations or fear of injury to the child. While these biases may be well-intentioned, they are preventing children with physical challenges from enjoying physical activities and exercise. First be sure to consult with the child's doctor or physical therapist and discuss with him or her the child's full range of mobility and what they can (or can't do). You would probably be surprised to find that in most cases children with physical limitations have a wider range of ability to perform in several activities, taking into consideration the nature of the physical limitation. For example, children with a prosthetic leg may be able to walk with other children on a track or they may be able to participate in swimming activities. The most important characteristic to consider when developing physical activities with physically challenged children is to maintain an inclusive philosophy that incorporates activities with able-bodied children and with children with physical challenges. This exercise philosophy not only promotes inclusion of all children during physical activities, but may also promote children with physical challenges to engage in more activities in the future by increased self-esteem.

Generally school systems and the public in general have had biases regarding when children are capable of engaging in a sport activity. Able-bodied children as well as children who had physical challenges prior to the 1940's era were encouraged not to participate in sport activity due to fears of injury or that their bodies were not able to support athletic activity. Important developments in the world of children led to the gradual acceptance of sports for children. Children's activities, such as the Boy Scouts, YMCA, or the 4H Club gradually influenced the acceptance of children's participation in sport activity. More importantly, children who face physical challenges are now encouraged to participate in a variety sport activities and exercises. This was a dramatic change in the past where many therapists and experts felt that outdoor activity for children with physical challenges may have been physically damaging to their body.

■ A Modern Day Hero: Ms. Sarah Reinertsen

In an interesting article that addresses the tremendous influence a positive belief system can play with those who have physical challenges in the world of sports, Sarah Reinertsen is described as a 29-year-old young woman who is currently training for the Hawaiian Triathlon. The Triathlon is a very demanding race that consists of three individual sports: Swimming, bicycling, and running. Only athletes who have been training intensely for years are recommended to even consider participating in such an event, which actually requires a qualifying performance within each of the three sports. When you consider that the swimming distance is over one mile, the bicycling event is 100 miles, and the grueling run is the classic marathon (26.2 miles), the event is extremely physically demanding. When you also take into consideration the extremities of the climate (usually Hawaii is very humid), the challenge is even greater, as it is essential to keep fluids in your body throughout the competition to prevent dehydration and cramping. Any athlete who competes has a hard time finishing the race, but when you consider that some of the athletes are also participating with some physical challenges, such as those in wheel chairs, prosthetic devices, or visually impaired, the completion of such a race is truly remarkable.

Ms. Sarah Reinertsen is an incredible athlete who has been competing with a prosthetic device on her left leg just above the knee. What makes Reinertsen unique is that her left leg is a prosthetic device made of metal and plastic. Currently Reinertsen holds the world record for the half-marathon and full marathon for above-the-knee amputees and now wants to complete the Hawaii Triathlon for 2005. Last year she was the first female amputee to even compete in the race, but unfortunately had to drop out due to nausea and high winds. She views her initial failure as an opportunity to try again: "There are tri-athletes who race their whole life and never get to do Hawaii . . . and the fact that I have an opportunity to do it again is special." However, what makes Reinertsen special as an athlete is her giving attitude to help others. She says that she does not consider herself a "poster child" and is always ready to offer help and assistance to other athletes who face similar problems. Athletes with physical limitations or disabilities need special training and positive reinforcement. Reinertsen says that other special athletes with physical limitations need to keep working and to keep trying: "You may not want to run a 10K or do a triathlon, but to keep up in everyday life you need to remain fit." Reinertsen is a remarkably positive example of how to overcome physical limitations and to achieve your goals. She is currently training for the 2005 Hawaii triathlon and says that she is "very pumped up and excited." She currently trains 10 to 15 hours a week, in addition being a marketing manager of Ossur North America, a prosthetic company based in Aliso Viejo. Given her tremendously positive attitude and spirit, we have every reason to believe that she will achieve her goals.

Research on the athlete with physical challenges is limited to a few studies that look at personality profiles. For example, Porretta and Moore (1996, 1997) determined that after extensive analysis of personality profiles that compared able-bodied athletes with athletes with physical challenges, very few differences emerged. One common personality test that reviews anxiety and mood profiles, the Profile of Mood States (POMS) determined that the mood profiles of athletes with physical challenges closely matched those profiles with able-bodied athletes. In other words, both groups of athletes experienced and responded to emotional and psychological mood states (such as anxiety and frustration) in similar ways. Similarly, Roeder and Aufsesser (1986) discovered that several of the elite wheelchair athletes they interviewed had very similar personality characteristics with able bodied elite athletes, and those wheelchair non-athletes had several personality characteristics with able bodied non athletes.

■ SIMILAR PERSONALITY CHARACTERISTICS AMONG ABLE-BODIED AND PHYSICALLY CHALLENGED ATHLETES: ONE ABLE-BODIED BECOMES ONE PHYSICALLY CHALLENGED ATHLETE

We have been discussing how the personality characteristics of the professional or elite athlete is very similar in many ways to the personality of the physically challenged athlete. In many personality assessment tests (i.e., *The Profile of Mood States or The Iceberg Profile*), empirical data suggests that many of the competitive and personality characteristics are nearly identical. More specifically, these personality tests identified areas of goal-setting, importance in goal attainment, visual rehearsal, mental imagery, participation motives as being very similar among the physically challenged and able-bodied groups of athletes. In a striking example that serves to reinforce this theory, former NFL player Curt Marsh (45 years old) recently had his right ankle amputated after 12 operations trying to repair the damage of a broken ankle. In an interview with the *Los Angeles Times* (January 31, 2005, Super Bowl XXXIX edition), Marsh said while playing with the Los Angeles Raiders his right ankle became swollen in 1986 after a game and told the team doctor: "I kept telling him that there was something wrong, but he didn't want to look any further . . . it's kind of like when you are in college and your car is broken, you don't want to find something bad, so you don't look." Marsh experienced excruciating pain every time he stood up, and eventually discovered that the right ankle was actually broken. Unfortunately, after 12 unsuccessful surgeries, he decided he would rather use a prosthetic device and walk, then keep the damaged right ankle and use a wheel chair for the remainder of his life. He was also promised that the pain would subside, but he comments that he still experiences pain even after the surgery. Marsh describes his rampant use of Novocain, and how the doctors then were just focusing on keeping athletes in play despite the severity of the injury. He comments and now laments the fact that the prosthetic for his right ankle was supposed to "take the pain away . . . but now I've got a lot of pain."

This tragic example illustrates several things—perhaps most importantly, when an athlete becomes injured, make sure you get competent and professional advice from a medical expert who is unbiased (i.e., not associated with the team). Marsh comments that doctors need to remain impartial in their professional work with athletes. Furthermore, Marsh's comments come at a pivotal time for Philadelphia NFL player Terrell Owens who currently also has a severely sprained right ankle and broken right leg. Owens is considering playing in the XXXIX Super Bowl game even with this serious injury—a decision that Marsh wants him to reconsider. Marsh comments: " I just hope that he has somebody close to him who cares about him . . . it's not worth the risk, you have to realize that you have your whole life ahead of you." Marsh should know—he was in a similar situation and decided to play despite the injury. That decision cost him his right ankle. Thus, physically challenged athletes and able-bodied athletes have much in common, and in some cases, they are one in the same.

■■ MOTIVES FOR THE PHYSICALLY CHALLENGED ATHLETE: WHY GET INVOLVED IN SPORT?

The motives for the young athlete with physical challenges to become involved in sport activity can be basically summarized in one word: Fun! First and foremost, we need to encourage youths today to enjoy the experience and the process of exercise activities. All too often adults "forget" how to enjoy leisure activities and how to have fun. Many adults seem to have difficulty in "letting go" of responsibilities of their normal work routine and cannot experience the pleasure of exercise. Youths today need to be taught how to enjoy and participate in sport activity. Several authors have identified the fact that a contributing factor for young athletes to participate in sports is simply to enjoy their activities with other youths and to have fun in the process (Skubic, 1956).

■■ CHAPTER 17 QUESTION & REVIEW

1. Generally describe your attitudes towards training and exercising with an athlete who has some form of a physical challenge—have you ever participated in any form of team sports or training? How do you think you might feel in competing with an athlete with a physical challenge? If you happen to be an athlete with a physical challenge, what are your thoughts and experiences in training with able bodied athletes?

2. Take the Bias Against Disabled Athletes (*BADA*) questionnaire and score your responses—were you surprised by your results? Administer the questionnaire to some of your friends or family and compare scores. How rampant is bias against athletes with physical challenges? What are some of the things that we can do to reduce this bias?

3. Describe some of the unique challenges facing the athlete with physical challenges—how can we overcome some of these challenges to make the training facility more exercise friendly?

4. Identify some of the reasons why cardiovascular health is of particular concern for the athlete with physical challenges—how can we improve overall cardiovascular health among athletes with limited mobility?

5. Describe your own personality type when competing with other athletes—is it similar to other competitive athletes with physical challenges? Do you consider yourself to have much in common with the athlete with physical challenges? Explain your reasoning.

Chapter 18:
Contributions by Individual Authors in Sports Psychology

Exercise and Concentration
by fitness expert Bruce Gaims

■■■ INTRODUCTION

Many exercisers already apply the two most basic physical training principles. They make efforts to increase their intensity (Overload Principle) and try to select exercises to improve certain areas of their performance and/or shape (Specificity Principle). Whether applying these principles consciously, skillfully, or haphazardly, they should be encouraged to learn more. Overload and Specificity are cornerstones of any successful pursuit of exercise.

However, in this chapter, as we shall discuss, human beings are not robots. Exercise, or any other endeavor worth pursuing, depends on more than mere physical principles and simple faith that a particular stimulus will engender a particular response. For example, take the following exercise prescriptions:

> ➤ To improve your cardiovascular fitness and to burn calories, do 30 minutes on the stationary bike, 3 to 5 times per week. Keep your heart rate between 65–85% of your maximum heart rate.
> ➤ To strengthen and tone your gluteus and quadriceps muscles, do 2 to 4 sets of squats, 8–15 repetitions per set, 3 times per week. For resistance, use 50–85% of your one rep max weight per set.

In and of themselves, these prescriptions are fine. The stationary bike is effective for improving cardiovascular fitness and burning calories. The squat is a good exercise for working the gluteus and quadriceps muscles. However, these prescriptions do not consider many personal and practical factors. Do you have access to the equipment? Do you enjoy the exercises? What complementary exercises should be performed? Are you able to do the exercises properly? Are you wearing the right clothing? Furthermore, even if all of the personal and practical factors are positive, what does that mean for your future? Starting next Wednesday, you will begin riding the bike and doing squats until the end of time or until you reach your goal? Who wants to do that? In the long term, few would look upon such a regimen as anything but drudgery. It's just not that natural (fun?) to live by prescription week after week even if you do get in better shape!

Why then are so many Americans in search of an "exercise prescription?" Of course, the answer (drum roll, please) is . . . results! Some people have neglected to exercise for years and others have started exercising before and have failed to reach their goals. They are disappointed in themselves. And faced with the prospects of failing or failing again, they want a prescription "guaranteed" to get them results.

In the American marketplace, they have no lack of options. Billions of dollars every year are spent on exercise machines, club memberships, classes, books, videos, and training aids. For such products and services, any number of experts (medical doctors, university researchers, therapists, trainers, athletes, and celebrities) are more than willing to offer enthusiastic endorsements. After all, if a television star says you're going to lose thirty pounds on the Giraffe Strider, you're going to lose thirty pounds on the Giraffe Strider! Undoubtedly for some, there is a return on their exercise investment. They find an instructor, a machine, or a new type of exercise that serves as a catalyst for their program. It happens. If one hundred thousand consumers buy a Giraffe Strider, somebody's life is bound to be changed! Whatever the catalyst, these people learn to exercise consistently and reap long term benefits.

But what if you are one of those who want to "do the right thing", but nothing you buy or try seems to be an answer? Perhaps, you have a Giraffe Strider, used it for two months, and now the machine is a hanger for delicates that can't be tumble dried. In case you would ever forget, you are reminded many times daily by newspapers, magazines, television, and the Internet that your lifestyle needs a change. What do you do? Maybe the world will change and make it easier for you to change. Maybe the day is coming when much of the hype and misinformation about exercise will dissipate. Society will become more proactive. More resources will be directed towards promoting active, healthful lifestyles and awareness among people of all ages. The power of healthier living will temper the power of commercial interests that rely on sales to an unhealthy and ignorant populace. Or...maybe you need a different approach to exercise. The cultural landscape hardly seems likely to evolve dramatically enough to galvanize your personal transformation. The odds of that are about the same as your finding a "miracle" machine, class, pill, etc. to do the same thing. We're not being cynical—just realistic! In your culture (that would be America, circa 2005), exercise is mostly bought and sold in the marketplace rather than learned and shared as a part of daily life.

In plain terms, you will have to change your world. Within your busy schedule, amidst the demands of work, family, and friends, you must find time to open your senses and exercise your body regularly. This will result in not only your own transformation, but will have positive effects among your family, friends, and your fellow workers and students. Rather than waiting for the world to change, you will change the world. It's a heck of a lot easier that way, trust us.

Exercise is usually packaged as a commodity. Much emphasis is placed on a prescription for what to do and what to buy. If you want to learn to exercise, such commerce is counter intuitive. We prefer and will introduce an approach whereby your own senses and experiences inform your choices. Exercise is an action performed by a living, breathing animal. Written words and pictures can impart only so much about physical training. However, you can embrace concepts that reduce your dependence on irrelevant information and relieve you of an endless search for the "perfect" program or machine. You can learn about strategies for developing your fitness instincts. You can begin to apply specific techniques that help open your senses to feedback provided by your own body.

This chapter has no evangelical ax to grind. No person has a moral or spiritual obligation to exercise. There are plenty of heroes and saints whose fitness level falls well below our society's standards for healthy living. But for those who desire to be fitter, this chapter is about *how* to exercise. Not about *what* to do, but about *how* you can come to know, to enjoy, and to guide yourself while exercising.

▬▬ EXERCISE CONCEPTS VS. EXERCISE TERMS

Let's pretend that you are so frustrated by your lack of conditioning and motivation that you go to see a psychiatrist. You say, "Doctor, thank you for seeing me. I am desperate. My body is falling apart because I can't stick with my exercise program. What do you think is wrong with me?"

The doctor responds. "Well, according to the results of your Rorschach ink blot test, your id is sublimated at heart rates above 70% of your VO2 Max. Furthermore, you have an oedipal complex that is clearly operative whenever you lift weight over your head. And you also show symptoms of delusional paranoia in any situation that requires coordination or balance. That will be $200.00, I would like to see you again next week for a check-up."

The doctor's diagnosis may be absolutely correct, but now you have two problems. One, you still aren't exercising regularly. And two, you didn't get anything from what he/she said. All of the fancy words and terms may mean something in the doctor's world, but they don't mean a darn thing in yours.

In this chapter, you will not be asked to memorize terms. Rather, we will introduce and develop exercise concepts and ask you to try to make them mean something to you. For example, we are about to discuss concentration. Random House dictionary defines concentration as "exclusive attention to one object." This definition is not of much use to us here (don't memorize it!). We are more interested in how it *feels* to concentrate *during exercise*.

▬▬ WHY CONCENTRATE?

Life is not very passionate or interesting without concentration. Concentration is the marshalling of your senses (sight, hearing, touch, etc.) for action. Different actions (reading, writing, dancing, running, making love, singing, chopping wood, etc.) may demand a different balance of your senses. You are most yourself when all of your senses are awakened and ready to contribute.

This is not earthshaking news. Most people appreciate the value of concentration. For example, parents gather at tee-ball games and watch their child learn to hit a ball. As the youngster watches a bird fly by or turns to look at the stands, they exhort him/her to "focus" on the tee. They know that the child will not be rewarded with the satisfaction of a good hit unless he/she learns to concentrate.

But who among us does not need a reminder about the practice of concentration? We can all become stuck in patterns of behavior that render us a passive spectator rather than an actor in our own lives. We waste time watching television and overeating. We squander opportunities to develop our own lives. We consume insatiably and join the populace characterized in the famous lyric by the musical group, Nirvana: "Here we are now, entertain us!"

If you are disappointed or bored by exercise, then the first question to ask yourself is, "Do I concentrate when I exercise?" Be honest! Are you one of those people who watches television, reads a book, talks on the phone, flips through a magazine, gossips with a friend, does the crossword puzzle, or files your nails while you ride a bike or walk on a treadmill? Then, the answer is no. You're not doing a very good job at hitting the ball off the tee. You want something from exercise, e.g. protect your health, feel good, look good, etc., but are not much involved in the process.

You might ask if is it *necessary* to be involved to get results? That's a fair question. Simple acts like walking on a treadmill, riding a bike, or lifting weights do have some fitness and health benefits regardless of whether you concentrate. However, as we have already noted, exercise is awfully boring and hard to continue when you are just biding time. And more to the point, you cannot expect meaningful, lasting results without concentration.

For example, improved cardiovascular fitness is strongly correlated to many of the results that most people seek. If you are adapted to do more work at any given heart rate level and to exercise at higher heart rates, you use more energy per unit time, reduce stress more effectively, and burn more fat in the recovery period after harder exercise. As we shall see, you must pay attention during exercise and monitor your intensity closely in order to achieve these progressive results.

However, the best answer is that it is not *necessary* to be involved, it is *desirable*. Why do parents beg their child to concentrate and to hit the ball off the tee? They know it is more fun and rewarding to be *in the game*! It is unlikely that you'll ever go to listen to an orchestra and see a TV on top of the piano so the pianist can watch a sitcom while playing. It's much more enjoyable to *play* than to act like you are playing. If you have not yet learned and/or are not learning how to concentrate during exercise, you are not playing. Many adults have a tough time playing, regardless of the game or situation. They subject themselves and/or others to standards and pressures that have nothing to do with playing. A company softball game is treated like a World Series finale. A pick-up game of basketball gets overly physical. Guests at a party refrain from dancing to music that they love. It is no different in most exercise facilities or settings most people are swallowed up by the environment and their own expectations.

Don't worry. We are not going to tell you that you've lost your "inner child". Although a pre-school playground is certainly wilder than most health clubs, children get a lot of regular free time and are in the habit of concentrating on play. Furthermore, kids get bored, cranky, tired, overly competitive, etc., unless some talented, hardworking adult(s) is there to keep things fresh and interesting. Even kids need to learn to concentrate in order to experience the true spirit of play.

■ CONCENTRATION IS LEARNED

No one is born a master of concentration. Mozart played chopsticks. Michael Jordan shot air balls. Shakespeare wrote clumsy prose. In your own life, there are already many things upon which you have learned to concentrate. You might be an accomplished chef. You might be a video game expert. You might be a dedicated gardener. Maybe you can juggle, whistle, fly fish, or do magic tricks. Somewhere on the road of life, you made time to learn and to get beyond the basics.

And life is a heck of lot more fun beyond the basics. Think of the times that you have helped somebody with something that you can do well. You explain the basics and ask them to relax and get into it. You know if they practice this approach that they will soon be able to advance to higher levels of concentration and enjoyment.

■ BE A GOOD TEACHER TO YOURSELF

If you think a little deeper, teaching somebody else offers a valuable lesson about the learning process. Often at the same time your student or protégé is most frustrated and sure that he/she can never learn or progress, you have your clearest view of his/her emerging abilities and talents. That is when you offer your strongest words of encouragement. Question: are you in the habit of offering yourself the same positive support when you are frustrated? Your exercise program will prosper if you are an honest and compassionate teacher to yourself. If you have not been making time or concentrating when you do have time, then you have to be honest enough not to make excuses for why you are not getting results or enjoying your exercise routine. If you have been making time and concentrating, you have to be compassionate enough to give yourself a pat on the back if your results and abilities seem to be more elusive than you would like.

Many athletes respond to questions about their performance and character in the third person, i.e. "Bo knows when it's winning time." Although this may seem odd or even arrogant to many people, we might also recognize that in this scenario the "teacher" is answering the questions and protecting the student's ongoing efforts and attitude. We are not suggesting that you begin using the third person when conversing with friends and family ("Teresa does not eat French fries while training!") but you get the point.

We will now begin speaking directly about concentration during exercise. It is an opportunity for you to practice being a good teacher to yourself. Please take a break before reading further. We want you to be fresh. We want you to have the energy and curiosity to get as much as possible from the thoughts and exercises that are to follow.

▬▬ FIVE FITNESS COMPONENTS

> *Cardiovascular or Aerobic Endurance*
> The ability to do moderately strenuous activity over a period of time. It reflects how well your heart and lungs work together to supply oxygen to your body during exertion and exercise. Also called aerobic fitness.
> *Muscular Endurance*
> The ability to hold a particular position for a sustained period of time or repeat a movement many times. This could be the capability required to hold a two-pound weight above your head for five minutes or the effort required to lift that weight 20 consecutive times.
> *Muscular Strength*
> The ability to exert maximum force, such as lifting the heaviest weight you can budge, one time. It is possible to have muscular strength in one area, say your arms, while lacking strength in another area such as your legs.
> *Flexibility*
> The ability to move a joint through its full range of motion; the elasticity of the muscle. This is how limber or supple you are.
> *Body Composition*
> The proportion of fat in your body compared to your bone and muscle. It does not refer to your weight in pounds or your figure. For exercise professionals, fitness is divided into the five components defined above. This chapter is not a vocabulary lesson (we promised!), and we only ask that you think a little bit about the definitions. Is there anybody or any athlete who would rate number one in all of these components? Which components do you think are your strengths and weaknesses? If you are doing any exercise now, what components are being improved or tested by your training? How does aging affect the components? What types of activity or exercise might you do if you want to improve in one or more component areas?

In regards to exercise concentration in this chapter, we will be using the first two components (cardiovascular endurance and muscular endurance) to illustrate our ideas. This does not mean that the other three components are not important or essential. All of the components are interrelated. If your exploration of exercise is sincere, you will undoubtedly learn that the ability to concentrate during an exercise that emphasizes one of the five components will facilitate your performance during exercises that emphasize the others.

▬▬ CONCENTRATION = BREATHING, RHYTHM, AND POSTURE

Although one might choose different and equally meaningful words to describe exercise concentration, we will use three: Breathing, Rhythm, and Posture. Without sounding too mystical, each one of these concepts contains the others. You cannot maintain your posture without breathing and rhythm; you cannot breath properly without rhythm and posture; you cannot make rhythm without breathing and posture.

Don't be scared! It is not the same as thinking about three things at once! You just need to learn exercise habits that allow breathing, rhythm, and posture to work together. After you invest some time and thought into your training, you will soon know and *feel* that they do. In fact, you will no longer want to exercise *without* the feeling of breathing, rhythm, and posture working together.

Involuntary and Voluntary Breathing

Some of your body's actions are involuntary, e.g. the response of your knee joint to the tap of a doctor's hammer. Others, like breathing, are both involuntary and voluntary. You cannot willfully stop yourself from breathing. However, you do have considerable control over how you breathe. One can understand why breathing has to be involuntary. In very general terms, breathing is the mechanism by which your body maintains its oxygen supply. Oxygen is essential in the circulatory and chemical processes related to the function and maintenance of your organs, muscles, nerves, and bones. But what about the voluntary aspects of breathing? What does it mean that you have a great deal of control over the nature (depth, rhythm, pressure, etc.) of your breathing? Is it another practical burden to you like the rent, tuition bills, car insurance, or the cost of new shoes? We hope not. We agree with the evidence provided by experts (from medical researchers to yoga teachers) that regular breathing exercise is one of the best ways to fortify your health and well-being.

Chest Breathing vs. Stomach Breathing

Most of us have read or have heard that there is a distinction between "chest" and "stomach" breathing. While the terminology is limited and misleading (your chest and stomach muscles don't actually breathe for you) there is certainly something important to understand here. During our fast paced, but often largely sedentary lives, we either never learn or get out of the habit of breathing fully. Instead we carry tension in our neck and breathe shallowly. We slump and sip air when at rest and lift our chest and tighten our upper body when we need more air.

Shallow breathing ("chest" breathing) is part of a vicious cycle. Shallow breathing contributes to poor posture and muscular tension; conversely, poor posture and muscular tension make it difficult to breathe fully. But what does breathing fully ("stomach" breathing) mean? One good way for you to grasp the concept is try the following exercise:

Breathing Exercise #1

1) Sit in a chair with your feet flat on the floor in front of you.
2) Sit so that you are not using the back or arms of the chair for support.
3) Place your hands on your thighs and let all of the air go out of you. Let your body and head fall forward. Relax.
4) Move your hands to your belly, spreading your fingers across your stomach.
5) Inhale steadily and gently through the nose and "pump" up your stomach gradually like a balloon. When the stomach is full, continue to fill up your lower chest.
6) Allow your body to sit up straight. Do not tense your shoulder and neck muscles.

Breathing fully means taking advantage of the full volume of air space that you have. Doing the exercise above, you can feel how taking a full breath allows you to support your body and to sit up straight. That does not mean that you did not feel awkward or strange. Perhaps, you may be thinking, how am I supposed to pay attention at a lecture, concert, or movie if I am paying such close attention to how I sit? People will think I am crazy!

Breathing and Identity

Let's assume that you have no problem relating to the basic need to breathe and circulate oxygen. After all, when your breathing cycle is interrupted, e.g. too much pizza in one bite, you do find yourself suddenly very concerned with opening the airway!

Can we also now agree that beyond this involuntary instinct that your breathing patterns affect many voluntary behaviors and actions in your life? For example, you cannot speak or sing without breathing. Your voice, its character, volume, and tone, are literally created by your body and its breathing patterns. And are not all of your relationships and social interactions closely tied to how you speak and communicate? In fact, one can argue effectively that breathing patterns also affect the way you think, move, sleep, digest your food, build your muscles, etc..

From *Breathing Exercise #1,* you have physical proof that how you breathe influences your posture. This alone is enough reason to concentrate on breathing when you exercise. Your posture is a reflection of the relative strength and flexibility of your muscle groups and their ongoing effects on the alignment of your bones and the range of motion in your joints. In short, your body's development depends a great deal on how you breathe and support your spine.

Doing breathing exercises (like #1 above) and thinking about breathing may seem disconnected from your previous ideas about exercise. However, if you are not in the habit of breathing fully, then all it takes is a little, consistent practice to begin building stronger habits. These habits will carry over or make up for times when you are in a more casual mode—attending a lecture, concert, movie, etc.

Breathing and Cardiovascular Endurance

Cardiovascular (aerobic) exercise includes running, biking, swimming, cross country skiing, roller skating, rowing, etc. During cardiovascular exercise, your heart rate is elevated over a sustained period of several minutes or much longer. Your heart pumps faster because your working muscles need more oxygen (carried to them in the blood pumped by the heart) than is required at rest or for shorter, non-aerobic activities. Your cardiovascular exercise intensity is often expressed as a percentage of your maximum heart rate (MHR). Depending on your health and conditioning, the American College of Sports Medicine recommends that you train at least three to five times per week, for 30 to 60 minutes, at 60–90% of MHR:

Your Estimated Maximum Heart Rate (MHR) = 220–Your Age

Many cardiovascular exercise machines now have built-in heart rate monitors so you can check your training intensity. Personal heart rate monitors are priced fairly economically ($25.00–75.00) and can be worn anywhere.

In order to supply your heart with enough oxygen to satisfy the energy demands of your working muscles, your rate of respiration (breathing) also increases with exercise intensity. You don't have to be a rocket scientist to know that you breathe faster and more intensely when you have to work harder. It's an involuntary response. However, you may not be in the habit of exerting voluntary control over the rhythm, depth, and efficiency of your breathing.

Most people doing aerobic exercise have an object in mind while they are exercising: lose weight, sweat, burn calories, drop inches, etc. They do not monitor their breathing, and consequently they either breathe too heavily or not heavily enough. Often, the intensity and quality of their workout depends on their mood prior to the workout. Did they have an argument with a friend or family member? A tough day at work? Are they guilty because of the burger and ice cream sundae they had at lunch?

On days when you punish yourself and breathe too heavily, your posture during exercise falls apart. You strain your heart, your joints, and your muscles. You tend to overuse certain "favorite" muscles and not wake up other muscles that have been ignored and need to be exercised. This type of workout may "work" in the short term, but eventually you get injured, sick, and or exhausted.

If your workouts tend to be lackadaisical, then you do not test your heart and circulatory system, your joints, and your muscles. Perhaps you are self-conscious about sweating, fearful of injury, or concerned about how you will look. This type of workout does not produce much physiological change or personal satisfaction. You get bored very quickly.

Here are some breathing fundamentals for cardiovascular exercise that apply no matter what type of exercise and regimen you choose:

1) Nose to Mouth—Inhale through the nose and exhale through the mouth as quietly and smoothly as possible. Try the best you can to maintain this type of breathing even during more intense intervals. If you begin "gulping" air through your mouth, it is a sign that you are nearing exhaustion and should allow yourself to rest or recover at a lower intensity.

2) Use Your Diaphragm—Breathe deeply into your diaphragm (stomach breathing) and avoid shallow chest breathing. The air you breathe not only supplies your working muscles with oxygen, but creates thoracic pressure that stabilizes your spine so you can maintain proper posture. Do not exercise so intensely that you are unable to "feel" the support for your spine that is provided by each breath of air.

3) Establish A Rhythm—Use all of your senses to establish a rhythm. Tune into the feeling of the inhalation and exhalation phases of each breath. Make that feeling consistent. Feel your heart beating and relax to its beat. Listen to the sound of your breathing, your feet, the rustle of your clothing, etc. Make that sound consistent. Relax your eyes, focus on a distant object, and give yourself over to a rhythm. If you cannot create a rhythm, then modify your workout; lower the intensity, choose another type of exercise, or change the environment.

4) Practice—Pay attention to your breathing during each workout until the fundamentals become second nature. Some workouts may be better than others in terms of "being in the zone", but don't disengage from the experience or the learning process.

5) Progression—Challenge your breathing fundamentals safely and progressively. Develop a solid "base" of 30 to 60 minutes at lower intensity levels before pushing yourself. Then, if you can control your breathing well at a particular intensity, gradually begin introducing more difficulty for short intervals. Do your best to relax, breathe deeply, and establish rhythm during these intervals. Lengthen them as soon as your body and your breathing have adapted.

Before we move on, you deserve a break! Here is a breathing exercise that will help demonstrate your voluntary powers over your breathing:

Breathing Exercise #2

1) Take a walk anywhere where you can proceed uninterrupted for several minutes (around a room, around the block, etc.).
2) Warm-up for few minutes.
3) Then while walking, take a deep breath, and then hold that breath as you continue walking.
4) Keep a steady walking rhythm and count the number of steps until you need to breathe again.
5) You'll be surprised how you learn to take a deep breath, relax, and rely on rhythm to extend the breathless interval!

Breathing and Muscular Endurance

Your muscular endurance is improved by performing resistance exercises that target specific muscle groups. Your body has hundreds of muscles, but most of the time resistance training applies major muscle groups rather than smaller muscles like the ones that wiggle your nose or curl your lip. The American College of Sports Medicine recommends that you train the major muscle groups of your body, i.e. arms, legs, back, and torso, etc., at least two times per week, doing at least 2 sets of 8 to 15 repetitions for each muscle group per workout.

Resistance training comes in many forms: weight training, calisthenics, rubber bands and tubes, etc. You may do some kind of resistance training but not think of breathing as an essential part of the exercise. It's understandable. Breathing just "happens" during cardiovascular exercise, because your rate of respiration escalates involuntarily. However, unless you are encountering heavy resistance or doing a non-stop circuit of resistance training, you may not feel the "instinct" to breathe during resistance exercises.

Another possibility is that you know that you are "supposed" to breathe but have forgotten about when and how to breathe while resistance training. Do I exhale on the way up or the way down? Do I wait until the end to exhale? Do I breathe in before I start or after I finish?

Let's first affirm that breathing is an important part of resistance training. Although your working muscles do not depend on "aerobic" quantities of oxygen, your breathing must be coordinated to ensure that your blood pressure is moderated, your spine is stabilized, and your posture is maintained. You may be able to do a resistance exercise without breathing, but you will not be as effective at isolating the muscles that are supposed to do the work. You will also tend to generate more wear and tear on joints that are being used out of proper position.

Advanced exercisers such as Olympic lifters and other athletes may use advancing breathing techniques to facilitate and to enhance their performance. For our purposes here, we will stick to the basics. You exhale during the active (concentric, positive) phase of an exercise. The active phase is when you are moving your body or a weight against gravity, e.g. lifting the weight stack, or when you are stretching a band or tube. You inhale during the recovery (eccentric, negative) phase of an exercise. The recovery phase is when you are moving your body or a weight with gravity, e.g. lowering the weight stack, or allowing a tensed band or tube to shorten.

Rather than bend your mind to remember the concept, try this breathing exercise to help you imprint the process:

Breathing Exercise #3

1) Sit in a chair with your feet flat on the floor in front of you.
2) Sit so that you are not using the back or arms of the chair for support.
3) Place your hands on your thighs.
4) Breathe fully and naturally in and out through the diaphragm—as you learned in Breathing Exercise #1—to support your spine.
5) Lift your hands gently and place them against your upper stomach as if you were going to push an object away from your body. Continue your breathing in and out
6) Then, as you exhale, push your hands away from your body. Imagine that you are pushing against a steady resistance.
7) As you inhale, pull your hands back towards you gently.
8) In both directions, synchronize the movement of your arms with your breathing. It should feel as if your arms are breathing for you!
9) Repeat.

Now let's reverse the action.

10) Repeat steps 1–4

11) Lift your hands gently and place them about 18 inches in front of your upper stomach. Continue your breathing in and out.

12) Then, as you exhale, pull your hands toward your body. Imagine that you are pulling against a steady resistance.

13) As you inhale, push your hands away from you gently.

14) In both directions, synchronize the movement of your arms with your breathing. It should feel as if your arms are breathing for you!

15) Repeat.

No matter what the exercise, upper or lower body, weight or rubber resistance, you want to make sure to breathe fully and to synchronize your breathing with the motion of the exercise.

Breathing Power and Posture

In the breathing exercises above, we have already experienced that full, rhythmic, and synchronized breathing is essential for good posture. Resistance training is safest and most effective when you are able to maintain posture and isolate the muscles (prime movers) that you want to train. While the prime movers work, your body uses other muscles (stabilizers) to keep your alignment and balance in place. Full, relaxed breathing gives you the best opportunity to tune into how your body is coordinating its muscles, joints, and bones to overcome resistance. Think of your diaphragm as the your center of power, which generates energy with each exhalation and renews with each inhalation. As in Breathing Exercise #3 above, your breathing and the movements of your body originate from that center of power or "core". Let's see how well you can breath, stabilize, and work from your core while in a standing position:

Breathing Exercise #4

1) Stand with your feet shoulder width apart, knees relaxed, and feet turned slightly outward.

2) Let your arms dangle by your sides.

3) Hold your chin level. Relax your neck and shoulders.

4) Begin breathing fully and naturally in and out through the diaphragm—as you learned in Breathing Exercise #1—to support your spine.

5) Squeeze your rear end (gluteus muscles) slightly.

6) As you inhale, let your arms float up gently to the sides. Do not "lift" them with your neck or upper back.

7) Then, as you exhale, push your arms back towards your body. Imagine that you are pushing the air out a balloon inside your upper stomach.

8) In both directions, synchronize the movement of your arms with your breathing. It should feel as if your arms are breathing for you!

9) Repeat

Now let's reverse the action.

10) Repeat steps 1–5

11) As you exhale, let your arms push up to the sides. Do not "lift" them with your neck or upper back. Imagine that you are pulling on strings that tighten a net around a balloon in your upper stomach and force out the air.

12) Then, as you inhale, let arms return smoothly toward your body. Imagine that you

13) In both directions, synchronize the movement of your arms with your breathing. It should feel as if your arms are breathing for you!

14) Repeat

Your next challenge is to do Breathing Exercise #4 with some "real" resistance in your hands (try 1 to 3 pound weights per hand). Do not change any of the steps in the exercise.

■ LEARNING TAKES TIME

Breathing, posture, and form are not just things that you think about during the actual exercise performance. Warm-up, cool down, flexibility training, cross training, and strength training all contribute to your comfort, results, and enjoyment of a particular type of exercise.

We do not have the space here to be specific about form and mechanics for the many different types of exercises. We do encourage that you embrace the learning process. Only short term results are possible until you open your senses and your mind to new feelings and ideas. Do not take your "knowledge" for granted. For example, most people would do well to think more about how they walk; many individuals have a stride that contributes to foot, back, knee, or hip problems.

Remember, you are already well on your well way to learning a great deal if you practice breathing fundamentals while you exercise. Breathing deeply to support the spine and maintaining a steady rhythm opens your senses to the clues that your body provides about your form: muscular tension, alignment, impact, symmetry, etc. You will be free to experiment back and forth between breathing and form until the two are inseparable.

■ SEEK GOOD, QUALIFIED TEACHERS

Finally, you get good at something because your own desire and persistence are resonated by the presence of a good teacher. In life, you have many teachers—parents, school teachers, camp counselors, coaches, etc. As a child, you do not always have the privilege of selecting your teachers. Unfortunately, most of us can count the number of good teachers that we have had on one or two hands. . . .

As an adult who wants to enjoy exercise and its benefits, you have the freedom to find instructors that you like. As part of being a good teacher to yourself, you should seek exercise instructors and environments that make you feel comfortable. The status of an institution or an instructor's reputation are irrelevant. Whether an instructor is in perfect shape him or herself is also not the point. If an instructor does not make you feel good about yourself and/or is not providing safe, productive, enjoyable training, then look for other alternatives.

The fitness industry has many certification organizations and credentials. The standards and exams vary greatly. Some better known organizations include American Council on Exercise (ACE), National Academy of Sports Medicine (NASM), Aerobic and Fitness Association of America (AFAA), American College of Sports Medicine (ACSM), and the National Strength and Conditioning Association (NSCM).

Some facilities hire only industry certified fitness instructors. If you are uncertain of an instructor's background and qualifications, ask for evidence of his/her educational and professional training. It's not a guarantee that you will click with the instructor, but you have some assurance of their basic skills and knowledge.

■ ADAPTATION

Regardless of your exercise goals or methods, your results are due to adaptation. If you gradually increase the intensity of an exercise, your body will adapt; you will undergo the physiological and chemical changes required to perform at higher intensities. At the beginning of the chapter, we called this axiom the Overload Principle.

For people of both genders and of all ages, sizes, and skill levels, the Overload Principle is positive news. Imagine an alternative reality where your earnest exercise efforts only yielded results about as frequently as the election of a new president or were based on odds equivalent to drawing a straight flush in poker. And you think you have a problem getting motivated to exercise in this world!

Of course, as introduced above, the Overload Principle is external and objective. It tells you what will happen to your body given a gradual increase in exercise intensity, but says nothing about your internal and subjective participation in the training process. Everyone from recreational exercisers to elite athletes must decide for him/herself, "what do I need to do, and how do I keep on wanting to do it?"

■■■ THE JOY OF FAILURE

In this chapter, we have suggested that concentration is the key to any endeavor including exercise. We have discussed how an exploration of breathing, rhythm, and posture will enhance your exercise skills and enjoyment. In conjunction with guidelines provided by fitness and health professionals, your have to learn to use your own senses in regards to the type exercise you do and how you do it (frequency, intensity, duration, etc.).

As you develop the power of your breathing and your awareness of rhythm and posture in your workouts, you will not worry about all the words and numbers (time, sets, reps, heart rate, cross training, muscle, joints, aerobic, etc.) that are used in the exercise world. You learn these concepts to serve your instincts. You do not follow them blindly in hopes of finding the promised land.

By definition, you will fail regularly when you exercise. If you are not concentrating, you will never learn to apply the overload principle wisely. It will always be a guessing game. Have I trained enough? Was that too intense? Am I burning enough calories? Will this shape my body? Without the feedback that you receive when you are concentrating, you and nobody else in the world can answer these questions.

Your senses tell you when your breathing, rhythm, and posture are breaking down (mouth breathing, too much impact, pain in the joints, stiffness in the spine, etc.). You learn make a compromise with your current levels of conditioning and your capabilities on a particular day at a particular time. You learn to push the body without hurting yourself. You train to a reasonable degree of failure. And you are happy because you felt so many things along the way and will be back again another day.

Many exercisers already apply the two most basic physical training principles. They make efforts to increase their intensity (Overload Principle) and try to select exercises to improve certain areas of their performance and/or shape (Specificity Principle). Whether applying these principles consciously, skillfully, or haphazardly, they should be encouraged to learn more. Overload and Specificity are cornerstones of any successful pursuit of exercise. However, in this chapter, as we shall discuss, human beings are not robots. Exercise, or any other endeavor worth pursuing, depends on more than mere physical principles and simple faith that a particular stimulus will engender a particular response. For example, take the following exercise prescriptions: To improve your cardiovascular fitness and to burn calories, do 30 minutes on the stationary bike, 3 to 5 times per week. Keep your heart rate between 65–85% of your maximum heart rate. To strengthen and tone your gluteus and quadriceps muscles, do 2 to 4 sets of squats, 8–15 repetitions per set, 3 times per week. For resistance, use 50–85% of your one rep max weight per set.

In and of themselves, these prescriptions are fine. The stationary bike is effective for improving cardiovascular fitness and burning calories. The squat is a good exercise for working the gluteus and quadriceps muscles. However, these prescriptions do not consider many personal and practical factors. Do you have access to the equipment? Do you enjoy the exercises? What complementary exercises should be performed? Are you able to do the exercises properly? Are you wearing the right clothing? Furthermore, even if all of the personal and practical factors are positive, what does that mean for your future? Starting next Wednesday, you will begin riding the bike and doing squats until the end of time or until you reach your goal? Who wants to do that? In the long term, few would look upon such a regimen as anything but drudgery. It's just not that natural (fun?) to live by prescription week after week even if you do get in better shape! Why then are so many Americans in search of an "exercise prescription?" Of course, the answer (drum roll, please) is . . . results! Some people have neglected to exercise for years and others have started exercising before and have failed to reach their goals. They are disappointed in themselves. And faced with the prospects of failing or failing again, they want a prescription "guaranteed" to get them results.

In the American marketplace, they have no lack of options. Billions of dollars every year are spent on exercise machines, club memberships, classes, books, videos, and training aids. For such products and services, any number of experts (medical doctors, university researchers, therapists, trainers, athletes, and celebrities) are more than willing to offer enthusiastic endorsements. After all, if a television star says you're going to lose thirty pounds on the Giraffe Strider, you're going to lose thirty pounds on the Giraffe Strider! Undoubtedly for some, there is a return on their exercise investment. They find an instructor, a machine, or a new type of exercise that serves as a catalyst for their program. It happens. If one hundred thousand consumers buy a Giraffe Strider, somebody's life is bound to be changed! Whatever the catalyst, these people learn to exercise consistently and reap long term benefits.

But what if you are one of those who want to "do the right thing", but nothing you buy or try seems to be an answer? Perhaps, you have a Giraffe Strider, used it for two months, and now the machine is a hanger for delicates that can't be tumble dried. In case you would ever forget, you are reminded many times daily by newspapers, magazines, television, and the Internet that your lifestyle needs a change. What do you do? Maybe the world will change and make it easier for you to change. Maybe the day is coming when much of the hype and misinformation about exercise will dissipate. Society will become more proactive. More resources will be directed towards promoting active, healthful lifestyles and awareness among people of all ages. The power of healthier living will temper the power of commercial interests that rely on sales to an unhealthy and ignorant populace. Or . . . maybe you need a different approach to exercise. The cultural landscape hardly seems likely to evolve dramatically enough to galvanize your personal transformation. The odds of that are about the same as your finding a "miracle" machine, class, pill, etc. to do the same thing. We're not being cynical—just realistic! In your culture (that would be America, circa 2005), exercise is mostly bought and sold in the marketplace rather than learned and shared as a part of daily life. In plain terms, you will have to change your world. Within your busy schedule, amidst the demands of work, family, and friends, you must find time to open your senses and exercise your body regularly. This will result in not only your own transformation, but will have positive effects among your family, friends, and your fellow workers and students. Rather than waiting for the world to change, you will change the world. It's a heck of a lot easier that way, trust us.

Women's Physical & Psychological Health:
The Costs of Caring Too Much or Not Enough
Julie N. Wallach, Psychology Teaching Assistant,
California State University Northridge

In this chapter we will explore the importance of women maintaining a balance of physical and psychological well-being. We believe these go hand-in-hand, and will illustrate how women's self-perception can enhance or prevent them from feeling their best.

I have always been physically active. As a young girl I participated in gymnastics, modern dance, swimming, paddle tennis, and soccer. I rode my bicycle along side my father when he trained for marathons. As I grew older I became interested in staying fit not only for the 'fun of it' but for outward appearance. When I was 18 years-old, it was crucial that I look my best for my first boyfriend. I became an aerobics instructor at a local YMCA and trained with weights, played racquetball, swam, and ran. I could not exercise enough; it became an addiction. I felt out of shape if I missed a day of training. My boyfriend expressed concern that I cared more about the shape of my body than spending time with him.

After years of compulsive exercise, I realized that I must maintain a balance in my exercise regime in order to achieve psychological well-being. I had my first child when I was 30 years-old. Although I gained weight when I was pregnant it was a priority that I lose the weight in a healthy manner. I noticed that many of my friends lost themselves in their children, and did not loose their "pregnancy weight." They forgot about their husbands' need for an attractive, sexy wife who cares about herself and their own need for adult relationships beyond their friends in "Mommy & Me" classes. They did not exercise and few of them ate well-balanced meals. The extent of their exercise was holding their babies and carrying the car seat (although they are very heavy!). I made sure that this would not happen to me. Every day – without fail – I walked steep hills with my daughter in her stroller or carrying her on my chest in a baby carrier. The extra weight of my daughter and the stroller helped the pounds fall off quickly. I ate nutritious meals and nursed my child.

In order to stay psychologically healthy, I joked about my daughter being attached to my body and using me as a pacifier when I nursed her. I wrote prose as a way to express my feelings about the psychological challenges of being a new mother. I did not hide behind a vale of smiles and stating that I was so thrilled about our baby that nothing else mattered; rather, I was honest that I felt a loss of identity as an individual and needed to transition to a maternal frame of mind.

The bottom line is that I accomplished what I set out to do because as a wife, mother, and self-aware individual who values physical activity, I knew that I needed to maintain balance in my life. After being married almost ten years and having a five year-old daughter, I still make sure to "check in" with myself when my life is out of balance. It is by no means a perfect science, but it is vital for me and those I love that I take care of myself physically and psychologically.

The goal of this chapter is to offer suggestions to women so they can pay attention to themselves–not too much and not too little. Our goal is to move away from blaming cultural forces that exacerbate women's poor body image or lack of balance in her life. The media, fast food restaurants, sexism, and countless other reasons for describing *why* these behaviors occur create a divide between women wanting to feel and look their best. Women must accept and embrace that it is imperative to obtain and maintain optimum health both psychologically and physically.

A caveat here is that I will not take the approach that we must 'accept who we are' whatever our weight or state of mind. Although some of the ideas expressed here are unpopular and often looked down upon in the 21st century (e.g., women are supposed to be more concerned about their career, children or both, than maintaining a "spark" in their marriages), we assert that it is completely acceptable and natural for women to want to have a positive body image and maintain psychological well-being. When women feel positive about themselves, it positively affects their lives on a global scale: Relationships with their children, husbands, extended family, friends, and co-workers are more positive and fulfilling. Overall, we encourage women to embrace the following beliefs and attitudes:

- Women want to feel good about their physical appearance and health.

- There is always time to be physically and psychologically healthy.

- Being a mother does not mean that women should neglect their physical and psychological needs.

- Women want to be physically attractive as a way to meet a potential mate.

- Women want to feel energetic.

- Women want to be viewed as being physically attractive by others.

- Women do not want to hide behind clothing that covers as much of their bodies.

- As women age, they still want to be and can be physically attractive.

- If women are not overweight, this does not automatically imply that they are healthy.

- We must stop chastising married women with children who wish to look their best and take the action to do so.

Perhaps women have forgotten that they want these things. Maybe it has been so long since they felt a physical and psychological balance that they do not realize how good it felt or how important it is to them. However, after being reminded that their physical and psychological well-being are the most important aspects of their lives, they will take action to improve their lives. They may think this is selfish: Their children, parents and other family members are more important than taking the time to go for a run. Although this seems logical and kind, if women are unhealthy how can they give as much physical and psychological energy to their loved ones as they deserve?

Perhaps women have stood at a crossroads, wondering why they cannot let themselves go and (dare we say!) enjoy dessert every so often without feeling fat afterward, or wishing that they could use food as a means of nourishment rather than comfort. Maybe when their children are taking a nap and they are mopping the floor in between loads of laundry, they wonder what happened to the part of them that made the effort to run five miles per day and dress nicely for their husbands.

Many women believe that it is sexist to place importance on women's physical attractiveness, and that women should be valued based on their performance as mothers. Mothers can be viewed as selfish if they spend time striving to look and feel their best. There is a dichotomy between the pressure we have to look our best and the criticism we receive when we work hard to look good. Women who exercise every day, eat a balanced diet of healthy foods, apply make-up, style their hair, and take time to get dressed so their look my best are often asked why they are so dressed-up (they are, after all, only going to the market!), and criticized for being too self-involved. However, we believe that women who state that it is unimportant to be e beautiful, sexy, and have toned muscles are lying to themselves. They are being untruthful if they claim to "not care what others think" or that they are "too busy to bother with fancy clothes." They do not have to spend a lot of money to look and feel their best, but they must spend time exercising and taking the time to present themselves to the world in the way they want to be seen.

Balance as a Barometer to Physical & Psychological Well-Being

We are not advocating that looks are the most important aspect of well-being; rather, women's global thought processes and actions will bring balance to their lives. For example, well-balanced women may take the time to

- exercise

- eat well

- create and maintain a healthy sexual relationship with their spouse

- be of service to others

- play with their children and not merely watch their children play

- sleep well to restore their energy—one of the most important items on a mom's "to do" list

- laugh often

- stimulate their intellect

- maintain supportive friendships

- achieve relaxation

- take in the beauty and serenity of nature . . . the list goes on and on.

This list is an example of the various ways that women can create a balance in their lives. The price women pay for caring too much or not enough about their appearance (e.g., eating disorders, compulsive exercise, or conversely, ignoring their appearance completely) can have serious ramifications. The bottom line is that looking good cannot occur until women FEEL good about themselves, and the only way this can happen is if there is a healthy balance in their lives of whatever *they* deem important.

In the following examples, we illustrate the negative consequences faced by women who are out of balance. We begin with a hypothetical college student, "Sally the Skinny Salad Eater," who is earning excellent grades but feels overweight. As a result of reducing her caloric intake to an unhealthy amount, she loses weight (her goal) but feels weak and tired, which negatively affects her academic performance. Sally feels an overriding need to be physically attractive at the expense of her physical and psychological health.

We move on to discuss "Sandy the Soccer Mom," who is so consumed with her children's needs that she has forgotten about herself and her husband. Perhaps "Sandy" lost track of what it means to her husband to have a wife who takes the time to look and feel her best. Sandy may feel that her excellent performance as a mother will override the dullness of her marriage, but this has serious ramifications. We argue that a marriage in which both husband and wife are happy is essential to family unity.

Sally the Skinny Salad Eater

Sally is a 19 year-old woman who attends a four-year university. She gained 15 pounds during her first year of college, felt unattractive, and perceived herself as 'fat.' At the beginning of her sophomore year, she decided to go on a diet that would allow her to lose weight as quickly as possible. She skipped breakfast, drank large amounts of diet soda throughout the day, and ate steamed spinach for dinner. She felt proud of herself when she noticed that she had lost more than the original 15 pounds she gained: Overall, she lost 20 pounds in three months.

Sally's life changed dramatically when she lost weight. She began dating an athlete who took great pride in his physique and was quite popular. At the same time that things were going so well,

Sally felt that her energy level was abnormally low. She could not concentrate well in school and noticed her grades were suffering. She always felt hungry and was lightheaded when she walked from campus to her apartment. Once she was home and she was able to eat, she would grab whatever she could as fast as possible to overcome her hunger. Mostly, she ate her roommate's junk food because Sally kept almost no food in the house. Although her roommate's food was unhealthy, she had more energy because she was eating carbohydrates. This energy did not last for long, though, so she needed to keep eating.

Sally followed this pattern and soon noticed that she gained five pounds. She began feeling 'fat' and vowed to herself that she would go back on her diet. She ate less and lost the weight quickly, but noticed again that she had little energy. It was more important to Sally that she be thin rather than energetic, and although she could not accomplish tasks the way she used to she was happier being thin.

The irony is that Sally is consumed with "looking" good and less concerned with the benefits that optimum physical health can have on her psychological health. By maintaining a body weight that *appeared* healthy, Sally believed that she has no reason to incorporate exercise into her life, relying more on body weight and outward appearance as indicators of positive body image, rather than true physical health.

The Scale as a Measure of Confidence

For Sally, outward appearance relates to maintaining the "perfect" weight. She weighs herself every morning, and her mood is contingent on how much she weighs. If she eats dessert one evening, she frantically weighs herself the next morning to determine whether she has gained weight. If the scale shows that she is a bit heavier this negatively affects her mood for the rest of the day. To make up for eating too much the day before, she eats almost nothing the following day as a method of losing weight and gaining control of her food intake. Once she is back to her "happy weight," she feels better.

Conversely, if she weighs herself and finds that she has lost weight, her mood is better and she feels more confident about her appearance. It seems that on these days, people compliment her on her clothing or ask if she changed something about her hair or make-up. The difference they observe in Sally is her level of confidence in her hard work paying off. The problem with is that her hard work is not exercise and maintaining a healthy diet, but starving herself so the scale shows lower numbers.

Muscle Weight: "Why am I Fat if I am Exercising?"

Sally has a friend, Ellen the Exerciser. On occasion they meet at a restaurant near the university for lunch. Ellen notices that the only food Sally orders is a small house salad with no dressing and expresses concern that Sally is not eating enough food: She looks thinner than ever–almost too thin. She also told Sally that she looks pale and worn down. Sally does not admit to Ellen that she is eating almost nothing, but says that she is so busy that she has not had time to pay attention to eating well.

As an avid exerciser with a healthy physical and psychological balance in her life, Ellen explains to Sally that if she really wants to look her best, she needs to exercise and become strong by eating a wide array of foods, such as meat, vegetables, fruit, and healthy carbohydrates. She also explains to Sally that there are exercise machines she can use to tone her gluteus muscles, and that Sally would be excited to see the outward results from such an exercise routine. As a supportive friend, Ellen tells Sally that she would be happy to go to the university gym with her and show her how to use the equipment. She would also be willing to make a regular date with Sally so they can exercise together. Sally takes Ellen up on her offer but has little energy to follow through with her routine. She follows through despite feeling lightheaded, but is ravenous and exhausted when she completes her workout. Ellen notices that Sally is tired but is proud of her for working hard and showing up to the gym. Sally and Ellen decide to make a regular exercise schedule with each other. Within a few weeks, Sally feels that she is gaining muscle and is pleased with the results from her routine.

Sally continues to weigh herself every day, sometimes two times, before and after exercising. Unfortunately, Sally is unaware that by exercising and building muscle, she is gaining weight. By virtue of seeing higher numbers on the scale, she becomes anxious about maintaining an exercise routine. Additionally, when she trains she requires more calories and feels hungrier. Sally worries that if she eats more she will gain weight; but what she does not consider is that her body needs a healthy amount of calories in order to burn calories efficiently. She needs to understand that her body shape will improve as a result of regular exercise, regardless of what the scale says.

■ SALLY THE SKINNY SALAD EATER: WEIGHTS & MEASURES FOR PHYSICAL & PSYCHOLOGICAL WELL-BEING

- List ten reasons why she believes that her diet of skipping breakfast, drinking diet soda and eating spinach for dinner every night is healthy for her body. Support her reasoning with medical research that has been conducted on such an eating plan.

- Rate her energy level three times per day

  1 = very low, 2 = low, 3 = normal, 4 = high, 5 = very high

- Rate her ability to concentrate when she is studying.

  1 = very low, 2 = low, 3 = normal, 4 = high, 5 = very high

- List ten reasons why it is important that she maintain her current body weight. Honestly assess the reasons and decide whether they are for physical reasons (e.g., "I am maintaining a lower body weight because I do not want to experience Type II diabetes, high blood pressure, or other side effects of obesity") or because she feels unattractive unless she maintains her "perfect" weight.

- What role does exercise play in having a "good body"?
  Is it a means to an end, i.e., something you must do in order to look better?

  Does your physical health play a role in your motivation to exercise?

  If you exercise for outward appearance only, do you only train on equipment that works certain areas of your body (glutes, etc.)?

- Have you ever exercised for the pleasure of the activity in which you are engaged? Have you enjoyed a particular activity so much that you forgot that you were actually exercising?

We believe that Sally can achieve a balance of physical and psychological health when she comes to terms with three important concepts: 1) She is doing more damage than good to her body when she essentially starves herself; 2) If she works at achieving the type of body she desires, she must incorporate exercise and increase her caloric intake, and, 3) work toward a balance of psychological and physical well-being by finding activities she enjoys and concentrating on accomplishing other goals, such as succeeding in school.

"Sandy the Soccer Mom"

We see her in the supermarket, telling her four young children to quiet down, and if they are quiet she will buy them their favorite cookies. The children wait patiently for 30 seconds then tell Mom that they have been quiet, so will she PLEEEEASE open the bag of cookies RIGHT NOW? She sighs and says yes, hoping this will allow her to shop in peace. (She'll do anything for a moment's peace!)

While the children are gobbling up the cookies as fast as they can (and perhaps sneaking an extra behind Mom's back), Mom heads for the bread aisle. She makes sure to buy a loaf of "*honey-wheat*" bread because it appears healthy. She's onto the next aisle and sees that potato chips are on sale so she buys two extra bags to have in the house "just in case."

Uh-oh! Time's up! The children want another cookie and now they are thirsty, too. She gives them a cookie and goes straight to the cold soda aisle where she finds them sugary drinks to quench their thirst. While they are gulping down their sodas, she realizes that the zipper on her jeans broke. She wonders how long she had been walking around like this. Did people see this and not say anything? Or, worse than this, did *anyone* notice or is she invisible–too generic and matronly for anyone to talk to about her appearance?

It is not supposed to matter what she looks like: Mom is the heroin without a face or a name. All that matters is that she does a great job raising the kids. BUT WAIT! This is where we stop the show. Mom, get to the check-out counter immediately, because it is time to go home, drop off the children with your mother, friend, or neighbor, and go on a journey to find the place where *you* got lost.

As you drive in reverse looking for yourself, you see remnants of the person you love. Maybe there were the few times you went out with your husband to a social event and he said you look beautiful. Perhaps one evening while you were doing dishes he walked over to you, put his arms around you from behind, and said that you are the sexiest woman in the world.

You realize that amidst the chaos of schedules and your children's wants and needs, you lost yourself. When did you stop caring about your looks? When did your uniform become jeans or sweatpants and a t-shirt? When did you ever NOT care about yourself as much as now?

Mostly, "Sandy" knows that the emphasis she places in her life is her children's happiness, not her looks. She thinks that if she is hanging around the house or going to the park that there is no sense in dressing "up" or trying to look her best; what's more, it seems like yesterday when her little girl was still spitting up on everything, not to mention how busy she is teaching her children values, changing diapers, helping with homework, creating and maintaining tradition in the home, demanding respect, heating the bathtub just right, making the best dinners, listening, admitting when she is wrong, and cheering on all of the kids during their games.

"Who has time to put on make-up or exercise?" the Soccer Mom asks.

The point is that the Soccer Mom has lost track of what is important. Where did she go in the midst of being a mom? What happened to the desire to feel good about her appearance and look good for her husband, to keep the sensual and sexual component of her life alive? Why, if she can take time to slip on a pair of jeans, can she not put on a skirt and take a few minutes to apply make-up, particularly if her husband will feel flattered that she is making the effort to look nice for him? These questions and concepts are unpopular – to the point of being offensive in Western culture–but they exist for a reason. Wives who want to look their best for their husbands are sending a positive message about their marriage. How much good are they doing for their children if their marriages are either stale or unhappy? If they are concerned about being a positive role model for their children, why are they teaching them that it is unimportant to be romantic in a marriage?

There is a myth that mothers are too self-involved if they care about their appearance. We strongly disagree; rather, at every stage of women's lives they should care about their physical and psychological well-being. Two examples of this involve breast milk and oxygen (bear with us; it will make sense, we promise!):

- Nursing: When a mother nurses her child she must nourish her own body with a healthy diet. If mom is unhealthy, her infant will not receive the necessary nourishment to grow normally. Mothers cannot go on a crash diet after giving birth if they are nursing, as they and their newborn will suffer physically. Mom must take care of herself so that she can take care of her baby.

- Oxygen: When a stewardess explains that in case of an emergency, an oxygen mask will fall from above our seats, we should apply it to ourselves first, then young children. This way, we will have enough oxygen to stay alive so we can help the child. If we do not have our own oxygen, we are no good to anyone else who may need us.

■■■ SANDY THE SOCCER MOM: "RUNNING AFTER MY KIDS ALL DAY" IS NOT A FORM OF EXERCISE!

➤ Give new meaning to the term "Soccer Mom." Soccer cleats come in all sizes, so buy a pair for yourself and other family members. Families can engage in an activity that will foster close, fun relationships with each other. It is meaningful to children when parents take an interest in their hobbies and help them improve their game. Do you remember what it felt like to have a parent do what you liked to do, along side of you? When they wanted to learn about an activity you loved and your parents asked *you* to teach *them* how to do it? If it happened to you, it was probably quite a positive experience, and if not it may sound nice to you. Imagine, as a child, your parent(s) buying soccer cleats or ballet slippers? Or going outside while you are playing handball and asking to join the game? Combine your gift of giving to those around you with things you enjoy and that are healthy for you. Everyone will benefit, particularly if you play soccer with your family in an evening gown and a full face of make-up!

➤ Perform at least 40 minutes of cardiovascular activity every day. You may think that you are too tired to exercise; however, exercise will provide you with more energy to get things done. You will feel stronger, your hips and back will not be in pain from carrying the baby, and you will be able to lift all of those heavy boxes from the warehouse store. You will sleep better. You will burn calories more efficiently. You will feel sexy. You will accomplish something that is all yours. You will have time to concentrate on your muscles and your heart beat.

➤ Enroll your children in swimming, ballet or other classes at a facility that offers classes for children and adults (e.g., YMCA or your local park) and use this time to exercise. You can take one hour for yourself while the kids are in their class.

➤ Men get blamed by women for pressuring them to look like "Barbie," or at least making a considerable effort to look as attractive as possible. Women complain that if only men were more accepting the imperfections of women's faces and bodies they would feel better about themselves and more eager to stand naked in front of their boyfriend or husband. This way of thinking is a waste of time! Men are merely reacting to a biological instinct. Men are not following a herd; rather, they are responding to their senses, to what they deem beautiful. I have yet to figure out what is wrong with this.

The man in your life should be physically attracted to you. If he is not, and it is because you are not taking care of yourself physically, change the way you look. The rationale behind this seems foreign in our society today, but it still holds true.

Looking good for him should be your desire, not a chore or something you do with resentment. Although we must be active and healthy mainly for ourselves, if our relationships are important to us we should want to keep the "spark," which, in part, is linked to physical appearance.

If you do not feel good about your health, fitness, and overall appearance, your mood may change (e.g., cranky, negative). This could lead to lower quality relationships with those around you, particularly the man in your life. It is not fair to take out your lower self-confidence on him with the behavior that follows it.

➤ We believe that you truly want to look beautiful; feel confident when you feel beautiful, and feel beautiful overall when their physical and psychological health are synchronized. Why, then, are men being blamed for the give-and-take of physical attraction between the sexes? Who cares if men want women to be physically attractive? Women, please admit that it feels good to feel healthy, muscular, energized, pretty, well-put together, and, dare I say, "done up." Own up to this, and balance this truth with other aspects of your life that are meaningful to you.

You need not neglect the most important aspects of your life—health and psychological well-being—because you are too busy with your successful career, children or other hobbies. In fact, a healthy lifestyle will enhance all other parts of your life and is likely to keep you alive longer so you can enjoy all of the people and things you love.

Chapter 19:
Outdoor Environments & Outdoor Activity: Exhilarating Exercises Enhanced by Nature

"I only went out for a walk, and finally concluded to stay out till sundown, for going out, I found, was really going in."

—John Muir

In the last several chapters we have been discussing the impact of activity on various components of physical and psychological health. We have identified several characteristics of exercise and training that has been shown to be highly effective with obesity, depression, self-esteem, and several other important behavioral characteristics. One component of exercise that we perhaps have taken for granted is the actual environment where the physical activity is taking place—we assume that exercise may occur inside a gym or spa and typically people tend to disregard the important effects of physical environment on behavior. In the vast majority of cases of individuals who have been exercising or training in physical fitness, the environment in which they exercise is typically indoors. The lighting, crowded spaces (i.e., signing a wait list for a popular exercise), ventilation and equipment within the indoor spa or gym have a profound effect on the psychological experiences and well-being of the individual while exercising. We have become so exposed and accustomed to indoor training that most people have forgotten (or at least have never experienced) the value and positive experiences that are associated with green outdoor environments. What limited vegetation or "greenery" that does exist is usually a silk (fake) plant or an improvised water fountain used in the gym to represent some characteristic of the outdoor environment. You may often even see a giant mural of a beautiful green hillside or mountain landscape on a wall improvised in the gym or spa to motivate athletes to exercise or train harder. The concept behind the use of these murals or pictures of nature on the wall is quite simple—to help people "visualize" a more calming or relaxing environment that will have positive consequences on the overall experience of the exercise itself. In other words, the mural exists as a means to help us "pretend" that we are somewhere else while exercising. Our point here is quite simple—why visualize (or "pretend" to experience) greenery or nature when you can have the best of both worlds, such as a challenging exercise in beautiful outdoor environments?

An important component of this chapter is to help the reader familiarize himself or herself and rediscover the tremendous psychological and physical benefits of the outdoor activity. Most individuals who have been exercising or training for a period of time have indicated that they in fact do prefer training outdoors, but certain problems that have been associated with exercising outdoors have limited their ability to do so. For example, many men and women indicate safety as a factor in exercising outdoors, as traffic and dark or unlighted areas may pose as safety problems. Additionally, the most commonly cited preventative factor in training outdoors is the "time" factor—many people indicate that they think training outdoors means excessive time traveling to some remote part of the hills or mountains, but this simply is not true. In many cases, the natural benefits of outdoor exercise may be as simple and close as right out your front door, your local park or even an undeveloped vacant lot. We will help people familiarize themselves with locations to train outdoors that are within easy reach (even living in congested areas, such as Los Angeles) and experience the benefits of outdoor exercise. One final point to note in comparing the physical outdoor environment with the indoor environment (i.e., spa) is that our bodies physically adapt very quickly to the demands being made upon them. Thus, if you have been reporting to the spa or gym regularly three or four days a week at 7:00 a.m., it is common to fall into a very predictable routine, and our bodies adapt to that routine. For example, you may exercise on the treadmill for 20 minutes, followed by light weights, then followed by 15 minutes of stretching and then get dressed for work. The body adapts to these routines and builds tolerances to the types of physical training. In order to maximize efficiency in exercise and training, we must continuously change or exercise programs so our bodies do not build up tolerances to our exercise routine. When we train or exercise outdoors, usually most of the major muscle groups are being utilized and we are able to maximize an efficient physical exercise routine. This routine is very difficult to match in indoor training—this is why most expert runners always encourage runners for long distance to begin cross-country training outdoors and avoid the treadmill.

This chapter will now focus on the physical characteristics of the environment (such as outdoor and indoor environments) and the impact on motivation in physical exercise, self-esteem, and psychological reports of well-being. Recent research shows exciting results regarding the dynamic interaction between the physical environment, physical environment, and psychological levels of self-esteem and wellness. We have established the fact that regular and challenging aerobic activity is essential not only to physical health (such as in cardiovascular health), but more importantly with psychological benefits, such as self-esteem and wellness. In a very interesting study that specifically explored these variables, Pretty and colleagues (2003) discovered that those individuals who engaged in regular physical activity not only showed higher levels of self-esteem, but also were able to show greater levels of resiliency and emotional stability. Thus, not only does regular aerobic activity show greater resilience to physical illness and gains in psychological adaptation, but also subjective reports of well-being and reduced depression. The positive benefits are numerous, where individuals who are engaged in regular exercise and physical activity outdoors report higher levels of happiness and even an "antidepressant" effect (see figure 19a).

Think for a moment when you were last outside on a beautiful day—what are the components that we take for granted while being outside? For example, think about the following: The bright sunshine, the clean and fresh air, the ability to observe and see all of the beautiful plants and vegetation that surrounds us are just a few examples of the many natural benefits available to those who choose to exercise outdoors. In a very interesting study that documented the positive effects of outdoor activity and less congested (rural) environments, Lewis and Booth (1994, *Psychological Medicine,* 24, 913–915) discovered a significantly lower prevalence of mental disorders than those individuals living in congested urban areas. The key psychological factor that proved to be most beneficial was living in green areas and open spaces, such as garden areas. In a related study that explored prosocial behaviors in outdoor environments, Walter (1982, *The Human Home: The Myth of the Sacred Environment*) discovered that the existence of noise that is typically associated with urban areas (such as traffic from automobiles in freeways or planes in airports) resulted in significantly fewer cases of prosocial help and altruistic behaviors. In other words, the more noise a given environment has, the less likely people are to help each other. These are just some of the more negative characteristics that we may encounter when exercising in congested environments. Additionally, research suggests that individuals who live in an urban and congested environment may be more at risk in suffering a variety of stress-related disorders

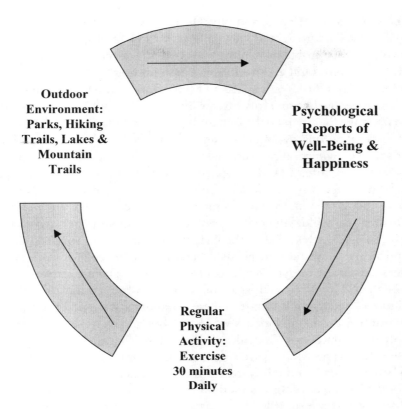

Figure 19a   The Psychosocial Cycle of Health

(Rainford and colleagues, 2000). Indeed, Rainford and colleagues determined that almost 30% of the women surveyed indicated that they had experienced a "large amount of stress" in the past 12 months that may have been attributed to circumstances that were associated with urban living. Specific factors, such as delinquency, vagrancy, crime and vandalism were cited as the most common negative factors associated with risks that were associated with congested urban living.

■ THE PROBLEM OF ARCHITECTURAL GREED AND URBAN SPRAWL: NO ROOM TO PLAY

The more pervasive the problems are in living in the congested urban areas the more we tend to appreciate the beauty and tranquility of rural areas. Paykel and colleagues (2000) noted that children living in country or rural areas had significantly lower rates of mental disturbance than children who were living in urban areas. The question arises why and what factors exist that make urban living so negative and counter-productive to mental health and hygiene. While there may be several factors that are associated to this provocative question, one point that needs to be addressed is the physical structures that are associated in the urban environment and the proximity in which we live from one another. The very fact that our physical proximity among one another in living and recreational activities has increased significantly is beyond dispute. Thirty, forty, and fifty years ago homes and shopping centers were constructed with aesthetic beauty and safety; homes were typically small (under 2000 square feet) but yard spaces were vast and spacious, typically expanding beyond one two or three thousand feet. Children had room to play and they learned to appreciate the value of play. Children played outdoors with their parents and friends, and typically there were few factors that disrupted play that unfortunately exist today. Children could kick balls, play catch, and spend the day outside with little concern about noise or safety problems. Unfortunately, many developers are now tearing down those beautiful old homes that were built on spacious lots and putting up two or even three small homes. No room to play for children, little yard space and too few (and too small) parking spaces create an unhealthy recipe where people become frustrated with each other not because they dislike each other, but rather they do not have their personal space in the outdoor environment. The typical distance that humans roamed in search of food over the last several million years was an incredible 26 miles daily, thus, the need for space in living and recreational activities is very much needed in our society today. The problem of greed in architectural development is clearly a problem, as our psychological and mental hygiene is being sold out by developers. The more the architect can design buildings to house more people on fewer acres of land, the more money he or she can make. The more the developer can build in housing in an already bloated environment, the more money they can make. The problem is frustration and psychological stress due to the lack of open and green spaces for recreation.

However, if individuals have become accustomed to living in urban sprawl, or training and exercising while indoors or in a spa or gym, we forget the psychological benefits of recreational outdoor activities. Many of these beneficial factors of outdoor activity may have been lost in the process while exercising indoors and living in congested environments. We tend to become insulated within the protective environment of being indoors while training and exercising and forget the therapeutic effects of simply being outdoors. Consider the numerous luxuries that we now take for granted while being indoors: Television while exercising, spas and saunas, refreshments are available when needed, music to help stimulate and motivate our training, and reading and chatting with other people are just some of the examples of the distractions that influence our exercise while training indoors. The problem with many of these so-called luxuries is that they often deter and prevent us from concentrating on the exercise that we are performing and they prevent us from outdoor participation. When we train or exercise indoors, we are removed from the natural environment that helps stimulate and promote good physical health, such as circulation and respiration when walking or jogging.

The advantages to exercise "friendly" environments are numerous—when we are able to train and exercise outdoors in environments that are green, spacious and healthy, we experience numerous psychological benefits. Consider the following:

Valuing Outdoor Activity: Get Out There & Just Do It!

a. Individuals who had access to recreational activity were more than twice as likely to get recommended exercise than those individuals who did not have access to recreational activity (i.e., living near parks or open areas);

b. Those individuals who did have access to natural recreational facilities (i.e., hiking paths, jogging trails) were 43% more likely to exercise at least 30 minutes than those individuals who did not have access to such facilities;

c. People not having access to the outdoor recreational facilities were significantly more likely to experience cardiovascular problems and be overweight;

d. The closer the proximity to a bike path, the more likely people are to use it;

e. When people felt that they lived in "safe" places (less crime), they were more likely to receive the recommended level of physical activity than those who reported living in "unsafe" areas.

f. When people feel as though there are more outdoor available opportunities for them to participate in, they prefer exercising (such as walking, jogging or bicycling) outdoors rather than indoors;

g. The ecology of the recreational and exercise environment is also critical. When safe areas are made available for special populations (i.e., the elderly and children), older adults as well as children are significantly more likely to use these facilities.

These results confirm the hypothesis that how a city or rural environment is constructed makes all of the difference in the world in getting people to get out and exercise. When people perceive an environment as safe and beautiful, they are more likely to take advantages of the facilities made available to them.

■■ SINGLE PARENTS AND RECREATION FOR CHILDREN

As a final note regarding "exercise friendly environments, we should note how the changing dynamics of the household has impacted children's levels of activity. Latest surveys indicate that in California, over 52% of children are raised in single-parent households (U.S. Census Bureau, 2004). This figure is very alarming in itself. However, given the fact that if one parent is raising one child (or more children), support systems are necessary to provide supervision for the children while the parent is working longer hours. Several years ago (in the 1960's, 1970's and the 1980's) we lived in a safer environment and children generally were able to go outside and play without adult supervision. However, many single parents have indicated that they simply cannot trust people living in their neighborhoods and thus feel compelled to keep children inside while they are working. The impact of trust, communication and cooperation have influenced how we experience and value outdoor recreation and exercise. When we live in an environment with people that we are unfamiliar with or simply do not trust, we cannot enjoy our neighborhoods and recreational facilities. This is why we see community awareness programs as being vital to the existence of safer parks, schools, and outdoor environments. When we live more cooperatively and communicate with each other, we feel safer and can trust each other. Numerous research studies supports the hypothesis that the social environment significantly influences the rate and frequency of outdoor exercise and recreation. Trust, tolerance, and perceptions of safety dramatically influence the quality and type of exercise that is performed in the environment (see, for example, Cooper and colleagues, 1999; Wilkinson, 1996, 2000; and Kawachi and colleagues, 1997. In *English Nature Research Reports,* May, 2003).

There are now several studies that are available that document the importance of outdoor training and exercise, not only citing and identifying the advantages of outdoor physical activities as being beneficial to psychological health, but even preventing depression such as seasonal affective disorder (SAD) and more recently attention deficit hyperactivity disorder (ADHD). We will now explore specifically how outdoor activities may help improve our psychological well-being through outdoor activities.

■■ OUTDOOR ACTIVITIES AS EFFECTIVE MEASURES IN TREATING ADD: GO OUT & PLAY!

In a very interesting article that identifies several positive characteristics that are associated with outdoor physical activity, researchers Taylor, Kuo and Sullivan (*Environment and Behavior,* V33, 2001, pp. 54–77) identified specific characteristics that are associated with outdoor activity as being highly instrumental in addressing and in the treatment of children diagnosed with ADD. The current rate of children who are diagnosed with ADD is over 2 million and the rate is growing annually (Taylor and colleagues, 2001). The symptoms that are associated with ADD include impulsive behaviors, difficulty in concentration, inability to sit even for short periods of time, and difficulty in listening and following even simple or routine tasks. Other psychological factors that are associated with ADD include low self-esteem, academic failure, peer alienation and rejection, anxiety and depression. Children who are diagnosed with ADD clearly have difficulty in adjusting to school, peer relationships, and home situations with siblings and parents.

In the current study, Taylor and colleagues wanted to determine the effects (if any) of the types of environments (outdoor or green environments, paved or concrete urban environments, and indoor environments) that may have influenced how the children who were diagnosed with ADD interacted with each other. The parents of the children who were diagnosed with ADD were asked to observe how the children interacted and played with each other in these different types of environments. Parents were asked to record the styles of behaviors of the children assessed with ADD, and the results were significant. Those children who were instructed to play outdoors that were rich in vegetation (i.e., plants, flowers, trees, grass) and greenery had shown significantly more positive results than the group of children that were instructed to play indoors or in asphalt or paved concrete environments. Specifically, the ADD children who played in the green environments showed the ability to focus and concentrate more effectively and were able to play with other children more cooperatively. These results are very encouraging, given the increasing number of ADD among children today. Note that the study did not even consider diet when exploring ADD behaviors among children. Imagine the positive results that may exist if ADD children are afforded more "green" environments to play in and if their diets are closely monitored. The results are very positive and encouraging for the future.

■ OUTDOOR ACTIVITY AND SEASONAL AFFECTIVE DISORDER: GETTING OUT & AVOIDING DEPRESSION

The American Psychology Association (APA) has published a document that allows psychologists to identify a wide range of psychologically-related disorders known as the *Diagnostic and Statistical Manual of Mental Disorders* (DSM IV). In this well known document, a wide range of diagnoses exists to help therapists and psychologists diagnose individuals with a wide range of psychological disorders. One of the specific classifications of these disorders is mood disorders. A mood disorder is characterized as any psychological problem that involves depression involving suicidal thoughts and sadness. The condition must last over two weeks and involve problems in thinking and cognition (such as concentration), low self-esteem, hopelessness, and even delusions and hallucinations. There are several categories of depression:

a. Depression with melancholic features;
b. Depression with psychotic features;
c. Depression with catatonic features;
d. Depression with atypical features;
e. Depression with post-partum features; and
f. Depression with seasonal onset (SAD).

While all of these categories of depression and important to review, we will explore seasonal affective disorder (SAD) as this category clearly relates to outdoor training and exercise. Depending where you live, you may already be familiar with the effects of a long winter or cold season: We are kept inside or indoors most of the time, we have limited physical activity outdoors, and most importantly, we may not see the sun and outdoor green plants during the colder months. The symptoms are relatively simple: People with a history of SAD become depressed when the daylight hours are short (such as during winter in the northern hemisphere) where in some cases only two or three hours of daylight are available. Interestingly, those individuals who have been diagnosed with SAD show *reverse* symptoms when daylight is more pronounced. Thus, the symptoms of SAD are similar with Bipolar Manic Depression, where hours of exposed daylight have been associated with full manic episodes. An important factor to consider with SAD is that *only* changes in daylight hours are the contributing factors to depression. Other factors (i.e., unemployment) that contribute to depression would fall under another diagnosis (such as chronic or major depression).

We have mentioned in the beginning section of this chapter how often we take for granted green outdoor environments and the positive effects of physical exercise outdoors. You may wish to conduct your own experiment that evaluates how exercise outdoors may improve your levels of psychological well-being. For example, try conducting your own informal experiment where you spend a minimum of 45 minutes outdoors engaged in some form of physical activity or exercise, such as walking, jogging, gardening, or hiking. After approximately three to four months of a consistent and regular exercise program involving outdoor activity, evaluate yourself on the following topics relative to psychological health and well-being:

a. Self-esteem;
b. Happiness;
c. Stress levels;
d. Self-Efficacy; and
e. Motivation.

Now, compare these results or scores of the above psychological constructs with three or four months of indoor activity. If our hypothesis is correct, we would speculate that those activities that were performed outdoors would yield higher scores in psychological levels of well-being and happiness. We will now include a survey that explores individual responses and differences in how people perceive exercise outdoors as compared to indoor gyms or spas.

Outdoor Exercise Activity Questionnaire

Please answer the following questions, where a score of "1" indicates absolutely not true, "2" indicates not true; "3" indicates no opinion; "4" indicates true; and "5" indicates absolutely true.

1. When I exercise outdoors, I generally feel better physically than when I exercise indoors in a spa or gym; _____
2. When exercising outdoors, I tend to feel more aware of events occurring in the physical environment more clearly; _____
3. When I exercise at least 20 minutes a day outdoors, I feel that I am better able to concentrate at work or school; _____
4. I prefer working out or exercising outdoors than exercising indoors; _____
5. I tend to avoid gyms or spas that are crowded with too many people;_____
6. I prefer natural environments (trees, grass, and flowers) as compared to gyms with televisions, radios, and internet sites; _____
7. If I cannot exercise outdoors, I feel that I am missing an important activity in my life;_____
8. I feel that it is healthier to exercise outdoors and more rewarding to work out in the natural environment than exercising indoors;_____
9. I feel that plants, trees, and flowers are a necessary component of physical health and psychological well-being;_____
10. I don't think people should use cell phones when training in the gym or even watch television when training in the gym____;
11. I primarily go to the gym to meet people and to socialize;_____
12. It is important that people notice me when I am exercising;_____
13. I exercise more for physical appearance rather than how I feel inside;_____
14. It is important to me when I exercise to have people to talk to;_____
15. I am happy to stay indoors most of the time_____

■ ECONOMIC LINKS TO PREFERENCES IN OUTDOOR EXERCISE & TRAINING

The survey of the Outdoor Exercise Questionnaire was administered to a wide range of individuals who comprised different ethnicity, socioeconomic status and educational levels. The survey was given to community college students, four-year state university undergraduate students, and graduate students in psychology. The measure also looked at gender differences in the responses to each question. The results of the survey supported the hypothesis that outdoor activity is very important to a wide range of students, and that outdoor activity is valued as an important experience relative to psychological states of well-being. We found interesting differences in the responses to the Outdoor Exercise Questionnaire among the Compton Community College students and the California State University (CSU) students. For example, Compton Community College is a two year college in a predominantly lower SES environment that serves historically Latino and African American students. In this area, many students do not go out at night due to safety reasons. Crime is significantly higher in these areas, and the existence of crime in the urban area appears to have influenced the community college student's opinions regarding the value of training outdoors. The Compton College students in the lower SES environments did not value the experience of training or exercising outdoors, whereas the CSU students in a higher SES environment did significantly value the experience of outdoor exercise. The scores were extreme and significant in describing the differences and preferences in outdoor training among high and low SES environments: Students in lower SES preferred training and exercising indoors in a gym (over 65%), whereas the higher SES students (CSU and Pepperdine University) significantly and overwhelmingly preferred outdoor environments in training and exercise (over 85%). These results are very significant if we wish to improve the overall physical health of lower SES children who have limited access to outdoor activity. We need to create a safer environment in the urban areas where people can exercise and train outdoors and feel safe as well.

In an interesting study that supports our anecdotal findings, Jules Petty, Murray Grifin, Martin Sellens, and Chris Pretty (2003) determined that outdoor activity is critical to healthy and positive psychological states. Furthermore, their findings seem to suggest that individuals find outdoor activity benefits both physical and psychological levels of mental health. When interviewing several students who were actively involved in exercise programs, several of them indicated that they would have preferred exercising outdoors, but found many problems and difficulties in outdoor training. For example, those individuals living in an urban or suburban area had indicated that there were few parks, if any near them, and the few that were available were unsafe to exercise in. This problem was mentioned by several of the female respondents indicating that while they had shown an initial preference to outdoor activity, they were concerned about their personal safety which impacted their subjective reports of pleasure.

■ OUTDOOR ACTIVITY AND REDUCED HEART DISEASE: INCREASED CIRCULATION IS THE KEY TO LONGER AND HEALTHIER LIVING!

We have described several advantages to increased outdoor activity, ranging from reduced levels of depression linked to dormant seasons (SAD) and reduced likelihood of children suffering from ADHD. One more advantage to add to the list of the benefits of outdoor activity includes improved circulation and reduced likelihood of cardiovascular disease. You may be thinking why someone has to be outdoors to improve their levels of circulation, and why shouldn't indoor training be considered just as effective as outdoor training? The issue lies in preferences of the environment where the training occurs, the personality dynamics of the individual, and the nature of the exercise itself. If you will recall from earlier chapters (chapter 2—"Personality Characteristics and Modern Sport") we described how the school of behaviorism may explain why people participate in sport and exercise from a learning perspective involving rewards and punishments: People tend to repeat those behaviors that produce positive consequences and avoid those behaviors that involve punishment. In health activities and exercise, the vast majority of individuals indicated their preferences in training outdoors, and a preference to incorporate some form of aerobic or cardiovascular activity while being outside. These activities may include hiking in the hills or mountains, bicycling on a sunny day, or stretching/flexibility exercises outside on a lawn.

Given the fact that the vast majority of Americans over 54 have some form of cardiovascular disease, it is imperative that we develop some form of exercise for older adults that are enjoyable, practical, and most importantly capable of being done outdoors. Given the significant proportion of individuals who prefer exercising outside, involving cardiovascular exercises with outdoor exercises seems most logical and practical. Outdoor exercises are clearly less expensive that indoor (gym) training, and can be performed just about any where and at anytime. The most critical factor that is associated with cardiovascular health has very little to do outdoor activity and aerobic exercise is the circulatory system. Our hearts will beat approximately four billion times throughout our lifetime and it is considered to be a remarkable muscle that seldom encounters problems provided that we are responsible in our exercise and training. The problems with heart attacks do not start with problems in the heart, but rather problems with the circulatory system. If the circulatory system becomes clogged with plaque that is associated with a sedentary lifestyle and high (saturated) fat foods, the lining of the coronary arteries slowly become caked and clogged with plaque deposits. Similar to galvanized pipes that become corroded with rust and calcium deposits, our coronary arteries become less efficient in transporting blood to the heart with the build-up of plaque. As the heart therefore works several times harder to "push" the blood through constricted coronary arteries, the stress and work placed on the heart increases significantly thereby increasing the likelihood of a heart attack. Increased outdoor activity may help "unclog" the arteries and thereby reduce coronary heart disease.

■ OUTDOOR ACTIVITY & THE NEED TO SWEAT

Many times individuals who are exercising may be exercising for physical appearance (i.e., trim and muscular appearance). However, looks may be deceiving, as what appears to be attractive physically (on the outside) may not have anything to do on the inside of the body, such as our hearts or coronary arteries. Many doctors now recommend exercising at least 30 minutes where we break out in a sweat to maximize the positive effects of exercise. When we increase our physical activity outdoors and sweat during the exercise, we actually carry healthy proteins (called cytokines) to various parts of the body that improves flexibility of joints and reduces increased plaque. The important point to note is that when we go outdoors for increases in physical activity, we should increase our heart rate for at least 30 minutes. In doing this we not only reduce the risk of heart disease, but we also feel better both physically and psychologically.

Sometimes when we see a muscular person, we assume that he (or she) is automatically healthy. However, physical fitness in outdoor activity includes physical and aerobic activity. For example, many people may appear to be physically fit through lifting weights, but if their exercise program has not involved any aerobic training, they can still be at risk for heart disease. The key factor to remember with outdoor aerobic training is that the aerobic activity releases key proteins that play a vital role in coronary health. In physical exercise and activity, it is essential that we place some form of a demand on the muscle that we wish to strengthen. This is the basic philosophy behind all muscle development: When you lift weights, you virtually "tear down" some of the muscle tissue that needs to become repaired and rebuilt. It is precisely through this rebuilding process where key proteins and substances develop that play a role in reducing heart disease. Cytokines are released during various activities that involve aerobic movement (typically outdoor aerobic movement, such as hiking or bicycling). The cytokines are like the "roto-rooters" of the body that clean out the plaque from poor diets (such as high saturated fats) and sedentary activity.

The problems of urban living and safety have also several other ramifications addressing health and physical well-being. For example, when individuals feel compelled to remain indoors longer (due to a variety of reasons, such as safety or convenience), sedentary lifestyles are likely to emerge which impacts cardiovascular health. If society is able to create a safer outdoor exercise environment, people will more likely participate in meaningful active programs outdoors and also enjoy the psychological benefits (see figure 19b).

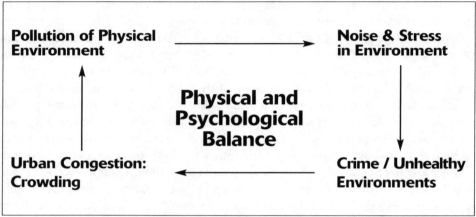

Figure 19b   Antagonistic Characteristics Regarding Exercise Environments (ACRE)

ACRE

■■ CHAPTER 19 QUESTION & REVIEW

1. Describe the relationship between outdoor activity and mental health and psychological states of well-being;

2. Describe the role of architectural design and development in urban areas and mental health among people living in those areas—how important is it to have open, safe and green yard space for children to play in?

3. Describe the role of outdoor activity and ADHD and SAD;

4. Take a moment and complete the Outdoor Exercise Activity Questionnaire. Score your results and determine how important outdoor activity is to you. Why do you feel that open and green environments is critical to psychological states of well-being?

5. Comment on the influence of SES and the responses to the Outdoor Exercise Activity Questionnaire.

Chapter 20:
Conclusions: Future Directions in Sport Psychology & Careers in Sport Psychology

The last several chapters have hopefully provided you with an understanding how sport psychology is an important discipline in psychology. We have described sport psychology from many perspectives—from a historical overview, to comparing sport psychology to the traditional theorists, reviewing collective and individual cultures and the impact they have on sport participation, and finally how the personality and body type of the athlete may influence sport performance. This final chapter will attempt to link these concepts together from a psychological and empirical research perspective and finally provide the reader with information how to pursue sport psychology as a viable means of economic support and personal fulfillment.

When individuals question the origins of behaviors, we often attempt to delineate the physical world from the mental or psychological world. We often hear people describing behavior from either the "biological perspective" or the environmental perspective. These names (however "official" and impressive they may sound) really try to explain the same thing, but from different perspectives. If we are trying to understand how Michael Jordan became one of the greatest basketball players in the NBA, or how Tiger Woods became one of the greatest golfers in the PGA, we cannot "split" or dichotomize their world as either being socio-environmental or biological (often referred to as the social constructionist theory and the biological essentialist theory). In order to best understand behavior, we must consider both paradigms as being relative and influencing each other in a reciprocal relationship. In other words, the Michael Jordan's of the world probably have been gifted with superior genetics (i.e., eye-hand coordination) but also have been fortunate with ideal training environments and experiences in playing basketball. The biological characteristics have merged with the social environment that has produced an exceptional athlete. This reciprocal process of learning is not limited to sports and sport psychology—it is the fundamental characteristic in understanding the basis of all human learning.

■ NOW THAT I UNDERSTAND SPORT PSYCHOLOGY—WHERE CAN I GET A JOB?

Sport psychology is increasing tremendously in popularity and interest among a wide range of individuals. More and more people are beginning to discover the link or the connection between psychological levels of preparation and their own performance in exercise activity, as well as the intricate relationship between mental thoughts and performance in the sports environment. As more and more individuals are working longer hours and relying more on technology and automation to get things done, they are finding it increasingly difficult to incorporate adequate levels of exercise activities into their lives. This book was written primarily to help people realize their exercise and health related-goals. It was also written to help people focus on a wide range of skills that they can employ to achieve these goals. This chapter now focuses on how individuals who are interested in sport psychology and exercise can implement these principles in a variety of ways. In this chapter we focus on the various types of employment that exists for those interested in sport psychology, as well as what people can expect from health trainers while participating in an exercise program. Coupled with this tremendous interest in the dynamics of sport psychology is the need to provide the public with competent and adequately prepared professionals trained in sport psychology to help them achieve their personal and professional goals.

The most important ingredient in a successful career in sport psychology (or any career, for that matter) is a passion, desire and love of the sport. Good sport psychologists take pride in their careers and enjoyment in helping people reach their personal goals. This is something that is inherent in your relationship with the people that you are working with—pride and satisfaction in working with others in reaching their goals. This next section in the final chapter will address several techniques how you the student and interested individual in sport psychology may pursue a career in this fascinating area.

■■■ SPORT PSYCHOLOGY CAREERS

Academic

Along with the tremendous interest in physical performance and psychological methods of preparation comes the opportunity to serve individuals in sport environments. Individuals who (after reading this text) wish to pursue sport psychology as a professional career have several options. Some people say great teachers are born—not made. In our view, teaching is one of the most rewarding and personally satisfying careers in the world. Certain "people skills" that are inherent in the teaching profession should come naturally, such as in knowing how to develop rapport with individuals and how to "tap into" a person's emotional base to find out how they feel about working out. As with any professional who seeks to work with the public in a counseling environment, a doctoral degree is typically required. Many individuals who serve as sport psychologists also work within a university environment and typically combine teaching with research in sport psychology. Additionally, individuals who primarily have academic careers may also serve as experts in sport psychology or conduct small private practices (which require licensure) serving individuals who wish to improve physical health through training or who wish to achieve personal goals (i.e., weight loss). Academic careers involving sport psychology usually address research topics in sport psychology, psychological momentum of the competitive athlete, visualization skills, and tolerance levels. Professors then typically incorporate their results in their lectures in courses specifically addressing sport psychology or they may publish their findings. Academic careers are very rewarding to most teachers of sport psychology, as the professors typically incorporate two areas of their own interest, such as teaching students and conducting research.

Health Trainer

An increasingly popular career for many individuals who are interested in sport psychology is the field of health training. A health trainer has several roles, but the primary role is in working with individuals in the gym or spa who are interested in improving their overall levels of physical conditioning. The effective health trainer has the unique ability in establishing positive rapport with a wide range of individuals and has an ability to help people realize that they can achieve their personal goals. The health trainer does not "solve the problem" for the client, but rather allows the client to see the important issues in their lives that need attention. Furthermore, and perhaps more importantly, the effective health trainer has the unique ability to allow clients to realize that they have the power to reach their goals independently and maintain a healthy style of living. This process is what we may refer to as "health related insight" and is only achieved within the context of a positive and trusting relationship.

Additionally, the health trainer should enjoy working with a variety of different people, have excellent communication skills with those people and possess the ability to establish interpersonal rapport with clients who have different needs. The health trainer works with several clients who initially may become frustrated and who have a low frustration tolerance. The trainer needs to be sensitive to the history of each client and why they are specifically seeking his or her help. The more we understand and appreciate the unique circumstances of each client the more effective we may be in identifying programs that suit their needs. Clients may come to they gym for several reasons, but perhaps the most common reason is to improve physical health, improve their diets, and typically drop anywhere from 10 to 30 pounds (or more). Perhaps the most effective skill of the health trainer is in establishing a trusting relationship with his or her client and gradually help them "discover" their internal power or their ability to achieve their own goals. Similar to the nurturing parent who teaches their child adaptive living skills, the trainer teaches his or her client a new way of living that makes them become more resourceful, adaptive and productive individuals. The effective health trainer knows the capacity and skills of the clients that he or she is working with and possesses the techniques that allow the client to discover those skills.

Earlier in this text we described an important component of sport psychology was in discovering each individual's source of motivation by determining their goals. Without specific and concrete goals, behavior typically becomes unmotivated and without drive. The effective trainer not only clarifies the client's individual goals, but helps establish a program for him or her that improves success in achieving the goal. The role of the trainer, therefore, is to serve as an inspiration and to help clients discover within themselves that they have the drive, the power and the capacity in not only achieving their goals, but in maintaining them on a regular basis. The health trainer in the gym is perhaps the most important component of what the facility represents. The health trainer's responsibility is to establish a positive relationship with clients who are entering the gym, answer questions regarding exercise and conditioning, provide support when individuals may be feeling negative or critical of themselves, and finally provide realistic goals (see figures 20a and 20b).

Certification Issues: Credentials Required for Careers in the Health Industry

Perhaps the single most important factor in determining the legitimacy of sport psychologists and health trainers is in the certification process. Who actually can refer to himself or herself as a "sport psychologist" or "health trainer"? The Association for the Advancement of Applied Sport Psychology (AAASP) is currently one of the largest governing agencies that directs and controls the certification process. Required criteria for AAASP certification includes:

a.   Membership in AAASP;
b.   Completion of a doctoral degree;
c.   Knowledge of AAASP ethical standards;
d.   Knowledge of sport psychology principles;
e.   Knowledge of biomechanics;
f.   Knowledge of the social, philosophical and historical components of sport;

g. Knowledge of research design;
h. Supervised practical experiences and consultation experiences; and
i. Knowledge of research design and statistics.

Research in Sport Psychology

An effective component of sport psychology is through empirical research that tests ideas and theory in sport psychology. Without empirical research in sport psychology, our ability to determine a "cause and effect" relationship would be compromised. For example, assume that you are a beginning researcher in sport psychology and you want to determine the effects (if any) in the quality of training with a training partner or training independently. You've heard anecdotal accounts from both arguments that they are both highly effective training techniques, but you want to find out for yourself and test this idea. As with all excellent research articles in science, great hypotheses begin with intriguing and compelling ideas. An example of the research hypothesis in sport psychology is described below.

Personality Characteristics As Effective Indicators of Individual Styles of Exercise

Hypothesis #1: Exercise and physical training is more rewarding and satisfying when training with an exercise partner than when training independently;

Hypothesis #2: A positive correlation exists among individuals who prefer training individually and the sport-introverted personality type; and

Hypothesis #3: A positive correlation exists among individuals who prefer training with a partner and the sport-extraverted personality type;

Hypothesis #4: Subjects will exercise more vigorously when exposed to a second (unknown) athlete who is training within their personal area.

Procedure

Fifty undergraduate students from California State University Northridge were selected for the current study. Subjects were first pre-tested for running speed, strength and stamina by timed running distances of 400 meters, sit-ups, push-ups and jumping jacks. If subjects in the pre-test were not capable of running 400 meters or completing 30 sit-ups and 30 push-ups within a two minute limit, they were eliminated from the study. Subjects were also administered The Athletic Personality Test (APT) measuring athletic personality introversion and extroversion characteristics. A baseline assessment was measured and recorded as the pre-test information:

Average running time for 400 meters:
Average number of sit-ups completed in two minutes:
Average number of push-ups completed in two minutes:

Additionally, subjects were administered the APT and scores were identified with each subject's performance. Subjects were then randomly selected into two groups: 10 subjects were placed in the experimental group and 10 subjects were placed in the control group. Subjects who were administered the APT test showed positive correlations between preferences in training and exercising alone with the sport introversion, and those subjects who were administered the APT test and preferred training with a partner showed positive correlations with sport extroversion.

These results suggest that personality characteristics have profound influences on the types and styles of exercise that individuals participate in. The more that we can understand the personality of the athlete the more we can improve styles of training and the overall quality of the exercise experience of the athlete.

Athletic Personality Test

Please answer each question with scores ranging between "1" through "5" where:

1 = Absolutely Not True;
2 = Not True;
3 = No Opinion;
4 = True;
5 = Absolutely True

E scale
1. Exercise is a very important activity in my life _____;
2. When I do not exercise, I feel as though something important is missing in my life _____;
3. I feel that I can train and exercise better with an exercise partner _____;
4. I prefer that my exercise partner is a little stronger or faster than me when training so I can get a better workout _____;
5. When I exercise I like to be with people _____;
6. I like to have fun when I exercise _____;
7. I like to hear encouragement from others when training—I think that it makes me work harder _____;
8. If I am jogging or running and someone runs past me, I have to try to catch them and pass them up _____;
9. When training with groups of people, it is important to me to try to be the best _____;
10. I think that groups of people who are exercising can improve individual levels or quality of exercise _____;

I Scale
1. I think that I can get a better work out when training by myself _____;
2. I feel self-confident when I exercise or train in groups of people _____;
3. People tend to distract me when I am exercising _____;
4. I feel that no one can "push" me harder than myself _____;
5. When I jog or run on the track and someone passes me by I usually keep my own pace _____;
6. Sometimes when I exercise with groups of people I feel self-conscious that people are staring at me _____;
7. I think that I can get more accomplished by staying focused and exercising by myself _____;
8. I feel that people who exercise in groups are not serious athletes and use them just to socialize _____;
9. I am my own best critic when it comes to training and exercise _____;
10. I think that no one understands my body better than myself _____.

Scoring the APT

Add up the point values for questions 1–10 and rank each score:

E scores:

The Independent Athlete (Low Extroversion): 0–15 = Low scores in extroversion—athlete prefers training individually; Avoids attachment to the group;

Social Moderation (Moderately Extroverted): 16–30 = Moderate scores in athletic extroversion—athlete enjoys working and exercising with other people but may also exercise individually as well; Recognizes the value in training in groups but can also work and exercise independently;

The Social Athlete (High Extroversion): 31–50 = High scores in athletic extroversion; athlete craves groups and social situations and feels that groups are necessary to have a successful exercise activity; feels uncomfortable when exercising in isolation.

I scores:

(Loner Athlete) Low Introversion: 0–15 = Introverted athlete who still recognizes the value of groups as a vital key in reaching goals and motivation. Dislikes groups, but feels that they are necessary in achieving personal health goals;

(Compatible Athlete) Moderate Introversion: 16–30: Introverted athlete that can tolerate training and exercising in groups but prefers exercising alone; This athlete may participate in both team and individual sports;

(Egoistic/Autonomous Athlete) High Introversion: 31–50: Athlete actively avoids training in groups primarily because he or she disregards the value of exercise groups; Primarily views groups of athletes in training as a distraction to him or her in reaching goals; Prefers training individually as they feel that few people can understand their dynamics and motivating factors in exercise; Distrusts groups and prefers the responsibility training and glory in winning.

Anecdotal reports of exercise. Please elaborate or explain the following:

1. I enjoyed this type of exercise because:
2. I feel that I was able to reach my goals in exercise and training:
3. What I liked best about this type of exercise and training was:
4. On a scale of 1 (lowest) to 10 (highest), I would rank my exercise activity as _____
5. I think I will probably be continuing to exercise in the future:
6. I prefer training with/without a partner because:

Ethical Principles for Exercise and Fitness Experts

While psychologists have their own specified criteria for ethics in practice and in research, health and fitness experts and sport psychologists perhaps are even held to a higher standard of ethics. In the health industry, we are frequently working with individuals who are vulnerable and the need for a trusting and ethical relationship is paramount for success in their exercise and health activity program. Furthermore, in exercise training many individuals place their trust and faith in the skills and competence of the trainer. The health trainer must be aware of the magnitude of the responsibility that they are assuming in their relationship with people who are concerned about their physical appearance and psychological well-being. The health trainer must also be adequately trained and competent in sport and exercise theory and physiology as well as understand the psychological components (i.e., self-esteem) of exercise. The following ethical principles are offered as guidelines to protect the welfare of the client in training with the health trainer:

Ethics of Health Trainers: "The 6 C's of Ethics in Sports"

1. *Competence > Theoretical.* Health trainers must know what they are talking about and should be considered expert in their area. Health trainers should consider themselves as scientists in physical performance and movement and should be able to transmit accurate information to the layperson in a simple and accurate manner. Health trainers should also frequently review new principles in exercise and sport activity, and must be able to answer a wide range of questions addressing physical and psychological components of health. For example, if a client asks, "How can I lose weight in my hips?" or "How can I strengthen my arms?" or "What is the Karvonan Formula?", the health trainer should know exactly how to respond to such questions. Health trainers should also review and record research in journal articles in sport psychology and apply them to their clients in training exercises. Examples of remaining theoretically competent and updated include:

    a. Updated information regarding exercise and health training to help with clients in their own exercise program;
    b. Renew all forms of required certification (AAFA, ACSM, AAASP);
    c. CPR and First Aid certification updated;
    d. Can the trainer respond to commonly asked questions by clients in an informative and accurate manner? Trainers must frequently review new materials and information and pass this information on to clients.

2. *Competence > Physical.* Health trainers are often viewed as role models—individuals view the trainer as someone to model and emulate. Therefore, effective health trainers have an obligation to stay in ideal physical condition and serve as role models to those who strive to achieve optimum health and fitness. Imagine, for a moment, that you are the client trying to lose weight or develop muscle mass and your trainer does not represent a healthy image of what you aspire to become. This can clearly have a negative impact regarding your ability to achieve your goal. Trainers should challenge themselves with the same enthusiasm and rigor as the client does in physical training. This not only sensitizes us as a trainer in terms of what the client is experiencing in terms of physical exertion, but also helps us to become better trainers by being in better physical condition.

3. *Caring & Respect for the Client.* Trainers must respect not only the potential of the client, but also respect his or her physical limits. Trainers need to help motivate clients to train within their limits to experience the full psychological benefits of health activities and exercise. Below (figure 20a) are some examples of the most important key characteristics of effective trainers. Most importantly, those trainers who push clients beyond their ability may risk client "burn out" or a significant loss of self-esteem. The trainer should work with clients gradually and progressively to help them realize their goals in a structured process. Trainers may have the best of intentions when trying to motivate clients to achieve their goals, but even the most ambitious trainer must recognize the physical limits of each client. Indeed, if overzealous trainers push their clients too hard (i.e., beyond their physical and psychological limits) the trainer may lose the client. When clients have become pushed beyond their capacity, they become frustrated and "burned out" and are at risk of dropping their training programs altogether. Trainers should always respect the limits of the client and remain cognizant of what those limits are throughout the exercise program. Trainers should remember

that in order to retain the confidence and trust of the client we must respect training limits and create training programs within those boundaries;

4. *Commitment to Client Success.* Good trainers work with clients and meet the minimum standards of performance in the client—trainer relationship, such as showing up on time to train. However, outstanding and most effective trainers are those that have a genuine commitment to the physical and psychological welfare of the client and are willing to "go the extra mile" for the client. They care about the success of the program for the client's sake and treat them as a dynamic and constructive individual who in fact is capable of achieving his or her goals in health management. Effective trainers are committed to working with clients regardless of the nature of their physical problems or the attitude of the client. Once a potential client can see that his or her trainer is committed to helping them achieve their personal health goal, they are more significantly more likely to achieve them. More importantly, when clients see the levels of authentic commitment by trainers they realize that their goals are more likely to be achieved. They will work harder because they now know that someone is watching and monitoring their progress. *This is critical to health training as no machine or automated device can do this*—this is the "human element" that is vital in all successful relationships. Trainers do not allow personal differences or perceived personality conflicts to influence their commitment in working with each client;

5. *Confidentiality of Relevant Information.* Trainers do not compromise personal information of the client to the public. This includes personal information, such as weight loss or other personal information that may be sensitive to the client. Additionally, trainers should not discuss personal and relevant information of one client to other clients, as rumors can be very detrimental to the morale of each member. Clients need to know that what information they divulge to their trainer will remain confidential and private. Effective trainers are trusted by the client and sometimes a confidante; the trainer should not take this special quality of the relationship lightly;

6. *Community & Social Commitment.* Effective trainers not only make personal and professional commitments to their clients, but also to the community. Trainers should often contribute to community programs and providing information that is relevant to health and exercise training. The more trainers can reach out to individuals who need accurate health information and exercise principles, the more we can help the general public. Examples of recommended community activities include trainers going out to public schools and communities teaching underrepresented groups the value diet and physical activity. As health issues become more apparent in our society (i.e., obesity, diet and activity), it is becoming increasingly more important that health trainers share and contribute their knowledge to various populations in society. For example, health trainers may wish to visit primary schools or high schools to teach proper exercise and training methods. Hospitals and assisted-living centers are also very important to teach the older adult how to maintain active lifestyles with minimal risk to injury. Giving back to the community such vital resources as exercise knowledge and inspirational discussions are vital to maintaining a healthy community. Trainers are also aware of the fact that in order to reverse the unhealthy trend of obesity in our society we need to start teaching children and young athletes health eating habits and to incorporate active health programs into their lives. For example, teaching children the phrase: "Taking Care of Our Bodies Through Exercise! . . . Exercise is Fun! And Exercise for Life!" will help remind them the importance of daily activity in their lives.

Seven Key Characteristics of Effective Health Trainers

a. Maintaining Positive Support and Friendly Demeanor to Persons in the Gym—make yourself easily approachable so people may ask questions freely;

b. Encouragement and Effective Communication Skills—always encourage people to keep training and offer positive feedback wherever possible. Remember: Always focus on the positive behaviors and reward them. People tend to repeat those behaviors that are rewarded;

c. Awareness of Client's Health Goals (i.e., losing weight, gaining strength)—Be clear in terms of what the client expects from you and what you expect from the client;

d. Setting Realistic and Challenging Goals for Client's—Challenge the client to work for realistic goals, but know when your client has reached their threshold for the day;

e. Knowledge of Useful Exercise Information: Trainers are continually aware of new methods and procedures involved in exercise training and maintain highest levels of certification;

f. Goal Setting: Effective health trainers determine goals (short-term and long-term) clients that are realistic and stimulate self-efficacy within the client;

g. Maintaining Personal Standards. Effective health trainers are role models for clients—if health trainers are physically unfit, then we become hypocrites. Trainers continually maintain their own personal standards of fitness that serve to inspire clients in the gym in achieving their own levels of fitness.

Figure 20a

In sum, the role of the effective health and fitness trainer is in establishing a positive and motivating relationship with clients as they begin to develop an exercise and health program. In the first phase of the exercise program, the client needs to communicate to the trainer exactly what his or her goals are—do they want to lose weight? Do they want to increase health and overall fitness? Are your clients interested in adding strength and muscle mass to their frame? There are several mechanisms that develop and unfold in the process of creating a successful and rewarding exercise experience for individuals in a health program, and the single most important factor in determining whether or not these goals have been met is through the development of a successful relationship with the health trainer.

Tips in Becoming a Great Health & Fitness Trainer: Incorporate CARING Principles

Creating a healthy and friendly relationship with each client. Health trainers most importantly want to create an environment that is friendly, courteous and respects each member of the gym or spa as an individual. Ideally, members should look forward to coming in to the gym to a welcome and healthy environment. They should want to talk to each trainer to get first-hand information how to improve their health. They should know that the information they are getting is accurate and personally tailored to fit their individual needs. Most people have very similar needs: To be greeted and to have people know them on a first name basis. Health trainers should allow members to gradually orient themselves to their new exercise environment and gradually provide direction and assistance when needed. The effective health trainer encourages members to train hard in achieving their goals but also knows the limits of each client. An important component in determining the goals of health and exercise lies in respecting the rights and limits of those individuals who are improving their health. Above all . . . health trainers create an environment where the client has fun in exercising!;

Always ask Questions. "How are you feeling?" "Does that movement feel good to you?" "Can you feel your muscles responding?" Good health training involves creating a challenging and realistic environment in achieving goals and allows the client to take responsibility for his or her success. Asking questions may begin with something as simple as "What kinds of things are you interested in doing today? Is today a 'cardio' day or stretching and flexibility day?" When trainers ask questions that are genuine to the client, the impression is that the trainer cares about the client first as a person and is concerned about providing a high-quality work out that will be rewarding to him or her. During the course of training and exercising, the effective trainer should periodically check and observe the actual quality of the workout of the client (especially if the exercise is a high-intensity aerobic exercise). Especially with the "Type A" client, they may be pushing themselves too hard, too fast and the exercise may actually become counterproductive.

Reviewing Basic Key Principles in Health & Fitness. Effective health trainers are knowledgeable in understand proper training techniques with exercise equipment and keep updated with certification procedures, such as CPR and first aid. The effective health trainer is not only competent, but continually strives to increase their knowledge base by attending conferences in health and exercise and conducting research in motivation and exercise. Trainers are certified and should be considered expert in their area. Reviewing basic skills relative to client safety is critical to running a successful gym or spa. For example, do the trainers and staff know where the fire escape is and fire escape procedures? What are the natural disaster plans? What to do when clients complain of the gym being too hot, too cold, or too stuffy? What do trainers do in cases of rude comments to members by other members? Sexual harassment issues? Reviewing basic guideline procedures in a manual is always good practice, as well as weekly meetings to discuss current issues in the gym;

Instruction. Effective health trainers are continually informing and communicating with clients, identifying specific procedures and exercises that are beneficial to clients and teaching them proper skill and technique in the execution of the technique of the exercise. This is especially true with those exercises that pose special problems, such as flexibility stretches, high-circuit weight training, and weight loss programs. The trainer frequently checks with clients when engaging in rigorous cardiovascular exercises and monitors health performance;

Note Taking Skills During Client Workouts. Effective health trainers keep logs and records of performances as key indicators of improvement in health training. These records are very important to individual members as they serve as empirical evidence of improvement in exercise and physical training. For example, if member "Bill" rows 5000 meters in 25 minutes, the health trainer may work with Bill and determine his split time to row the same distance in 24 minutes. In other words, good health trainers know exactly what clients have to do in order to improve the quality of their exercise and they maintain records and logs of physical performance and exercise;

Goal Setting: Achieving Goals Means First Identifying Goals. Communication with members and individuals interested in achieving better physical health will allow the effective trainer to identify meaningful goals for each client. Before any exercise program begins, the health trainer introduces the member to the gym and program and then listens to the ideas and goals of each member. After listening to the concerns of each member regarding health and fitness, the trainer and member both create an exercise program that is both fun and challenging. Identifying goals that stimulate an interest in improving and maintaining physical health are an absolute priority in training and exercise. Without goals, clients have no way of measuring their success or failure; goals provide the psychological impetus to keep trying as they serve as empirical evidence that the exercise program is indeed working. While developing goals for the client, the health trainer has extremely high levels of personal and professional integrity and does not create a conflict of interest by soliciting their personal training services during gym hours or confide personal problems to the client. Effective trainers also provide incentives for goal achievement, such as through acknowledgment in gym fliers or newspapers, and bulletin board notices with client names that acknowledge member accomplishments (see figure 20b). Finally, the health trainer with the highest levels of integrity never crosses the boundaries of professional ethics with personal interest.

Gaims Health Spa & Fitness

Congratulates The Following Members:

1. Mary Jones: Completing The Los Angeles Marathon (4 hours 33 minutes)!

2. Kevin McDonald: Rowing 40,000 consecutive meters!

3. Christy Holland: Certified Aerobics Instructor!

4. Ralph Jones: Completed one of training without missing one day!

Great Work!! Keep Going!! Look for Next Week's Heroes

Figure 20b   Methods Used by Gyms to Facilitate Member Goal Achievement

■ A FINAL NOTE: REMEMBERING WHY WE ENGAGE IN SPORT & EXERCISE

As a final note in our discussion of sport and exercise, we should remember that above all, we should enjoy the activity and the process of physical activity. Whether it is outdoor activity, aerobic activity, or working out with a partner, physical activity is vital and essential to optimal levels of physical and psychological functioning. With all of the emphasis regarding what we "should" be doing in medical research or what we should be eating, we may lose sight of the fact that we need to enjoy the process of exercise and overall enjoy our quality of life. If there is no personal enjoyment in the process of achieving our goals, then the activity itself becomes meaningless and futile. While exercising and participating in a series of healthy activities throughout your life—we recommend remembering the following tips:

a. *Enjoy what you are doing and have fun!* We are not saying that all of your goals and activities will be easy or simple, but the basic common denominator in all forms of exercise is the psychological need to enjoy the activity. If there is no enjoyment in the activity, you will eventually discontinue it and your overall levels of personal satisfaction will drop considerably. When members enjoy their exercise activity they look forward to participating in the health and exercise activity in the future. Exercise now becomes a reward where the body enjoys the physical activity either in the gym or some form of outside activity. Perhaps more importantly, individuals who enjoy their exercise activity are more likely to incorporate new styles of training into their lives;

b. *Health and fitness:* Physical exercise and health training require some time to notice positive changes. The effective health trainer knows how to encourage clients to keep training during that difficult period of time where they are investing much effort but do not see any change in their physical appearance. Health trainers need to provide a steady stream of support and encouragement during this difficult period of time. Furthermore, communicate to the client the importance of understanding that exercise is not temporary or some form of a fashion statement or fad. The health trainer may communicate to the client: "Incorporate the health activity into a permanent activity within your lifestyle. Just as when you wake up in the morning and get dressed and eat breakfast, your exercise program must become as regular and routine. You can do it be telling people about your goals and rewarding yourself for gradual and consistent participation."

c. *Family Recreation:* Teaching children the values and importance of activity is vital if they are going to incorporate exercise into their lives when they get older. Spending time together in outdoor activities is important for family health and close bonding. The activity itself need not be expensive—it can be simply a walk in the park or playing catch with a ball outside. Take time off to interact and have fun with your family while teaching children the value and importance of exercise. You will not only have a physically healthier family, but also a more communicative and closer family.

d. *Psychological levels of wellness.* When we exercise and enjoy outside activity, we feel better mentally as well as physically. Often, people forget the intrinsic value of just being outside and how important exercise makes us feel mentally. When you have had a particularly difficult day or stressful class during school, take a few moments and look outside. View the trees, the grass and any other natural part of the landscape. Now try (if possible) to go outside and think how these natural aspects of beauty makes you feel. Notice the distinction between the stressful indoor environment (i.e., office or classroom) and feel the relaxation of simply being outdoors. Make sure that you understand the distinction in feeling how your body responds to stressful environments and physically relaxing environments. When you feel stressed out in the future, think of these relaxing experiences;

e. *Goal achievement as a vital component of self-worth and happiness.* Part of what makes exercise rewarding is the activity, but also knowing that you are accomplishing something. Before beginning any exercise program, be sure to identify the characteristics that distinguish progress in achieving your goals. For example, if you are trying to lose weight, are you keeping accurate weekly/monthly logs of your weight? If you are a rower, are you keeping records of your time and distance? Only through understanding your goals and maintaining your structured progress will you ever be able to achieve or reach your goals;

f. *Remember the Critical Period in Teaching Children Sport and Exercise.* If you will recall earlier in the chapter we mentioned an important term in developmental psychology that is referred to as a "critical period." A critical period in developmental psychology refers to a limited opportunity of time to learn a cognitive skill, such as language. As parents and teachers we need to work more closely with children in helping them to understand and value exercise, health and nutrition. If we view the opportunity in teaching children and young adults the benefits of exercise as a form of a critical period, then the basic principles of exercise can be incorporated early on in development and most likely will remain a part of the child's lifestyle. Children need to be exposed to health styles and forms of exercise early on in development so they can understand their importance in overall health. If children see their parents participating in an active and healthy exercise lifestyle, they will more than likely imitate their behaviors and continue them well into adulthood. Just as an infant needs to be exposed to some form of a language at birth in order to speak that language, so too is it necessary in exposure to exercise activities in childhood. The role model or parent should view the activity as a healthy and active form of participation for all members of the family. In this way, children will regard exercise as an enjoyable activity that should be done on a daily basis;

g. *Evolutionary Theory and Competition: Why Do We Work Harder With Others?* Many athletes debate over the merits and advantages of training with a partner. Training partners help inspire us to reach our goals and help motivate us to work harder. Some individuals even claim that they cannot receive the type of training that they prefer without having a partner there to "push" them and provide the support that they need. Whether or not a training partner helps improve the quality of your exercise and workout perhaps has more to do with your individual personality trait and temperament than your type of exercise.

In the study that we conducted earlier in this chapter we explored the impact of training and exercise with a partner. We hypothesized that exercise and training with a partner helps us reach our goals that we would not have reached if we were exercising by ourselves. Furthermore, many of the athletes commented that a partner helped "push" them to reach personal goals that they felt would have been impossible to reach had they been exercising by themselves. Why is it that we work harder, exercise with more intensity and push ourselves with more intensity when training with a partner? This is especially true with athletes who have been running on a track and an unknown runner begins to pass them. Often the unknown runner makes us run even faster as we refuse to be passed on the track. Is this a "territoriality" issue? Perhaps a better understanding of evolutionary theory and competition in athletic sports may provide us with some answers.

■ SPORT COMPETITION AND EVOLUTIONARY THEORY

Competing with others and developing a health competitive attitude appears to have had evolutionary ramifications. Those individuals who were highly competitive proved to be able to outpace others and thus have advantages in the development of necessary survival items, such as food, water and safe living spaces. Clearly, the development of a competitive nature was an advantage in our evolutionary history because it allowed us to gain significant advantages regarding mates (fertile females) and food. By competing for important resources and winning those resources allowed us to survive over other less competitive individuals. Pacing with others in sport environments or the need to stay in proximity of others also appears to have been a very basic and primitive need that served some survival need in our evolutionary history. Those early ancestors that developed the ability to pace with others also had an advantage by developing the ability to create interdependent relationships and cooperation with others within the group. This pacing advantage in sports allows athletes to train harder, stronger and more efficiently as stamina increases. When modern athletes train today by pacing with partners (such as in swimming, rowing or cycling) they are able to maintain higher intensity levels of exercise that probably was an advantage in our evolutionary history.

■ CHAPTER 20 QUESTION & REVIEW

1. Identify some practical ways in finding work or employment in the field of sport psychology;

2. Identify and describe the seven key characteristics of health trainers;

3. What does it mean to be "CARING" health trainer?

4. Identify how individuals who are interested in sport psychology may become certified—why is the certification process perhaps most important in sport psychology?

5. Describe why empirical research is especially important in sport psychology—can you identify one area of research that interests you?

Appendix A: Fitness Measure For Skill Sports & Endurance Sports

Athlete's Physical Condition:	Poor	Moderate	Good	Excellent
I) Track: One half mile (minutes):	8	7	6	under 5
Long Jump (feet):	8	10	12	over 14
High Jump (feet):	3½	4	5	over 5
5 Kilometer run (minutes):	22	21	20	under 19
10 Kilometer run (minutes):	50	45	42	under 40
40 Kilometer run (minutes):	5	4½	4	under 3:45

	Distance	Stroke	Time
II) Swimming:	500 yards:	Freestyle	5:00 minutes
	1500 yards:	Freestyle	15 minutes
	3000 yards:	Freestyle	30 minutes

III) Football
Throwing Accuracy: Accuracy in throwing variety of distances
Catching Accuracy: Catch football while running (left & right)
Punting: Punt over 30 yards
Blocking: Defend quarterback from rushing team

IV) Bicycling
One hour moderate speed (3–5 mph)/Occasional hills.

		Moderate	Healthy	Excellent
V) Rowing	1000 meters:	4 minutes	3:45	3:30
	5000 meters:	20 minutes	19:00	18:30
	10, 000 meters:	42 minutes	40:00	38:00

VI) Dancing
15 minutes various styles of aerobic dance;

VII) Dead Hang
Hang from vertical bar one minute;

VIII) Circuit Weight Training
High intensity circuit training of light weight/High repetition;

IX) Basketball
Full Court Basketball 45 minutes minimum

X) Flexibility
Stretch/Flexibility training for 20–30 minutes (lower body).

Appendix B: General Fitness Yardstick for Adults

The key to understanding health and fitness is knowing how your body responds to the physical demands that are placed on it regarding a variety of exercises. For example, do you know what kind of cardiovascular fitness you are in right now? Are you aware of what type of upper body strength you have? What about your flexibility? In this section of the appendix we will review some very basic principles in determining overall physical health. The following guidelines are offered by the Cooper Health Institute in Dallas, the American College of Sports Medicine, and the American Council on Exercise.

A. Cardiovascular Test For Adults: One Mile Walk (in minutes)

	Men Under 40;	Females Under 40;	Men Over 40;	Females Over 40
Excellent	13 (or less)	13:30 (or less)	14 (or less)	14:30 (or less)
Good	13–15:30	13:30–16	14–16:30	14:31–17
Average	16	17	16:45	17:30

B. Strength Test (push-ups)

Excellent	25	10	20	8
Good	20	7	15	6
Average	15	5	10	5

C. Strength Test (sit-ups—in two minutes)

Excellent	50	40	30	20
Good	40	30	20	15
Average	30	20	15	10

D. Flexibility Test

Excellent	Straddle stretch stomach touching floor;
Good	Straddle stretch stomach within 6 inches to floor;
Average	Straddle stretch stomach within 12 inches to floor.

Appendix C: Athletic Personality Test

Please answer each question with scores ranging between "1" and "5" where:

1 = Absolutely Not True;
2 = Not True;
3 = No Opinion;
4 = True;
5 = Absolutely True

1. Exercise is a very important activity in my life _____
2. When I do not exercise, I feel as though something important is missing in my life ___;
3. I feel that I can train an exercise better with an exercise partner _____;
4. I prefer that my exercise partner is a little stronger or faster than me when training so I can get a better workout _____;
5. When I exercise I like to be with people _____;
6. I like to have fun when I exercise _____;
7. I like to hear encouragement fro others when training—I think that makes me work harder _____;
8. If I am jogging and someone runs past me, I have to try to catch them and pass them up _____;
9. When training with groups of people, It is important to me to try to be the best _____;
10. I think that groups of people who are exercising can improve individual levels or quality of exercise _____;
11. I think that I can get a better workout when training by myself _____;
12. I feel self-confident when I exercise or train in groups of people ___;
13. People tend to distract me when I am exercise _____;
14. I feel that no one can "push" me harder than myself _____;
15. When I jog or run on the track and someone passes me by I usually keep my own pace _____;
16. Sometimes when I exercise with groups of people I feel self-conscious that people are staring at me _____;
17. I think that I can get more accomplished by staying focused and exercising by myself _____;
18. I feel that people who exercise in groups are not serious athletes and use them just to socialize _____;
19. I am my own best critic when it comes to training and exercise _____;
20. I think that no one understand my body better than myself _____.

II) Anecdotal reports of exercise. Please elaborate or explain the following:

1. I enjoyed this type of exercise because:

2. I feel that I was able to reach my goals in exercise and training:

3. What I liked best about this type of exercise training was:

4. On a scale of 1 (lowest) to 10 (highest), I would rank my exercise activity as _____

5. I think I will probably continue to exercise in the future:

6. I prefer training with/without a partner because:

Appendix D: Workout Routine

Effectiveness of Exercise Training with Partners

Pretest (no training partners) Type of Exercise:	(pre-test) lbs. (individual)	(post-test) (Training Partner)
a. Flat Bench:	35	70
b. Lap Pull-Down:	120	140
c. Leg Extension:	50	120
d. Hamstring Curls:	70	100
e. Lateral Arm Raises:	60	90
f. Bicep Curls:	15	35
g. Tricep Extensions:	40	50

Notes

References

American Psychiatric Association. (1994). Diagnostic and Statistical Manual of Mental Disorders (4th Ed.). Washington, DC: Author.

Bandura, A. (1997). Self-efficacy: The exercise of control. New York: W.H. Freeman.

Bandura, A. (1986). Social foundations of thought and action. Englewood Cliffs, NJ: Prentice-Hall.

Bandura, A. (1977). Social learning theory. New York: General Learning Press.

Bandura, A. (1973). Aggression: A social learning analysis. Englewood Cliffs, NJ: Prentice-Hall.

Bandura, A. (1969). Principles of behavior modification. New York: Holt, Rinehart & Winston.

Bandura, A. & Walters, R. (1963). Social learning and personality development. New York: Holt, Rinehart & Winston.

Darwin, C.R. (1859). On the origins of species. London: John Murray.

Darwin, C.R. (1871). The descent of man. London: John Murray.

DuCharme, K.A., & Brawley, M.R. (1995). Predicting the intentions and behaviors of exercise initiatives using two forms of self-efficacy. Journal of Behavioral Medicine, 18, 479–497.

Erikson, E.H. (1963). Childhood and society (2nd Ed.). New York: Holton.

Faber-Taylor, A., Kuo, F.E., & Sullivan, W. (2004). Coping with ADD: The surprising connection to green play settings. Environment and Behavior, 33, 54–77.

Freud: S. (1900/1978). The interpretation of dreams. Birmingham: AL: Classics of Medicine Library.

Freud, S. (1920/1950). Beyond the pleasure principle. Oxford, UK: Liveright.

Freud, S. (1923/1961). The ego and the id. New York: Norton.

Hoffman, A.J. (1982). Effects of psychological momentum on performance among American athletes. International Journal of Sport Psychology, 14, 41–53.

Jung, C. G. (1928/1935). The relations between the ego and the unconscious. CW 7: 123–241.

Kitayama, S., Markus, H.R., Matsumoto, H., & Norasakkunkit, V. (1997). Individual and collective processes in the construction of the self: Self-enhancement in the United States and self-criticism in Japan. Journal of Personality and Social Psychology, 72, 1245–1267.

Faber-Taylor, A., Kuo, F.E., & Sullivan, W. (2004). Coping with ADD: The surprising connection to green play settings. Environment and Behavior, 33, 54–77.

McCullagh, P.D., & Landers, D.M. (1976). Size of audience and social facilitation. Perceptual and Motor Skills, 42, 1067–1070.

Miller, N. & Dollard, J. (1941). Social learning and imitation. New Haven, NJ: Yale University Press.

Molock, B., Zamora, L., & Hwang, T. (2005, May). Positive effects of training partners on exercise performance among individual athletes: You can do one more! Unpublished manuscript, California State University Northridge.

Paykel, E. S. (2002). Mood disorders: Review of current diagnostic systems. Psychopathology, 35, 94–102.

Rainford L., Mason V., Hickman M., & Morgan A. (2000) Health in England 1998: Investigating the links between social inequalities and health. The Stationary Office, London. Retrieved February 21, 2005 http://www.nelmh.org/content_print.asp?c=22&did=2387&fc=004012

Rogers, C. R. (1961) On Becoming a Person. A therapist's view of psychotherapy, Boston: Houghton Mifflin.

Rotter, J.B. (1971, June). External control and internal control. Psychology Today, 5(1), 37–42, 58–59.

Seligman, Martin E. P (1975). Helplessness: On depression, development, and death. San Francisco: W.H. Freeman; New York.

Skinner, B.F. (1971). Beyond freedom and dignity. New York: Knopf.

Thorndike, E. L. (1911). Animal Intelligence. New York: Macmillan.

U.S. Census Bureau.(2000). 2000 Census of Population (P.L. 94-171) Redistricting Data File. http://factfinder.census.gov

Vygotsky, L. S. (1930). Tool and symbol in children's development (A.R. Luria & M. Cole, trans.). In M. Cole, V. John-Steiner, S. Scribner, & E. Souberman (Eds.), L.S. Vygotsky: Mind in society. Cambridge, MA: Harvard University Press, 1978, chaps. 1–4.

Vygotsky, L. S. (1931a). Development of higher functions. In psychological research in the U.S.S.R. Moscow: Progress Publishers.

Vygotsky, L. S. (1931b). The history of the development of higher mental functions (M. Cole, trans.). Excerpt in M. Cole, V. John-Steioner, S. Scribner, & E. Souberman (Eds.), L.S. Vygotsky: Mind in society. Cambridge, MA: Harvard University Press, 1978.

Watson, J.B., & Rayner, R. (1920). Conditioned emotional reactions. Journal of Experimental Psychology, 3, 1–14.

Weiner, B. (1974). Achievement motivation and attribution theory. Morristown, N.J.: General Learning Press.

Weiner, B. (1980). Human Motivation. NY: Holt, Rinehart & Winston.

Weiner, B. (1986). An attributional theory of motivation and emotion. New York: Springer-Verlag.

Zajonc, R.B. (1965). Social facilitation. Science, 149, 269–274.